More Adventures with
DAVID GRAYSON

More Adventures with
DAVID GRAYSON

ADVENTURES
IN UNDERSTANDING

ADVENTURES IN SOLITUDE

GREAT POSSESSIONS

DOUBLEDAY & COMPANY, INC.

Garden City, New York

1946

FOREWORD

I HAVE been having moments of joyous remembrance. For the first time in many years I have been rereading three of the books I wrote long ago: *Adventures in Understanding, Adventures in Solitude, Great Possessions,* which the publishers are now about to reissue in a generous volume to be called *More Adventures with David Grayson.*

Each of these books has been reprinted several times, but never before in a combined volume, so that it can stand up side by side with *The Adventures of David Grayson* which includes the three earlier books by David Grayson called *Adventures in Contentment, Adventures in Friendship,* and *The Friendly Road.* To an author who is not yet accustomed to the publication of his books three at a time, this unexpected and delightful prodigality on the part of the publisher is somewhat overwhelming. He remembers no such easy profusion in the earlier days when his books came into being, one at a time, with a welcome all too scanty.

I have been recalling how carelessly and swiftly each new published book began to diffuse itself. It soon seemed no longer my own. Worse still, when I began to see how far short it fell of the dream I had of it, I felt like disowning it entirely. For a long time I did not even want to see it, much less read it. Even an extravagant review—or two!—failed to satisfy me. I found that in order to be happy again I must be at my far-gleaming, all-but-perfect *next* book. I kept always in mind, to comfort and encourage me, a maxim that I had somewhere picked up:

What's doing, that has life: what's done is dead

Do authors ever read their own books straight through? I wonder! They may nibble at them here and there, or their paternal instincts, being sharply aroused, they may fly to the defense of an abused chapter or battered paragraph. They may even search for a likely passage which they intend to purloin for a later book, or they may wish to verify a partly forgotten quotation—but to read his own books straight through, an author should make prayerful preparation. He should wait at least forty years, if he can spare the time—anyway, twenty or thirty. For in forty years even an author should have attained a chastened and philosophical spirit. He must be able to stand aside and look himself over. He must be able to laugh, or at least smile tolerantly, at what he finds. If the adventure then proves to be amusing, he may enjoy it to the full, without fearing the asides of an accusing conscience; but if the reading becomes insufferably dull, as it is quite likely to do, he is entitled, at that age, to let the book slip from his fingers, while he settles down in his winged chair and goes comfortably to sleep!

With these warnings and preparations in mind I have just been discovering what surprises, what a curiously absorbing interest a writer may find, even what amusement and pleasure, in re-reading his own books. Really it is quite an experience!

I find I have been reliving some of the best-remembered incidents of my earlier life—incidents that had grown lean and thin with forgetfulness, mere shadows of the past. And here they are overflowing with the delight of the moment in which I lived them first. The last thing I expected was to recover, not merely the pedestrian facts, but the *feeling,* the intense emotion, with which I wrote them. I am not here saying that I found them either good or bad, nor that they were written as well as they might have been. I found that I was not criticizing them as I had expected and intended to do. In no time at all I ceased to think of the solemnity that ought to have marked the reading of books soon to reappear in public, newly clad in gay colors, and eager again to fulfill the hope of the author and verify the challenge of the publisher. I must here and now make the naïve confession that I found myself quite simply fascinated by those old books. Other readers may not, of course, find in them what I found—all the strange off-stage incidents, all the dear remembrances of times and places, or recall all the things I had left out (this sometimes with regret), which came upon me with such a joyous sense of discovery.

What delight, for instance, I had in recalling my experiences with the English starlings as told in one of the chapters of *Adventures in Solitude*—the re-created picture of the grim hospital at Baltimore where I lay for so many weary weeks, when the end of life for me seemed near, when all the world was black—and the starlings came there to my window, bringing new hope, new courage. How I enjoyed them!—in a time when joy seemed abolished from off the earth.

What active, sprightly fellows they were, anyway! There was something jaunty, almost humorous, in the way they sidled about, cocked their heads, preened their feathers. I had thought them un-mannerly and raucous-voiced, but there was something positively charming in the little intimate, almost affectionate airs they put on as they sat together exchanging the gossip of a fine autumn morning. And so far from the harsh cries I knew them by I now heard, from my highly privileged place, their deliciously intimate conversation. They too, like our own native catbirds and thrushes, had their low whisper songs, though with them it was scarcely songs at all, but low, musical ejaculations and gurgling notes, and from time to time, as though some of the gossip had passed utterly beyond the pale of credibility or propriety, some bird would break in with a kind of ironical whistle, high, clear, and sweet, and as it seemed to me that morning, full of laughter. They reminded me exactly of a group of lively old ladies, all by themselves, at a tea party.

If I begin to speak of the unexpected discoveries I made in rereading my books, how can I resist the temptation to rewrite them—here and now! Another writer might do them better, but could I? Could I make myself any other than I am?

I can only advise the reader to try them just as they were and are. They have interested many people in the years since they first appeared. I know, because I have received innumerable letters about them. It may be that there will continue to be readers who enjoy them; even rereaders who may share my own delight.

Amherst   DAVID GRAYSON

CONTENTS

Great Possessions

ADVENTURES
IN
UNDERSTANDING

INTRODUCTION

A LUTE PLAYER," observes one of the wisest of the old
philosophers, "when he is singing for himself, has no
anxiety." So indeed it is with the writer. It is only when he is
writing for himself that he writes happily.

Always since my youth I have loved to make notes in small
books wherein I set forth the common adventures of my day,
describe faithfully the people I meet when I take to the road,
or report the interesting arguments I often have with them, in
most of which, since I myself write them down afterward, I
easily come out ahead. If I am sad I find comfort in setting
down the nature of my sadness, for I come thus to a kind of
philosophical understanding of it. If I am glad I turn with no
less eagerness to my pen, for a joy expressed is a joy doubled.
Thus I write away my sorrows and increase my joys. I challenge
thus my doubts: thus define my aspirations. In all this writing I
am without anxiety, for, like the lute player mentioned by
Epictetus, I sing for myself.

When I consider making a new book, I look into these notes
of mine and, having come upon an incident or an observation
that sets me aglow with remembered enthusiasm, I say to myself,
if it concerns a new friend, like the Iceman, "Now, wasn't that
a man worth knowing!" Or if an experience like my adventures
in Caliphry, "Who could have imagined anything more amusing?" Or if a bit of philosophy, I say, "It's true, it's true!" The
more vividly these fine things come back to me, the more clearly
it seems to me I understand what they mean, and the more I

think I should like to share them with my friends. They seem somehow to count in making this a livable world. So I straightway warm up to my task and out of such "adventures in understanding," developed and rounded out, I make my book.

I suppose this is a wayward and unregenerate process of writing, but it seems to be the only way I know. Not long ago—while I was setting down the chapter herein called "Jonas" (over which I had much delight) I ran across a delicious passage in Benvenuto Cellini's Memoirs which has given me no end of comfort, since it encourages me in my perversity.

Cellini here relates the disgust and anger of King Francis because, when the King orders him to produce "twelve silver statues," he appears with a "salt cellar and a vase and busts," to say nothing of "a heap of other things that quite confound me."

"That," said I, gloating over the passage, "is just like me. I start out to produce twelve silver chapters—and see what common things I make. Salt cellars!"

"You have neglected my wishes," said King Francis to Cellini, "and worked for the fulfilment of your own."

What a sinner!

"If you stick to your own fancies," continued King Francis in what must have been a terrifying tone, "you will run your head against a stone wall."

"Here am I," said I, "with my head already against a stone wall."

So here is my book—common salt cellars, vases that I have liked to make, busts without a torso or legs! Things that quite confound me when I consider them. But I have enjoyed writing every line of it. May you enjoy reading it.

DAVID GRAYSON.

I

WE GO TO THE WICKED CITY

"Sail forth! Steer for the deep waters only!
For we are bound where mariner has not yet dared to go,
And we risk the ship, ourselves and all."

WHEN the Great War broke into my quiet it changed all things for me. I am a settled countryman and love well the hills of Hempfield, where I live, and my own wide valley and the pleasant open fields; but in war you do not do what you wish but what you must.

I had to live in a City—at first sadly enough—and there I wrote laborious articles and books. For it was not with a sword, nor yet with a plough that I served, but with a pen. That drudgery!

But at the same time I was living another book—a high, free, true, adventurous book. And this I have been writing down a little at a time, as I could, for seven years. (It is more than seven years since "Great Possessions," more than seventeen since "Adventures in Contentment.") I have called it from the first "Adventures in Understanding," for it seemed to me that in the City I came to understand many strange new things, both without and within, new things about life and people, and the way to live.

I shall never forget the strange sense of adventure I had when we arrived at our chosen lodging: the old doorway with the fanlight over it and an aged wistaria vine tightly twisted into the rusty iron railings.

"That," said I to Harriet, pointing to a tree that looked hopefully around the corner from the alley into the street, like a gossipy old woman, "is a Tree of Heaven."

This old part of the city is full of such ailanthus trees, which have a peculiar personality of their own. I came later to wonder at them and somewhat to like them for the cheerful way in which they accepted the hard fate of growing in back alleys, in the crevices of brick walls, or among paving-stones. But Harriet looked sceptical and seemed to doubt whether a true tree of heaven could be so much at home in a city.

Presently the door opened at the hand of the redoubtable Mrs. Jensen, who, I promise you, shall be much better known to you in the future.

The curious smell of living when the door opened; and the mystery of the long, narrow, dim stairway upward.

"Here we are," said I.

Harriet said nothing grimly, but I know as well what she was thinking as though she spoke aloud:

"Now, I wonder who lived here before, and whether they were nice, respectable, clean people."

The English language has one adequate word to express Harriet's approach to these complicated wonders: "Gingerly."

I have since looked up this excellent word in my dictionary:

"Gingerly: in a cautious, scrupulous, or fastidious manner."

And the quotation given to illustrate the word:

"*Gingerly,* and as if treading upon eggs, Cuddie began to ascend the well-known pass." Scott: *Old Mortality*. Vol. II, p. 53 (T. & F., 1867).

Since then, whenever I think of Harriet with her umbrella and armadillo basket mounting those wild, dark stairs to our chosen tower, I say to myself, under my breath:

"Gingerly, as if treading upon eggs, Cuddie began to ascend the well-known pass."

As for me, I liked, at once, the old street and the old house with the lichens of human living upon it; and the old rooms which were to be ours, and the wide court at the back with ailanthus trees in it and little fenced yards, and, here and there, on a clothes-line, a domestic tragedy. An old street, in an old, forgotten, neglected corner of the town! But I liked such places: old quiet places, places to look out of; old, still, sunny places, and beautiful people going by. I like to think of windows that have been much looked through; rooms full of thoughts left

8

over out of life. There is a chill, inhuman cleanness about a new place; but something warm, familiar, pleasing in an old house. Here men have dreamed and women loved; here, possibly, one was born and one died. Here a fool meditated a selfish deed, thinking it would bring him happiness; and a wise man reflected upon the folly of taking anything for himself out of life that all other men could not also have for themselves upon the same terms (as Whitman says). Something, I scarcely know what, but it is real, seems to remain of all human contacts. Nothing human is ever wholly lost.

"But," said Harriet sensibly, "most people are so careless— so dirty!" (She thinks I have queer ideas.)

"Harriet," I replied, "I wish they weren't; but still I've got to have them. They're valuable. I can't get along without a single one of them. And," said I, "you remember what Henry James's artist replied to the critic who found so much dirt in Old Rome: 'What you call dirt,' said this artist, 'we call colour.'"

To this remark Harriet deigned no reply.

I may as well confess, first as last, that I found the early days of our life in the city not easy to bear. I used to find myself thinking of a little turning in the country road near the Hempfield creamery, where one catches the first clear view of the hills—I kept thinking of that particular turning and the smoke I could often see from our own chimney. I am a friendly man and love people who pass by. Often and often, in the country, have I stopped work in my field or orchard to beard a passing traveller in the road and "swop a lie with him," as we sometimes say. Your country traveller likes to be stopped and asked the price of apples or told about the condition of the weather (which he knows already).

But the people in the city streets: How they surged by entirely regardless of me! They did not seem to know that I was there. I was oppressed with populations, overcome with speed. It seemed to me that there was no place anywhere to be quiet or to think, no height from which I could look away to distant beautiful things.

Moreover, I found my labour heavy and difficult. A man should never write under compulsion: a man should write only when he is in love with somebody or something (as I am now). But in these days the Press was to me an inhuman monster, black with ink, roaring and ravening, pursuing me in a kind of nightmare race—pressing, pressing!—with me just escaping each week from being swallowed alive. All this, added to the sense I had of a thundering Great War going on just around the corner (or so it seemed), made it appear for a time as if everything fine, simple, natural, beautiful in the world had shrivelled up and blown away.

So often the only way to get a man to look up is to get him down. A man utterly on his back has to look up. I remember one evening, after many days of dull labour, glancing out of the window near my table.

It was May, with a kind of softness in the air. The sun was going down, but still glowed upon the upper stories of the houses opposite. On an iron balcony I could see a child leaning to look over into the shadowy valley below. Men and women were here and there in the curious little boarded yards, working or talking.

Suddenly, something down deep within me seemed to come alive. I cannot rightly describe it; but all at once this scene, which had scarcely before awakened any reaction at all within me—unless it was aversion—became strangely and suddenly interesting, curious, human. I seemed to catch a harmony I had not heard before.

I leaned farther out.

The ailanthus trees were coming into leaf and held up to me their new green whorls—the peace offering of spring. I could hear pleasant confused voices without catching distinctly any words at all.

Presently a girl's voice from some nearby open window—though I could not see the girl herself—broke out singing:

"There are smiles——"

An instant later the half-mocking voice of a boy, from another window, joined in: "smiles that makes you s-a-a-d"—and I heard the girl's voice trailing away in laughter.

All at once the oppression of the city, the oppression of too many people, left me. It seemed curiously and newly interesting to have all around me so many human beings, so much warm, strange, tragic, beautiful, brief human life.

I leaned still farther out.

Such a variety of odd activities! What were they all doing? What were they thinking about? Were they happy? Or miserable? What did they read? Had they any God? And, above all, why did they live all crowded together in such honeycombs of places, when there was room enough and to spare in the open country?

"How excited you look," said Harriet, when I turned to glance at her.

"Harriet," said I, "have you thought of all the extraordinary and interesting things that must be happening at this moment in these little pigeonholes of places, in these caverns and burrows and strange passageways?"

"No," said Harriet, "I have not."

"I think," said I, "that I have never before seen such a tangle of human life as there is right here under our eyes. I did not know it was here before. It seems to me I'd like to get down into it—all over."

It was then that I had the curious flashing vision (I'm going to confess everything!) of this room of mine at the dingy top of a city lodging house as a Tower. It improved it immediately. It was my Tower: and this was the City Wall I lived upon; high up, overlooking the world. It was something to live in a Tower on the Wall of the City, I would have you know. One could see much from a Tower!

"David," said Harriet, "what *are* you laughing at?"

"Do you remember, Harriet, when Nehemiah was rebuilding the wall of Jerusalem?"

"Yes," said Harriet.

"And how they got tired of seeing him perched up there and wanted him to come down among common human beings and be sociable?"

"Yes," said Harriet; "but—"

"And do you remember what Nehemiah said: 'I am doing a great work, so that I cannot come down.'"

When I said no more, Harriet asked presently, "What of it, David?"

"Well," said I, "it's extraordinary how many men think they are doing a Great Work and cannot come down."

"But Nehemiah *was* doing a great work," said Harriet.

"That," said I, "is different."

After that my nights and Sundays began to be much more cheerful. I began to go all about our neighbourhood, first, like a careful explorer, near shore, but little by little I ventured into deeper waters and sailed by unknown countries. And I began to look upon these shores for some native I could pounce upon, like a kind of good-humoured pirate, and carry off captive to my Tower. It seemed to me that there must be a way, if one could find it, of getting to these strange people.

When once we come to this mood, adventure is never far in the offing, and comes upon us in the most surprising ways.

If any one had told me that I should stumble upon my first adventure at the foot of my own Tower, I should surely not have believed it—but so it was. For adventure is like love—we do not have to seek far for it; we can begin anywhere. I think sometimes we mistake the nature both of love and of adventure; and sit by waiting for someone else to begin the loving, or for some fine and thrilling thing to happen to us. But true love is not like that—nor yet beautiful adventure. Love comes of loving first, and adventure, because we have it in the soul of us.

I had come down the stairs at evening and stood looking up the street. In the block above, an Italian was playing on a street organ. Rendered soft by the distance, it was somehow sweet to hear. An evening breeze off the harbour, with a touch of salt in it, came cheerfully in at one end of the street and went out at the other. I had to admit, grudgingly, that the city, after all, had a kind of beauty of its own.

Presently my eye lighted upon the substantial figure of Mrs. Jensen, standing below me in the little front area-way that led into her basement burrow. She had her hands folded upon her capacious apron and was looking out for a moment in the cool of the evening, benevolently, upon the passing world.

"Good-evening, Mrs. Jensen," said I.

"Good-evening," said she.

I think I profit by looking something like a farmer.

"Did you ever live in the country, Mrs. Jensen?" I asked.

"No," said she.

"Never had any hens, or pigs, or bees?"

"No," said she.

"Never made a garden?"

"No," said she; "but Jensen, he's crazy about gardens. Jensen, he makes gardens in the house."

She spoke in a rather guttural voice, with a slight foreign inflection.

"Does he? What kind of a garden? Right here in the city?"

"Sure," said Mrs. Jensen broadly. "Sure. Every year he has flowers, and sometimes vegetables. Oh, not many, but good. This year the vegetable he is planting is punkin."

"But how can he do it?" said I, in astonishment. "How can any one make a garden among all these stones?"

When Mrs. Jensen laughs she shakes in the middle. I could see I had her interested, and presently she was leading me down the steps and through a dark passageway to a large room at the back of the house.

"Jensen," said she, "here's Mr. Grayson, and he wants to see how you plant vegetables."

At this I saw a man, who had been stooping over at work near the window, rise up and face me. He was a slight man with grey-ing hair thrust back in disorder. He looked a little like pictures I have seen of Beethoven. A fine, sensitive, serene face, upon which was written as it were in capital letters, "Impractical." But I liked him at once.

Jensen smiled deprecatingly at this bold introduction. I could see that he was embarrassed.

"I'm from the country," said I, "and I like to see things grow I was surprised to hear about your flowers—"

"And vegetables," put in Mrs. Jensen.

"Oh, it is nothing," said he.

He said "iss nutting," for he had still more of the foreign burr in his voice than his wife. He was a Dane.

At that I discovered that the whole back window was full of bloom. On little shelves cunningly constructed close to the glass were many pots containing daffodils, narcissus, and tulips, now coming into full blossom and filling the air with as rare a fragrance as ever in the country.

"How fine your flowers are!" I exclaimed.

"It iss nutting!" And he spread out his hand apologetically.

"He makes nutting of ever'ting," remarked Mrs. Jensen.

"We have not here enough sunlight," he said. "They grow veak. It iss not like the country."

But they gave true evidence of much loving care. I know well the sign of the man who loves growing things: how his hands touch them gently. It took no time at all to warm him into enthusiasm. His face began to flush and a light came into his eyes. He told me of each variety and even the peculiarities of each plant, the obstinacy of this one, the enterprise of that one, how this one was tricky and that thirsty.

"But where is your vegetable garden?" I asked presently.

"This year," remarked Mrs. Jensen, "the vegetable he is planting is punkin."

Jensen led me out of the door into the little pocket-handkerchief of a stone court. I did not see so much as a square foot of garden space.

"There," said he with pride.

Close to the wall stood a large wooden box filled with earth. Jensen told me how he had brought in this earth pail by pail from a distant lot, and how he had gathered manure from the street outside; he showed me the cunning device he had invented for sprinkling his garden by way of a bit of hose from the kitchen tap just within the window. All around the edges of his box he had radishes and lettuce, already growing quite thriftily, and in each corner, with mathematical precision, he had set a cabbage plant; but what he especially pointed out was the new adventure of the year—pumpkins—which were

14

just thrusting their bent green knees out of the moist earth. Jensen tenderly flecked away a bit of earth here and there as if to help them in their struggle to emerge.

"Jensen, he likes vegetables," said Mrs. Jensen.

"But where in the world," I asked, thinking of the activities of a really energetic pumpkin vine, "are they to run to?"

This caused Jensen to laugh aloud, and with the greatest triumph. His face literally glowed.

"It iss so in the city," said he, "that there iss not room to grow out, so ve grow up!"

He illustrated this process vividly with both head and arms.

"So vit men, so vit punkins."

I saw then that here was a philosopher as well as a gardener—though I knew beforehand that all true gardeners become, sooner or later, philosophers.

Jensen showed me with delight a little trellis he was then building on the brick wall leading upward.

"Ve haf plenty room," said he, chuckling; "ve can go up to the sky!"

I had a vision of great yellow pumpkins adorning the side of the house all the way up, which was altogether so amusing that I couldn't help laughing.

"But when the pumpkins get large," I asked, "how are you going to keep them from breaking away or pulling the vines down?"

I wish you could have seen Jensen at that moment—tapping his head with two fingers, his eyes twinkling, saying mysteriously:

"I haf a great idea,"—but refusing to tell me what it was.

At this I glanced at Mrs. Jensen. There she stood, shaking her head slowly from side to side and saying:

"Jensen, he lofes vegetables."

But the wonders had only begun. Jensen now exhibited another box, much smaller, so that it could be carried in, if necessary. He did not need to show me what it contained, for no sooner did he open the grated lid than I had olfactory information! Rabbits. He pointed out the pair and observed:

"There will be more soon," which I did not doubt.

From this we went inside, and I made the acquaintance of his sleepy canary birds, each in a cage of its own, for which Jensen had made curtains to keep out the evening light. There were also a bowl of goldfish and a cat. He came so near having a complete menagerie that I asked finally in my soberest voice:

"Where's the pony?"

They both looked at me in solemn surprise. Jensen recovered first.

"Ach, you are a joker." Only he said, "yoker."

Mrs. Jensen here put in, as though somehow to answer a reasonable question.

"Jonas, he hass a flivver."

Jonas, I learned, was their son. I had no premonition then of what possibilities and excitements were wrapped up in the "flivver" of Jonas. That is another epic.

I cannot tell what delight I took in all these simple discoveries. I suppose they could have been duplicated in a thousand cramped yards and area-ways in that great city, but they were new to me. And it seemed to me, in the warmth of my enthusiasm, that here, in this dim basement, was a kind of ideal life—nature indeed balked, but human nature somehow triumphant under handicaps. Here were people who managed to live interestingly. But it is a strange thing that people who get the credit of living ideal lives often do not see it in that light at all. No sooner did I try to express something of my feeling than I unloosened the floods.

"Ah," said Mrs. Jensen, in her guttural voice, "ve have great troubles."

I looked at Jensen; the glow was dying out of his face. He was beginning to be uncomfortable, for he plainly knew what was coming. A moment before he had been the master, exhibiting his triumphs, and Mrs. Jensen was the worshipful follower, hanging breathless upon his words; but now she turned upon him suddenly, with a kind of indignation:

"Jensen, he can't get vork. He try and try, and he cannot get vork."

Jensen hung his head but said nothing.

16

"He iss no good, Jensen: he iss afraid of ever't'ing. He goes to ask for vork, and when the boss says 'No,' Jensen goes avay. He should not go avay. He should ask, 'Why?' Iss there not vork in America? Do not Americans have books to bind?"

By this time she had become vehement and glared fiercely upon poor Jensen, who seemed more and more to shrink into his unworthiness. Yes, he looked like some dreamy Beethoven....

"So Mr. Jensen is a bookbinder," I said, to relieve the situation.

"He iss too much an artist for America. All they say in America is 'Qvick, qvick.' They do not want good vork, only qvick, qvick vork. And Jensen, he iss not qvick!"

And then, the hopelessness of the situation overcoming her, she seemed fairly to swell up in her indignation:

"Jensen, he vill not try qvickness. I tell him he live in America he must be qvick. But he say, 'I cannot be qvick.' Sooch a man!"

"I wonder," I said, "if any real artist is ever quick." But my remark made no impression whatever. She shook her head in complete helplessness.

"Ah, ve have such troubles. Food it costs so much and the rent is so high. And Jonas, he must have his flivver. Ah! ve have troubles."

Poor Jensen. He stood with hanging head, saying never a word. It was evidently an old experience with him.

"Well," I said, "I am interested in books. What kind of books do you bind?"

At this Mrs. Jensen started up with alacrity. "I vill show you," said she.

So she went to a drawer in a kind of dresser and took out a parcel carefully wrapped in paper. This she unrolled and took out a leather-covered box beautifully fitted together. Opening this with hands as tender as those of a mother, she drew out a book. Jensen stood still, hanging his head, and did not look up. Mrs. Jensen handed the book to me with every solicitude. I thought it at the moment truly the most beautiful thing of the kind I had ever seen, rich green morocco, hand tooled in red and gold; all exquisitely perfect.

"What a beautiful piece of work!" I exclaimed.

I saw Jensen's head slowly rising. I looked at the book more closely.

"How perfectly your satin inner covers match the morocco!" I said.

At this Jensen took a step toward me and half lifted his hands.

"And where did you get such a design for the lettering? It's wonderful!"

"Ah! So you like it!" said Jensen.

I wish you could have seen the change in the man; from deepest dejection all in a moment to pride and power. He thrust one hand through his hair as though he were about to sit down and play a sonata. Then he took the book from me, and with a touch of loving tenderness, turned it over and over in his hands; showed me each difficult excellence, the tooling, the lettering, the pasting, the pressing. His face was glowing again and his eyes shining. His whole aspect became one of masterly dignity and pride. At the same time Mrs. Jensen seemed to fade away or shrink down again into her former place as worshipful admirer. It was as good as a play. She stood by, occasionally remarking, in her guttural voice, and with unmistakable pride:

"Ah, Jensen, he iss an artist!"

Then she would pause a moment, as though struggling with herself, and add, shrugging, "But he iss not qvick."

Suddenly Jensen turned to me with a look of affectionate confidence, like a child:

"So you are interested in books."

"Yes," said I, "I like the outsides of books when they are like this: I like still better the insides of books."

He had told me that this was a book he had just finished binding for a rich book-lover. It was an exquisite edition of the "Odes of Horace." I opened it almost at random and came across the ode to Mæcenas, inviting him to the Sabine farm (which long ago I knew well), and I read aloud:

> "Lord of himself that man will be,
> And happy in his life alway,
> Who still at even can say with free
> Contented soul: 'I've lived to-day!'"

When I had finished, I was surprised to find Jensen taking hold of my hand with both of his—in quite an old-world way—and, after shaking it heartily, saying:

"Ah, ve know, ve know."

How I love to be accepted as a member of the Craft!

We had much more good and friendly conversation. I could hardly get myself away from these interesting people; and finally proposed that the Jensens come up some evening soon to see Harriet and me.

"There are plenty of questions in the world yet to be solved," said I. "You and I must get at them at once. They must be settled."

"Ve vill, ve vill," cried out Jensen, as I went up the stairs.

I heard the door shut behind me and then open suddenly, and Jensen's voice, full of enthusiasm:

"Ve've lived to-day!"

"We have," said I.

Then I heard Mrs. Jensen:

"Jensen, he iss an artist—but he iss not qvick"—and the door closed for good and all.

I came back to find Harriet much alarmed—thinking me lost in a strange city.

"Wherever have you been?" she asked.

"I have been out in society," said I. "Harriet, I've met an artist, a true gardener, and a philosopher."

"Who is he?" she asked.

This had not at all occurred to me before, and I said:

"Well, he's the husband of Mrs. Jensen——"

As I dropped off to sleep that night I said to myself:

"What a day! What a day! I could never have imagined it would be like this. It's no credit to a man in the country to have a garden; any one can have it and mishandle it in the country. But think of loving gardens so much as to make one among these stone caverns!"

I thought again of yellow pumpkins hanging to a brick wall, and went to sleep laughing.

II

I ADVENTURE INCOGNITO

A countryman may travel from kingdom to kingdom, province to province, city to city, and glut his eyes with delightful
objects, hawk, hunt, and use these ordinary disports, without
any notice taken, all of which a prince or a great man cannot
do.—*The Anatomy of Melancholy.*

I WONDER if ever you change human beings with arguments
alone: either by peppering them with little sharp facts or by
blowing them up with great guns of truth. You scare 'em, but
do you change 'em? I wonder if ever you make any real difference
in human beings without understanding them and loving
them. For when you argue with a man (how much more with
a woman), you are somehow trying to pull him down and make
him less (and yourself more); but when you try to understand
him, when you like him, how eager is he then to know the truth
you have; and you add to him in some strange way, you make him
more than he was before; and at the same time, and that is the
sheer magic of it, you yourself become more.

There is nothing in this world that people so much thrive
upon, grow fine and rosy and robust upon (especially women)
as being loved. This is true.

Yet there must be facts, and reasons, and arguments. . .

How I toiled those long spring days in the City, forging thunderbolts of argument, heaping up ammunition of fact, loading
great shells of truth. Oh, I was hot upon the business of bringing
down the enemy! I'd finish 'em off! Once they heard the ma-
chine-gun rattle of *those* facts, or saw *that* bomb burst white
in the sky, they'd run to cover! Every day I grew savager and
savager.

(Now, facts are not to be thrown at people like dishes or
vegetables, but somehow warmed into them.)

But, thank God, I had my blessed nights and Sundays; and

as soon as I began to look up and look around, I began, as surely, to come alive again. One Saturday morning I said to Harriet, "I'm going to stop work early to-day and take in the City."

Harriet, by her look—oh, I know Harriet!—seemed to imply that I'd better look out lest I be the one taken in; but, nevertheless, I set out full of curiosity and enthusiasm.

I shall never forget that vivid spring morning. I walked briskly down the street, looking all about me.

It was May in the City, and where is May not beautiful? The vines were coming freshly green on old walls, the elms were showing their new soft verdure, the little squares of lawn here and there by the street-side blessed the eye; and in many a friendly window I could see the beckoning welcome of potted daffodils or narcissus.

"The City also," I said, "is very beautiful."

I looked in at curious alleys and openings as I passed, and old area-ways and strange nooks and corners. I love such irregularities, unexpected passageways, unopened but inviting doorways; the odd shifts of human beings to meet the small difficulties of life.

Presently, as I walked, I began to have a strong sense, among all these hurrying people of the streets, of being utterly alone, aloof. It was as though I were wearing a magic cloak of invisibility, for it seemed that I could see all these passing people without their seeing me. They went by as though I were not there at all, had no corporeal existence. I became a kind of ghost, and quite depressed, there in the bright May sunshine—and yet felt that I was well worth knowing, if only someone would stop long enough to know me!

I paused on a busy corner to consider this curious problem.

"After all," said I, "I don't think I am really invisible. I am merely visiting the City incognito. I'm a kind of Caliph of democracy, arrived here from my palace in the country to visit, secretly, the humming streets of Bagdad."

This idea seemed to me so amusing that it ran away at once with my fancy. Ever since I was a boy, no story has interested me more than that of the Prince who goes out disguised among common people for a day of true happiness or a night of thrilling adventure. How all the ripe old Caliphs loved such doings! And, when you come to think of it, is not this about the most ancient and universal of the stories known to man? It began at the very beginning!

It was only a short time after this earth was created—according to the veracious record—that the Lord God himself, no doubt grown lonesome, as royalty must, upon his high throne, came down in the cool of the day to walk in Eden. And what an adventure he had; and what goings-on among the inhabitants! At that time the entire population of the earth had just discovered that it was naked, and had organised the first great industry—garment-making. What a thing was that to find—offhand—by a Monarch travelling incognito!

"But in these latter days," said I, standing there in an eddy of the city stream, "royalty is not what it once was. It has grown unadventurous and blasé. It is willing to take its thrills second hand. It lacks fresh imagination. It has quite lost the genius of wonder. We are all of us kings nowadays, in cities at least, with ballots of folded paper for our sceptres; but we are so unsteady on our thrones, so little certain of our royalty, that we dare not, even for a moment, trust ourselves down among ordinary, interesting Adams and Eves."

I liked this idea tremendously and quite forgot where I was in pursuit of it.

"No," said I, "the modern Caliph of democracy seems to fear that if he gets off his throne and goes down among all these Italians, Poles, Greeks, Jews, Negroes, he will not be able to get back again. He wants to feel his crown always warmly on his head—one hundred per cent on his head, as you might say. I suspect he wears it at night, perhaps ties it on with a pocket-handkerchief lest it fall off and get lost under the bed. I think the real trouble is that he does not feel, inside, quite royally democratic."

So I walked onward again, but now with a new and delightful idea, thinking myself truly a kind of Caliph come all unknown to visit busy Bagdad: "glutting his eyes with delightful objects." And being a Caliph disguised, of course these hurrying people would never recognise me. I must therefore make the advances myself, find out the heroes and the villains, and surprise adventure where she lurked. Afterward, at my royal pleasure, I could choose whether or not to disclose my identity.

(Did you ever take flight upon the wings of a wholly amusing and beguiling idea? Recklessly? Try it one day, friend, and be happy!)

By this time I had drifted well down toward the wharves of the city and was looking sharply at each man and woman I met, considering where I should begin.

"Someone," said I, "though he doesn't know it yet, is shortly to have a curious adventure."

But they kept rolling past me so fast that I could not seem to fix upon any particular person.

"The very next man," I said at last, "that I find standing still I will swoop down upon."

Hardly had I formed this grand resolution when, almost at my elbow, in the door of a little cubby of a street shop, stood a stout, swart man with black eyes and an inviting manner.

"Good-morning," said I promptly, recalling my decision.

"Good-morning," he answered, and at once backed into his shop and with a wave of his hand motioned me to one of his tall chairs.

He was a bootblack.

I certainly wanted no shine; but I climbed meekly into his chair, chuckling a little at myself because, after all my grand ideas of capturing some interesting human being, I had myself been caught in one of the oldest nets in the world and would presently have to pay the ransom of a dime to escape. . . . I was glad Harriet was not there.

The swart man went at his work with a will; and presently, watching his head bent down before me, my fancy went free again, and I said to myself:

"He evidently recognised my royalty by instinct. Has he not mounted me here, at once, upon a throne? Is he not making all these low obeisances to me? It's wonderful to be a Caliph."

It was a stuffy little hole of a place, no larger than a Hempfield hen coop, with four chairs in a row, a kerosene stove in one corner, and brightly coloured pictures of the King and Queen of Italy on the wall.

"How long," I asked, "have you been here blacking shoes?"

He looked up at me with his piercing black eyes and an ingratiating smile, a smile possible only to an Italian.

"Twenty-seven years," said he.

If he had struck me he could scarcely have surprised me more. Twenty-seven years blacking shoes; think of it! And all right here on this street corner.

"You must," said I, "have blacked a million shoes in that time."

"Mebbe—perhaps," he said, smiling until his teeth gleamed, "tinka two-three million. All pipple in city."

It was inconceivable. It defied all my notions of the city where, of course, people are constantly changing about, doing new things—and being rather miserable in doing them.

"Do you like it?" I asked.

"Sure, I like. I mak' money."

He said it jauntily; and looked as happy as a man could.

"Another ideal exploded," said I to myself, for my idea of the bootblack, as I think of it now with amusement, was in terms of the poor, starved, hungry street boy of youthful storybooks; starved to-day, but a mayor or senator presently; a miserable figure, through whom one could easily acquire, at trivial cost, the inner glow of the charitable. But this stocky, sturdy Italian had not only been at it twenty-seven years without becoming President, but actually seemed to like it. So I sat there marvelling on my throne, as surprised as the Lord God in Eden at what I found.

Just then a fine-looking young fellow, extremely well dressed, dark-eyed and trim, stepped into the little shop; and my bootblack, pausing a moment and putting down his brushes, took from his inner pocket a worn leather pocketbook, and from a

24

substantial supply of bills took out three and gave them to the young man. As he turned back to his work on my shoes, he said:

"He my boy."

"Your boy?"

"Yes, he go college this year; spend plenty da mon'."

"College!"

"Sure, he go college."

What next? I began at once to ask a hundred eager questions. This poor, down-trodden bootblack! Just outside by the curb he showed me his Car; no very grand affair, indeed, but nevertheless a Car, wherein he drove to work in the morning as fine as you please. Turning over a new customer to one of his helpers, he told me, as he brushed me off, of his wife and family, and then, seeing how deeply interested I was, he took from his inner pocket a couple of photographs (rather soiled), one of himself, his wife, and children, he with a starched collar and his moustache curled to perfection, and his family as robust and cheerful as one could wish to see.

"And that," said he, showing me the other photograph, "is my house."

His house!

He stood there smiling at my wonder.

"And you earned all this blacking shoes?"

"Sure, I earn. I mak' plenty da mon'."

Well, there he stood, a reality; to me, a new person, sturdy, vigorous, happy, with his cubby of a shop, his brushes, his car, his house, his black-eyed family, his son in college.

"I wonder," I thought, laughed at myself, "whether I am the Caliph incognito, or he."

"Well," I said aloud, "I think you have done wonders."

He smiled broadly.

"And I'd like to shake hands with you."

This was evidently something entirely new, but brushing his hand off on his apron he extended it to me.

"You're a real man," said I; "you're a true citizen. I want to call on you again."

"Sure."

"Sure" has come to be one of the most expressive words in the American language, said as he said it, with gusto and unction.

I left him there smiling broadly, with his greasy fat pocket-book just showing above his vest, and the tool of his triumph, his blacking brush, in his hand. I think he also enjoyed the adventure.

"Well, well!" said I, "if I haven't had my money's worth; if that isn't a story—just blundered into."

And walking across the street toward the wharves and turning these astonishing things over in my mind, and occasionally catching a blinding glimpse of the halo from my new-shined shoes, I said to myself:

"I like being a Caliph—as far as I have gone."

I stood for a long time on the docks watching a great rusty, weatherbeaten British ship discharging a pungent cargo of tea from Ceylon and teakwood timbers and baled cotton goods from India—and all in the clear May sunshine. A raw Scotchman at the donkey-engine bellowed and swore, and nimble little lascar sailors in woolly turbans and dirty cotton shirts darted about the littered deck. I watched with delight the husky longshoremen, their bare arms all knotty with muscles as they lifted and loaded and ran with the heavy trucks. I love the very look of outdoor men powerfully and easily at work. How deftly they lifted the great bales and timbers; and in the intervals how still they stood to rest. I liked the well-controlled power of the hoisting engine and the little plumes of steam, worried by a fresh breeze from off the bay, as they were torn in ragged gusts from the exhaust.

"What a world this is," I thought, "full of all kinds of strange and interesting people."

I had a great impulse to go aboard the ship myself and try to find out more about the Scotch engine-driver, the lascars, and the longshoremen.

"Each of us," I said to myself, "gets to thinking of himself as the centre of the universe. That great bellowing Scotchman clearly thinks so, and that little dark lascar out of India is no doubt sure that he is—probably thinks that all of us are in outer darkness; and that Jew, checking out the boxes of tea, is he not also to himself the centre of the universe? And how am I better than any one of them? Don't I think I am also the centre of the universe? Now, it is evident that we can't all be centres. There aren't enough universes to go around. If we keep on trying it, I can see nothing ahead of us but celestial collisions—and chaos. The question seems to be: How shall we all learn to live together agreeably at the centre of the only universe we are ever likely to know anything about? And how can we do that unless we understand one another?"

Musing upon these things I moved on again, thinking that one day I'd sail to India on just such a rusty ship and come really to know all these strange people.

So I came again into the streets of the city, considering where I should go next.

"Sooner or later," said I, "I shall have to honour some one of my fellow democrats by having him take me to luncheon. One must eat."

This idea amused me greatly, and I thought of all the different ways I could try to beguile one of these hurrying strangers not only to invite me to luncheon, but to be glad afterward that he had done it. No problem that isn't difficult is interesting, said I to myself, and to a true Caliph, said I, all things are possible.

So I walked up the long street from the wharves; and with the necessity of finding a luncheon somewhere looming greater every moment.

Presently I stopped at the window of a second-hand book-shop, quite a dusty, shabby place, but when I looked in at all the wares there exhibited I had a kind of love for it. I am not one who is much drawn to any book simply because it is old; and why such pother over a first edition when the same good contents are in the second or fiftieth? And yet old books are not unlike old houses: they wear upon them the marks of life. Often and often at a shabby stall have I picked up a book marked here and there by some former traveller: here a passage scored with approval, there one underlined with emphasis, or a word corrected or queried. In reading such a book it is almost as though you had an unseen companion looking over your shoulder, and before you get through you come to know pretty well what kind of man he was. Not long ago I found an old book in an old shop which delighted me greatly, for it bears the footprints of a furiously angry man. "Bah!" he writes on the margin, or "Piffle," or "The Idiot," or "Sophomoric." I turned each page with delight, expecting some new explosion.

(There is another advantage in old bookstores that I should put in parentheses: there one can get two or three books for the price of one.)

So I thought I would go into the shop and take up a book or two—luncheon or no luncheon. And it was here that I met my fate!

Harriet says that I am lucky; that I "fall into things." But I think it is only because I look like a countryman, and so, when I begin to ask questions, I make the stranger feel somehow superior, which is to him a comfortable, tolerant feeling and does no harm to me. And besides, a man has a kind of fondness for those for whom, in his superiority, he feels that he must make allowances. I know well the allowances that have to be made for me.

While I was in the bookshop I noticed there another customer: a middle-aged man with thin grey hair and a somewhat weary look. He was taking up a book here and there, but hardly looking at it before he put it back again. He seemed not to know what he wanted. And yet, by the way of him, he was a man of evident position—perhaps of some wealth. He might be one of those men who make believe that they have a passion for first editions. I watched him out of the corner of my eye.

"He looks," said I, "as though he were bored with life."

It struck me as an inspiration, so suddenly that I could feel a warm flush spreading through my body, that this was the very man I was looking for—to take the Caliph to lunch.

But how to do it?

I studied him sharply, pretending I was deep in a book, and

watched for an opening. There were the little familiar marks around his eyes that showed humour; and this was an element in my favour. For humour is the world's Esperanto.

Still I held back; and still he kept picking up and putting down various books. I tried to think up a clever speech to make to him; but have never in my life been able, beforehand, to think of anything clever to say. Presently, he all but threw down a book, as though in disgust, and, turning suddenly, walked out of the shop.

Though a Caliph, I was panic-stricken. He was about to escape me. I saw the prospects of luncheon fading away. But I stepped so quickly after him that we were almost face to face in the little entry of the shop. Now or never!

"Do you know," said I, "of a good place to lunch?"

It was not at all what I intended to say.

It seemed to take him a moment to focus upon me. I could see in his sharp glance the shrewd appraisal of the business man.

"Why, no," said he; "at least not around here."

"I am a stranger here," said I, "from the country. I do not know the City."

He seemed to be thinking about a place to direct me to. I was at the crisis now; everything depended on what I said next.

"I had a very amusing idea in the shop there," I said, looking him in the eye and smiling.

He did not answer, but looked at me again, this time with an air of vague curiosity.

"I am interested in books too," I said, "and I could see you taking them up and putting them down as though you were— well, disgusted with them."

Still he did not reply, but stood looking at me now half impatiently—though a kind of amused glint came in his eye.

"Who are you, anyway?" he asked, not ill-naturedly.

"I am a countryman," I said, "a kind of farmer."

"I can see that," he said, half smiling; "but you must be something more than a farmer, or you wouldn't be visiting old bookshops."

"Now," said I eagerly, "you are discovering me; the fact is, I *am* more than a countryman. I am here incognito."

"How is that?" he asked, plainly not knowing whether to be amused or irritated or alarmed.

With that I began telling him how I had started out that morning and how I had felt, a stranger in the streets, and how that had led me to the odd fancies I have already described. I made the whole story, including my experience with the Italian bootblack, as amusing and yet as matter of fact as I could. . . . But suppose he had no imagination!

"So you're now a Caliph incognito," said he, laughing.

"Yes," said I.

"Looking for adventure in Bagdad?"

"Yes," said I, "and I want to tell you where you come in."

He now looked thoroughly amused—with every wrinkle around his eyes in full employment. Blessed be, he *had* imagination!

"I decided," I said, "that you might well be the citizen of Bagdad who would take the Caliph to luncheon."

At this he laughed aloud.

"Well," said he, "whoever you are, you're a good one. And why not? I was going to my club to luncheon; but when a Caliph is in town——"

So we turned up the street together. I cannot tell how triumphant I felt. It was as though I had won a battle.

He was clearly still somewhat suspicious—your true City man is difficult to beguile—and opened up on the subject of books, I think as a kind of new test of me. As luck would have it, he fell outright upon an old passion of mine, George Borrow, and I soon found that my friend could easily floor me on the early editions and the bindings, but that I easily put him down when we came to discuss Isopel Berners and the Flaming Tinman.

By this time we were comfortably seated at an extraordinarily small table in a curious little restaurant kept by a Greek down a side street. The table was so small that it brought us close together at once. I think, by reaching hard, we could have touched noses across it. . . .

I cannot remember now one single thing we had to eat that day—and that is unusual for me. For once started upon our talk, or rather his talk, we never stopped. And such talk, and such a new human story!

Every last man and woman of us, in this world, goes about in daily drudgery, a dim, dull, uninspired daily life, expecting sometime, somewhere, a Miracle; every man and woman goes about among suspicion, and jealousy, and envy, expecting sometime, somewhere, to meet a Great Friend. . . . This is true.

I cannot here report the full conversation; it would make an entire book by itself; for the warmer grew my interest, the more earnest my questioning, the more eager seemed my friend to unburden himself.

"I don't know why I should say such things to you," he would say. "I never before said such things to any one."

"You can be free," said I, "with a Caliph."

The worn, dull look disappeared from his face; he seemed determined to talk away all the burden of unsaid things so long stored up within him. His name was John Cross Pitwell. (I have changed it only a little.) He was a business man in a way a little vague to my limited experience; at least, he had large and often difficult dealings, and much responsibility. He had made, I judged, a good deal of money. But these outward facts (though I did not learn them all on that first meeting), once we were started, became immaterial. Are they ever really important?

I have thought since much about the man's story; and if I could boil it all down into its essence I should say that it was expressed in a single sentence of his that I remember vividly:

"I've made money. I've been what you might call a success—at least my friends say so—but I'll tell you the truth. I've never done what I wanted to do or been what I wanted to be."

And that is why, ever since, I cannot help thinking of John Cross Pitwell as an unhappy failure, and his story, though simple enough in its elements, a kind of tragedy.

31

He referred to the chance of his being in the bookshop that day and meeting me.

"It was a mere chance," said he, "I suppose, of this spring weather. Every year at this time I have a stirring of the old restlessness. I wake up in the night with a feeling something like homesickness. I have a kind of self-disgust, as though I had deliberately wasted my life. Often something I see in a magazine, possibly a line of poetry, will start an ache in me I cannot describe."

"I know, I know," said I.

"And that is why I avoid reading anything serious; I want something exciting, absorbing, that will take me away from myself. But in spring days like these it sometimes gets the better of me. Once, a long time ago, I did have a number of keen interests. Books, old books and first editions, was one of them, and to-day, as I was coming down the street, I saw Cahan's bookshop and turned in. But it only bored me."

"I could see that," I said.

"Well," he continued, with a short and rather bitter laugh, "you see what I am now. I am a stodgy, uninteresting business man, uninteresting to myself and to everyone else, getting old and bald"—he turned down the top of his head to show me. "I do what every other man of my kind does, say what he says, think what he thinks. . . . It sometimes seems as though I had never lived."

He paused.

"We grow ashamed of the best things we have in us," said he; "and fail to be what we might have been—with a little more courage. I remember a poem written by T. B. Aldrich, which I should never dream of mentioning to my hard-headed partners. I knew T. B. Aldrich himself slightly when I was a boy, worshipped him afar off. My father knew him well. The poem I speak of describes me exactly. It is called 'Voices and Visions,' you may know it."

"No," said I, "I do not know it; but I should like to."

"Well," said my friend, "Aldrich begins by telling how

> "In youth beside the lonely sea
> Voices and visions came to me.
> Titania and her fertile broods
> Were my familiars in the woods.

"It is a picture of a youth full of visions—I won't bore you with all of it—a youth who goes to the city, where for a time the voices still follow him from street to street.

> "Strange lights my errant fancy led.

"But he does not respond, and the voices and visions grow dim—and dimmer. The concluding lines of that little poem are to me about the saddest I know:

> "Now one by one the visions fly.
> And one by one the voices die.
> More distantly the accents ring,
> More frequent the receding wing.
> Full dark shall be the days in store
> When voice and vision come no more."

He paused, and we were both silent for some moments.

"It isn't," said he, "that I have been unsuccessful, or that I have been soured by misfortune or ill-treated in any way that I know of. It's because the world is just plain—damned—deadly —dull."

I cannot tell how my heart went out to this strange, rich, unhappy man. For what does it matter, all the "success" in the world, when no longer "voices and visions" come to a man?

I told him, in parting, of my lodgings and of Harriet; and urged him to come and see us.

"We'll have some more great talk," said I, "about this wicked and miserable but altogether beautiful and desirable old world of ours."

I left him with an amused gleam in his eye.

"I'll come," said he, "I'll surely come. If you can be a Caliph in Bagdad, perhaps I can be a One-Eyed Calendar."

"No, you're Aladdin; you have only to rub your lamp and do what you will."

"I've lost my lamp," said he.

I warned him that he might meet other strange company there: Sinbad the Sailor, Jensen the Bookbinder, or even the Great Roc himself; but he assured me that nothing should stop him.

So it was that I walked homeward thinking this day one of the greatest of my whole life. . . .

As I was going to bed a line from a poem I like, a fine poem, came into my mind:

What is this world but our secret natures opened and stamped into cities?

III

THE MEETING IN THE TOWER

I EXPECT I was ridiculous enough in those early days in the City, even after I began to meet a few of the people, like Mr. Pitwell and the Jensens; but the countryman in me, and the countryman's inborn suspicion of the City, even the dislike of it, sometimes got the better of me. I was always thinking how much happier most of these hurrying people would be if only they could live in the country.

You are entitled to smile when I tell you that I used sometimes to go about the sunny streets rolling under my tongue certain fine old denunciations of cities—with plenty of "woes" in them.

> "Woe unto them that join house to house . . . till there be no place, that they may be placed alone in the midst of the earth."

It is truly one of the joys of the country I know to be "placed alone in the midst of the earth," where a man can look about him freely, look up at the sky, look down at the earth, look and think well of all the things he sees, and so, love deep. "Slowness," said Rodin, "is beauty"—but there is no slowness in the City.

Another of these denunciations came often freshly (and humorously) to my mind when I saw the great rich houses and stores of the City with the swift traffic rolling by. It is from Isaiah:

> "Their land also is full of silver and gold, neither is there any end of their treasures . . . neither is there any end of their chariots."

35

("The old fellow knew this City," said I to myself.)

"Their land also is full of idols; they worship the work of their own hands, that which their own fingers have made."

I love these strong old words, and while I said them humorously enough, there yet seemed to be a kind of sense and truth about them. People in the City are worshippers of the works of their own hands, and come easily to forget that God lives.

("God said, the heaven and the earth, think ye that We created them in jest, and that ye shall not return to Us?")

But the trouble, these charming May days, was that the City appeared not in the least shaken by my denunciations. The woes did not seem to touch the hurrying people! The streets, the tall buildings, the little open spaces with bits of greenery, had a kind of indescribable brisk beauty which I could not resist, and as for the people, although they were different indeed from the country folks I know best—the Scotch Preacher, Horace, and the Stone Mason—I began to be more and more interested in them. I played Caliph, as I have related, in meeting some of them, like Mr. Pitwell; but with others I came into contact in the most ordinary ways.

There was Mr. Tuney, whom I met soon after I arrived. He occupied a place in the publishing establishment I often visited. He had a flavour of his own, a somewhat bitter flavour, quite beyond my experience. The first time that ever I went to walk with him we stopped at the top of a little open square where we could watch the people streaming by like so many hurrying ants, to their evening trains. I remember the shrugging way he waved his arm and the tone of his voice when he said:

"Insects!"

That was actually what he thought of human beings.

Yet I found him extraordinarily interesting. He was new to me, and he rather shocked me (we like to be shocked—in the right tone of voice!) by calling me names.

"Grayson," said he, "you are a kind of Don Quixote."

Not to be outdone, I came instantly back at him:

36

"Tuney, you're a kind of Diogenes."

Well, he was.

So I invited him to the first of the gatherings in our Tower on the City Wall.

It seems to me I could make a whole book of that one evening, if I were to tell all about those who were there and how they looked and what they said. The *reality* of them—all sitting about in the cool of the evening with the windows of our Tower wide open and the distant, drowsy sounds of the City coming in! I think I see most clearly the old Dane, Jensen, there in our largest chair, with his great china pipe curving down upon his breast. It had a little cover over the top of it, this old-country pipe, like a pepper box, and occasionally he took it out of his mouth to remark, "Ach, vell," or "Vell, vell, vell," in a deep, guttural tone, full of comfort. In his best clothes, with his shaggy grey hair brushed back, he looked more than ever like Beethoven.

One thing surprised me very much: Mr. Pitwell, when he came in, at once greeted Jensen. Jensen had bound a number of valuable books for him, and they fell at once to talking of the lore of old bindings.

Mr. Tuney and our dry little Knightly, who is always quoting something or other, came in together, though they had not met before. Knightly often surprised us with what he carried about, all covered over with diffidences, inside of him.

(If only human beings would meet one another on the basis of what they have inside them, instead of outside!)

And, of course, Harriet was there.

In a company like this, of men so different, and strangers to boot, there was at first some ice to break; but long ago I made the discovery that the best thing for melting ice is warmth. If a man knows you like him he begins at once to thaw out, and that is the first step. The next step is to produce some kind of a conflagration which so raises the temperature that all those present begin, figuratively, to cry out, "Fire, fire!" and forget in their excitement all about themselves. For iciness always means that people are frozen with thinking about themselves, shivering lest someone take them for less than they take themselves.

37

It was fortunate that Mr. Tuney was there to begin with, because he and I strike fire on sight. In no time at all we were tussling furiously over the respective merits of city and country. As I think of it since, it makes me smile, for it strongly resembled a question which once, long ago, I heard debated in a country school:

"Resolved, that the country is better than the city."

It began when Mr. Pitwell asked me, as a countryman, of some of the things that struck me as interesting about the City—"interesting or different."

"Why," said I, "everything is interesting and different. There are a thousand little curious things at every turn."

"What, for example?" asked Mr. Tuney.

"Well," said I, "here's a very little one: I've noticed that nearly all the wooden clocks along the streets—you know, those that advertise jewellery stores—have the hands so pointed as to represent seventeen minutes after eight o'clock. Now, why is that? Why eight-seventeen, and not nine o'clock, or twelve, or four?"

"Is that so?" exclaimed Mr. Pitwell; "I never noticed it."

"Vell, vell!" remarked Jensen, taking his pipe out of his mouth.

"Try it the next time you are out!" said I.

"It ought to be five o'clock," remarked Mr. Tuney. "That's the golden hour of the day. It's the only hour anybody ever really seems to want."

"Nobody in the City," said Mr. Knightly, "ever truly looks at anything."

"But what does it matter?" retorted Mr. Tuney. "And what difference does it make? And why should Mr. Grayson here clutter up his mind with such worthless observations? . . . Is *that* all you see in the City!"

"I see," said I, "that I must dig deeper to satisfy Mr. Tuney. Well, take the matter of age and death in the City. That has struck me hard. With us in the country there is a kind of beauty and honour about age; and death is a pageant which has not lost all of its meaning."

("Hear, hear!" cried Knightly.)

"In our town," I continued, warming up to my subject, "there is one ceremony that it would satisfy your hearts to see. We have an official town cane, ebony, with a gold head, with which we honour the oldest citizen. When he dies it passes on to the next oldest. I wish you could have seen our selectman coming down the West Road not long ago, in his black coat, with the gold-headed cane in his hand, to bestow it with ceremony upon Old Man Norton. It had been known for days, ever since John Webster's death, that the cane would be coming down the West Road; and Old Man Norton sat at the window, looking up the road, waiting. I saw him there, with his white beard, his skull-cap, and his dim old eyes peering behind his spectacles. He was ninety-three years old. They said he cried when the selectman came in stamping the snow from his feet.

"'Where's old Mr. Norton?'

"'Here I am,' cried the high, cracked voice. 'I'm ninety-three, come April. I'm the oldest man in town.'

"Well, you should see the pride of the old man, walking about with that gold-headed cane. It has given him a bit more of happiness in his dull old hours, which he might never otherwise have had. But in the City, who ever sees or thinks of the old? Where are they, anyway? Who cares? You elbow them aside."

("Ach, vell," said Jensen, shaking his head.)

"And death," said I, "is not an event in the City, only an incident; to be smuggled out of sight and hurried through with. Both life and death, in the City, grow cheap and shallow."

It is one of the troubles with me that even when I begin with a humorous idea, I turn serious too soon; and to my embarrassment find myself making an oration.

But fortunately Mr. Tuney was there. He rose at once to the challenge. Of course the country had to make the most of the old people, said he, it had so few of the young! And as for himself, if he were having pageants, he thought he would rather have them deal with live men than dead ones.

"And how does it happen," asked Mr. Tuney, triumphantly, "if the country has all the charms you say, that the City should be so crowded with country people?"

Well hit—and a good laugh.

"Here you are, now, Mr. Grayson," said he, "living in the top of this City lodging, when you might be at home planting corn! Here we all are—enjoying ourselves!"

Well hit!

By this time the temperature had not only melted all the ice, but we were sitting about in delightful summer weather, coats figuratively off and fans going. Knightly had already quoted twice from the poets, and Jensen's pipe was smoking like a factory chimney. Pitwell had utterly ceased to be bored. As for Harriet, she looked delightfully alarmed—and afterward said to me:

"David, I *don't* see how you and Mr. Tuney can disagree so completely and call each other such terrible names and still be friends."

"Harriet," said I, "if everyone agreed with me, this would be a dull world."

Good conversation is like a brush fire: once well started the flames go every way of the wind. We talked of poets and potato-growing, bookbinding and bees—everything in the world! I cannot put down all that was said, but I must at least report Mr. Tuney upon the subject of masterpieces in America (I think in secret Mr. Tuney writes poetry!), because he spoke with the authority of a kind of minor prophet, say, Hosea or Micah.

"Trouble with authors in America," said he, "is that they don't put enough of 'em in jail. In old times they had the right recipe for masterpieces. They locked up the poets and prophets and fed 'em on bread and water, or drove 'em out into the wilderness—and the product was 'Pilgrim's Progress' and the 'Epistle to the Philippians' and the 'Inferno' and 'Don Quixote.' But nowadays, if anywhere a man shows the least symptom of breaking through the thin crust of civilisation with anything free, bold, original, instead of locking him up they immediately invite him to tea. Instead of taking away his liberty, they force more liberty upon him. They give him an automobile these days."

("They haven't offered me any yet," remarked Knightly.)

("Your turn'll come," said Mr. Pitwell.)

"They invite him to talk," continued Mr. Tuney, "to lecture, to visit innumerable colleges, chambers of commerce, women's clubs, and they sit hanging upon his words, although they care less to hear what he says than they do to see him squirm. The trouble in America is not that speech is not free, but that it is too free——"

("Hear, hear, hear!" exclaimed Mr. Knightly.)

"Oh, they wear him out! Everything that is fresh and original in him bleeds away in talk to audiences which want to be shocked just enough to make their return to their own strong-holds of opinion more delightful. That's the end of *him!* What we need in America is to put the really promising poets and prophets in jail—and keep 'em there!"—Mr. Tuney's face was flushed; and he now brought his fist down upon the corner of the table—"Keep 'em there on bread and water."

I wish you could have heard Mr. Pitwell laugh at these savage sallies, and the rest of us with him.

I had seen our diffident friend Knightly sitting over in the corner during these remarks, slowly filling up with something to say. I knew that he was a writer of sorts, one who hung on at the fringe of literature, too good to succeed and yet not quite good enough.

"How would you favour putting the authors in jail, Mr. Knightly?" I asked.

"It won't work," said he, smiling. "Now, I'm in jail, and produce no masterpieces."

We all looked at him with new interest.

"How's that?" asked Mr. Pitwell.

"Why," said Knightly, "I'm poor; and to be as poor as I am is to be in jail. No, jail won't do it. I see what Mr. Tuney really means: it's that your poets and prophets won't take time to be quiet and dig down into life, get some vital beliefs of their own about it. They don't take time to look at ordinary things and ordinary people until these ordinary things and people become extraordinary and so worth writing about; and, above all, they won't wait until they must write or sing or prophesy because it hurts them not to—and that's what makes true literature, and poetry and art, and"—said he, with his voice dropping—"I think religion too."

There was a distinct pause of surprise following these words of Knightly's; they were so unexpected, coming from such a dry, diffident, unassuming little man. Yet there was a quality of sincerity behind them that went straight home.

"Right," said Mr. Pitwell, "you're right. It's as Grayson says: we move too fast in the City to feel the spaciousness and continuity of life. We see only surfaces. I can see nothing for it but to move out to Grayson's farm and be happy."

"I invite you here and now," said I, "every one of you. There's room in the country to live, *really* live, and to look at life—and to think. There's even time to be tranquil, which is the rarest achievement of modern life. I shall go back there as soon as ever I can."

With that it came upon me with such a sudden wave of longing as I cannot describe, what Hempfield would be like on such May evenings as these: the meadows there, and the trees coming out in full leaf, and the lilacs in bloom. And the fine work to do there under the open sky, and how a man could be happy there! And as I looked about at the friendly faces all around me in the room, I said suddenly—for I had never thought of such a thing before:

"Will you let me read you something?"

"Go on," said they.

So I opened the drawer of my desk and took out one of my notebooks.

"It may amuse you," said I, "and seem even a little absurd— I don't care if it does!—but I've found a way of living a kind of country life right here in the City. I'll tell you how it is: For many years in the country I've made a practice of putting down every day in such little books as these—not diaries, but notebooks—some record of what I have seen, or heard, or smelled, or thought or felt, as I went about my work. For when you write about life, it is a curious thing, you get a double joy out of it. You sharpen up every impression; you get twice as much living out of the same experiences. So I have been going back every spring, while imprisoned here in this Bastille——"

("This agreeable Bastille," put in Mr. Pitwell.)

"—in this agreeable Bastille, to what I have written during many a spring in the country. In April here I had April there, and a fine April, too; and now in May here I have May there, and already I'm looking forward to June. Two lives, you see, I live—one here in this Tower on the City Wall——"

("Your agreeable Bastille," said Mr. Pitwell.)

"—my agreeable Bastille, and one in the hills of Hempfield."

"Where does the Caliph come in?" asked Pitwell; "you are not forgetting the Caliph?"

"That," said I, "is another matter."

"Go on with the reading," cried Mr. Tuney.

"So I thought I'd read you the very passage with which I comforted my spirit this morning. It was written only last year and almost on this very day in May. It's really nothing much in itself, but it brings back to me a moment of the past so that I can live it again. I call it:

THE BEES OF HEMPFIELD

"This spring, especially, have I loved the bees of Hempfield; and watched them long and too ignorantly. Some future life I shall devote entirely to studying the bees: all the varieties, until I know well their wise communities and all their regulated habits and trim manners. Since we have lived and planted upon this hillside, the birds have come to us in great variety, and many small, shy animals, including a one-eyed rabbit, a pair of Chinese pheasants, and a family of grey squirrels—but, more than all else, the bees. For in making beauty and abundance for ourselves with apples, peaches, plums, cherries, pears, and all the small fruits, to say nothing of many rich and sweet shrubs like the bush honeysuckle, we have given a friendly welcome to the bees. We have made a kind of bee paradise. I forget also the alfalfa and clover in our field below, now near blooming, and the tall hubam, which comes later. I estimate the bee population

43

upon our small acres on a bright day like this at not less than six hundred thousand to eight hundred thousand. And yet people will say that the country is lonesome!"

("Vell, vell," said Jensen.)

"Of these, of course, a large proportion are in our own colonies of honeybees; but we are hospitable and welcome great numbers of other bees of all kinds. Just now the rich flowering honeysuckles are veritably alive with them. That old giant, the bumblebee, is a noisy worker but fast! He averages twice as many blossoms in the minute as the honeybee. But his manners are far from good; he is rough, crude, direct—like one of our oil barons. He wallows over the blossoms, tearing down the anthers, plunging headlong among the petals, driving by sheer force through all obstacles and taking what he will without asking leave. Getting the oil! I have been watching him on the columbines. Here he is a regular robber and takes honey without paying even the usual toll. Instead of thrusting his tongue down through the corolla, and thus helping to spread the pollen—which is the price that nature demands from the law-abiding bee—he lights on the outside of the blossom and bites *through* the tender growth like a burglar, and steals the honey pot entire. Oh, he's a modern business man!"

("Hear, hear," cried **Mr. Tuney.**)

"How different the honeybee, how much defter and better mannered! She uses her brains to save her legs. She apparently studies each blossom before wasting energy upon it: hovering an inappreciable instant above it—does she *see* or *smell?*—and making her visit only when she is sure she will have some reward in nectar. I picked many blossoms which I saw the honeybees rejecting and tore them apart. In no case did I find the little, glistening, moist bit of nectar which the bees seek. How do they know? Apparently the bumblebee bumbles into all the blossoms without discrimination, and takes the chances of finding or of not finding a store of honey."

So I closed the book.

"It may not mean much to you," said I; "but it made me live over again that May morning in Hempfield."

"And it gave me an introduction to your farm," said Knightly, "that I shall not forget."

Mr. Pitwell and Mr. Tuney were both about to speak, when the door opened and Harriet came in with a tray. Some time before this I had seen her slipping out; and then presently, stealing in upon our conversation, came that most delectable of odours—good coffee. And here she was herself with her tray, the shining coffee-pot upon it sending off a delightful plume of steam; and a great pyramid of doughnuts at one side.

Of all the masterpieces of art in this dull world, fabricated out of common materials, what is there to excel a fine, rich, brown doughnut, with just a bit of powdered sugar to set it off and indicate its true inner virtues!

(I would also specify, without offence to other great artists in that field, that Harriet made them. Harriet has a way with her!)

Instantly, upon the opening of the door, Mr. Pitwell sprang up and brought forward the little table, on which Harriet placed the tray. Jensen sat forward, beaming, in his chair, his fat china pipe held unregarded in his hand.

"If this," said Mr. Tuney, "is what ordinarily happens in the country, I surrender."

"You'd better," said Harriet.

It may be that common ideas, or a common class, or race, draw men together; but not one of them equals in sheer magic the binding power of a good doughnut. After this experience I am sure of it. There we all were, picked up at random out of the flotsam of life—and like old friends. . . .

The pleasant excitement of the parting—the visitors all going down the stairs talking and laughing; and Harriet and I in the doorway to see them off, Harriet flushed and happy as I had not seen her since before we left Hempfield.

Only Knightly hung in the doorway, and seemed loath to go.

"It has been so friendly here," he said, wistfully, glancing at Harriet, and then, after an awkward pause, he said, half laughing, "I think I could really write—if I lived in the country."

("David," said Harriet afterward, "in some ways I like that Mr. Knightly the best of any of your friends.")

45

So I put on my hat and walked down with Knightly. We talked on the stairs, we stopped to talk on the steps, we walked slowly down the street talking, we talked on the deserted corner while the clock struck one, we turned the corner and came, still talking, to the square. . . .

(And that, I assert, is the true way to talk—all floodgates wide open and the water pouring recklessly over the dam.)

So I came back through the silent, mysterious streets of the sleeping City. And I thought of all the strange life throbbing around me within and beyond the walls of the darkened buildings—life so little seen or understood, because so few men take the time from their eager money-getting to stop and look at it, and thus come to know it and love it. I said to myself:

"I will look through these walls; the barred doors cannot keep me out, nor any customs or laws exclude me, but I shall go in and understand."

And I went up the stairs to our Tower with a strange, deep sense of having had, somehow, a great experience.

IV

THE ICEMAN

A MAN," says Emerson, "is like a bit of Labrador spar, which has no lustre, as you turn it in your hand, until you come to a particular angle; then it shows deep and beautiful colours."

I like people, all kinds of people, but especially first-hand, salty people. I mean people who have nothing between them and life; who, when they reach out a hand, touch things that have actual existence; who, when they look up, see life and, when they listen, hear life.

One of the amusing adventures I had in the City—perhaps because it came about with such utter naturalness—was that with the Iceman. I never recall it since without a thrill of enjoyment.

I saw him first in May. He drove his cart into our street: a great yellow cart with an arched roof like the prairie schooners I knew as a boy. I was on my way down to the printing shop of my weekly misery when he came in upon me. I suppose I had seen ice wagons and icemen a hundred times before, but not with the eye of enjoyment that I had that morning. Possibly it was because there was no other iceman quite like mine! He was just getting out of his cart as I chanced along; and there was something so easily strong about him, a splendid power in his great shoulders and muscular neck, that I could not help giving him a second glance.

His head, thatched with crispy yellow hair, was bare to the May sunshine; he had a ruddy glow upon his face and a rollicking look of the eye. A big, thick-chested, well-knit man, with shirt open at the throat and hands like small hams.

47

"Whoa," said he, swinging himself down, and the team of grey horses, powerful shouldered and shaggy hoofed, came to a stop.

He stepped to the back of his yellow caravan, took his tongs down from a hook, seized a block of ice, swung it easily out of the wagon, caught the hook on the scales, looked at the dial, and then, turning quickly to a girl who had just stepped out of a nearby basement door, remarked:

"Mornin', Maggie."

He looked at her with a broad smile, as though there were some good joke between them.

"Fifty this morn', Maggie? You bet."

With this he deftly cast his leather apron over his shoulder to protect his shirt, swung the block of ice upon it, and disappeared down the area-way, bantering Maggie as he went.

Well, there was something jaunty and clean-cut about it all that I liked. A kind of reality, a kind of joy of life! While he was gone I looked over his cart and his horses. It was a delight to see how neat and well arranged everything was: the ax, with one side sharpened to a pick, set in a leather holder, a place for the tongs and the pails, and the feed bags for the horses, and the blankets, and the coiled ropes—and from a hook in the hood the dinner pail of the Iceman himself, with his pipe and his tobacco pouch in a little box of its own near at hand. He even had the morning paper stuck in at the side of the seat. He could not have been more at home at his own fireside.

But it was the horses which most delighted me. Splendid great Percherons, with coats rubbed until they were like silk. Every spot on the harness that could shine, shone; every spot that ought to look oily and black, looked oily and black. And there were red pompons on the bridles and many red and white rings on the head straps, and brass knobs, so bright they hurt your eyes, at the top of the hames.

"That man loves his horses," said I to myself.

Above the collars, on the outer side, were brass plates bearing the words "Sylvan Pond Ice Company"—and these literally shone in the sun.

"Any man," said I, "who truly loves animals is well worth knowing."

I don't know why such common things should so delight a man, but they do. They seem to mean something interesting, alive, real.

I found I had walked entirely around the ice wagon, examining everything closely, and was just back on the sidewalk when the Iceman came out of the area-way.

"Good-bye, Maggie; see you to-morra."

("I suppose," I laughed inwardly, "he knows all the Maggies in the street.")

He hung his tongs deftly on their proper hook, stepped on the hub of the wheel, and slid easily into his seat. The reins were attached to a hook on the roof of the hood. He did not take them down, but merely shook them.

"Hey there, Lady," he called.

The ponderous horses stepped forward, the polished brass of the harness gleamed in the sunshine, the pompons tossed, the wheels of the great cart thundered on the stones—and the Iceman moved onward to new triumphs, new Maggies.

I looked after him with a kind of amused longing. I had not said a single word; and as for him, he had appeared not to see me at all. But I went on down the street somehow pleased and refreshed.

After that, every time my work took me out in the morning I looked up and down the street for my Iceman. I came to know the time of his coming and going, for he ran on schedule like a train. It may seem absurd, but sometimes I turned out of my way to pass him, or walked slowly down the other side of the street to see him in action.

"He is truly a popular man," said I; "if he were to run for alderman, he'd have this street to the last vote."

He joked the policeman at the corner as he passed. It is something to be able to call the policeman "Bill." He flirted with or bantered all the cooks, maids, and even the housewives in our street. Once, going by, I heard him having a lively set-to with the grocer's wife on the corner. At a distance I thought that it was an altercation about the weight of the ice; but as I came nearer, it turned out to be a heated disagreement as to whether it would rain or "turn off fair."

"Gee, it's hot," says the Iceman.

"Hot!" says the grocer's wife, "and you settin' in an ice wagon!"

"Sure it's hot; and me carryin' ice up three flights o' stairs."

I even found that Harriet had made the acquaintance of the Iceman—or rather with the head of him, for she never saw anything more than his head looking in at the little trap window where he put the ice into our ice box. He always wore a broad smile; and it was not long before the conversation spread from such cogent observations as "How much, miss?" or "Mighty fine weather, miss," to the disclosure of personal history. I defy any one, from a President to an iceman, to resist for long the impulse to tell Harriet how many children he has and whether girls or boys. The Iceman had four.

The oftener I saw him, the stronger grew my impression of him as a kind of Triumphant Character of the town. He had, it is true, no outriders going before him with trumpets; but his coming was not the less heralded. I could see in imagination the wave of preparation sweeping up street after street; the Maggies and the Sallies fixing the ice boxes, and then preparing to touch off the latch or open the area door. I could see flocks of youngsters—both boys and girls—ready to welcome him wherever he stopped and pick up bits of the ice he chipped off.

"A truly public benefactor," said I to myself; "a magician," said I, "changing about the seasons and importing winter into summer."

My amused speculations continued for two or three weeks and I had not yet exchanged so much as a word with the Iceman. But the more I saw of him, the more I wanted really to know him; to hear what he would say; to try him with questions and ideas and see what had come out of all this curious experience of life. I thought it would be interesting to know the ripe conclusions of an iceman about the universe, the solar spaces, the immortality of the soul, and the price of potatoes.

For it seems to me that no knowledge is better worth having, or more fascinating, than the knowledge of how people have come to be what they are; how they have managed to live in the world. And when I see a man like my Iceman who not only lives but does it boldly, joyfully, with a kind of triumphant air about it, it seems to me I can scarcely wait to be at him!

But how to do it? I thought of a hundred ways of saying exactly the right thing first—which is a difficult art. It is easy enough to imagine one's self playing the Caliph in Bagdad—and who has enjoyed it more than I, or kept quieter about my failures! But really to cross the line into the soul of another human being is not an easy thing.

It came to me in a flash one morning, as I passed the ice wagon, how I could do it. The Iceman himself had gone into one of the houses. When he reappeared, whistling, I was stooping over to run my hand down the leg of one of his horses. He looked at me in some surprise.

"I thought," said I, glancing up at him, "it was too bad that such a fine horse as this should have a spavin."

"Spavin!" he exclaimed. "Spavin!"

It was as though I had struck him. His precious horses!

"They ain't a cleaner-boned animal in America," said he explosively.

I smiled up at him and then stood up, slapping my hands.

"So I see," said I. "I like horses myself, and when I saw that lump on the leg——"

"That ain't spavin."

"No," I said, "I see it isn't."

Then I remarked, casually:

"I'm from the country, and I don't think that I ever saw as finely matched a team of Percherons as yours."

I could see I had hit him where he lived.

"They're not so bad," said he, but with pride in every tone of his voice.

We had some other exchanges. I inquired how much they weighed and how old they were and then remarked:

"I've been wondering how much such a team in the City would be worth."

Of course, they did not belong to him; but nothing could rob him of all the glowing pleasures of possession, even the delightful business of bantering a stranger upon the assumption that he might want to buy. He probably knew well enough that I was only "talkin'," and knew that I knew that *he* was; but when two horse-lovers meet in this wilderness of a world they easily set up a little stage of their own and play upon it. You need not think that he was idling, even while this bit of conversation was going on. He was pulling out blocks of ice from the cavernous depths of the wagon with a long-handled hook, chipping them deftly apart into smaller pieces (he could guess twenty-five or fifty pounds to a turn!), getting ready for coming deliveries.

So our acquaintance started. We had no more talk that morning, but on several days afterward, when we met, I stopped to swap a word with him, exactly as I might in the country with a friend passing in the town road. I have one great advantage in such contacts: I am from the country, and who in the City doesn't expect a man from the country to be a little odd? One must make allowances for a man from the country! I learned that his name was Curtis Haley—though everyone called him Curt— and where he lived, and how long he had been an iceman.

"You must have hauled ice enough in your day to fill St. Mark's Church."

(This was a huge Episcopal church we could see up the street.)

"St. Mark's!" said the bold Iceman, with scorn, "you can roll all the saints' churches in the calendar into one pile, and I've filled the dang-blasted lot of 'em clean up to the eaves."

He had a kind of hard, common-sense working philosophy of life, fragments of which I broke off, as it were, from time to time.

Here are two samples of remarks I heard him make at different times:

"What's the use o' kickin'? You gotta work anyhow."

"A man's gotta pay for what he gets, one way or another, that's certain."

I have sometimes thought of City workers as radicals; but so far as I can see most of them are conservatives of the conservatives. My Iceman was an example: he was a Republican without in the least knowing why. "My old dad was a Republican," says he, "and it's good enough for me." So he was a Methodist; "though I ain't workin' at it." So he respected savings banks and Masonic lodges.

I enjoyed these little contacts keenly; I felt like a portrait painter, touching in each day some little new characteristic of my Iceman, until he stood out, to me, a figure of robust reality.

"I'm none o' yer factory hands," says he, "punchin' out an eye hole or touchin' a button a thousand times a day. Me! I'm free."

And free, indeed, he seemed: a regular voyageur. Careering through the streets in his great caravan, brasses gleaming, harness rattling—to cool the fevered brow of the world.

Finally, one afternoon I chanced on the Iceman just as he was stepping into his seat.

"I'm empty," said he.

"Going back for a new load?"

"Yep," said he, and when I intimated I was going his way: "Get in, pardner."

So there I sat up beside him in his broad seat, rocking and bumping behind the mighty Percherons.

"Curt," said I, "I've made up my mind you're a benefactor of the human race."

"How's that?"

"You're a kind of miracle man. You turn summer into winter."

"Say, pardner," said he, "I never thought o' that before."

"It's a man's job," said I.

"You bet," said he.

"You're doing right now, every day, just commonly, what the greatest princes of the past couldn't afford to have done. Did you ever hear of the Emperor Alexander?"

"Sure," said the Iceman, "he was the old feller that cried because there wasn't any more worlds to conquer."

"Right," said I; "but with all his power and all his riches, he could not have had done what you do every day: have his ice box filled in July."

This seemed immensely to please the Iceman. He slapped his knee and roared with laughter.

53

"Say, I never yet thought o' that."

"Oh, you don't appreciate what a fine and great job you've got," said I. "It's one of the most interesting jobs I know."

With that I began to be genuinely fascinated—as well as amused—and though I had not imagined, ten minutes before, doing any such thing, I began to describe the process of ice-cutting, ice-packing, ice-carting, throwing in all the dramatic or humorous turns I could think of, showing what a curious and wonderful thing it was, all the complicated process by which the ice of up-country ponds was placed months later, as regularly as clockwork, in every ice box in the City. I grew strangely interested myself in the story; and wound up dramatically with a picture of the fevered patients in the hospital, who tossed less painfully because of the ice that the Iceman brought, and the babies that were saved, and life altogether made more agreeable to millions of human beings.

Since then I have looked back with some amusement, and yet with a kind of deep pleasure and satisfaction, to what I said that day to Curt Haley, who sat with eyes fairly glued upon me. I can see now that what I was doing was to sing him the Saga of the Ice.

"Why," said I to myself, "I was the Homer of this new kind of war. I 'smote me bloomin' lyre' and made a battle that seemed hard and dirty and long somehow beautiful and heroic."

I wonder sometimes if those Greek soldiers on the plains of Troy would ever have thought of their work as anything but hungry and hard—the humdrum butchery of Trojans—if Homer had not been there to sing.

It may seem absurd, but I've thought since that I'd like better than anything else in this world to be the Homer of many such dull but truly heroic occupations. Icemen, steel workers out on the tops of new buildings, a hundred feet from the pavement, risking their lives at every step, trolley-car motormen, miners, woodsmen.

Civilisation is like a great kettle full of rich life, carried by the whole of humankind. If one least man falters or lets go, or falls from hunger or discouragement, the kettle tilts and some of its precious content is lost.

I think I never saw a man more fascinated than my Iceman. It was as though he had never before heard of his own job.

"Say," said he finally, "that was some story."

"It's true," I replied, "every word of it."

"Sure it is," he remarked; "but who'd ever think of it?"

He rumpled his hand through his crisp hair, looked out toward the great fine horses, which were rocking along in a steady walk. He nodded his head slowly:

"Some job—bein' an Iceman," said he.

"Say," he added, "what's your job? I ain't never even thought to ask."

"My job," I said—and it struck me curiously, all at once; "why, I teach flying."

He looked at me wonderingly and a little sceptically; but I was as solemn as you please.

"I know I don't look it," I said. "But people often surprise you. You can't always tell what people have inside them by what they show outside."

"Sure, I know *that*."

"I'd like to teach you to fly," said I.

"Say, pardner, you're kidding me."

"No," said I, "I am in dead earnest."

"Real flying?"

"Real," said I, "the realest there is. In fact," I said, "I've been teaching you already. In the past you've never realised—you said so yourself—what an interesting job you had. You'll be thinking to-night, your mind will be flying to all the different things I told you today. They'll amuse you and interest you."

"So, that's what you mean by flying. I get you. You mean your mind flies!" He paused, and then added, "Say, you're the queerest fella I ever met."

I rode with him as far as the storage house, where he was to reload, and then I turned and walked homeward alone.

I did not see him again for two or three days, and then chanced

55

upon him unexpectedly. When he saw me a broad smile broke over his face.

"Flying to-day?" I asked.

"Sure," said he, "turnin' summer into winter. Sure—beatin' Alexander the Great."

After that we had a precious joke between us; which, if soon rather worn, never lost its friendly usefulness.

One hot day in July the Iceman appeared on the landing of our lodgings. When Harriet opened the door she found him there, looking like a warm gladiator, smiling broadly. He had a package in his hand. He had discovered where I lived.

"The flying-teacher isn't home, is he?"

Harriet said she didn't know exactly what he meant; she supposed I'd been joking again; but she replied:

"No, he isn't."

"Well," said the Iceman, "I want to leave him something."

He looked embarrassed.

"They got a big oversupply at the cold storage," said he, "and told us drivers to take 'em."

When we opened the package later it contained two very fine muskmelons. A bit of soiled paper was pinned to one of them, with the words:

"From Cuby. Curt."

"Harriet," said I, "this is surely an amusing world we live in."

"Even the City, David?"

"Even the City."

V

WE ARE THANKFUL

"Is nothing done
Any more for fun
Under the sun?"

ONE afternoon in that City—it was now come to be the autumn of the year—I was walking along the street looking in at the shop windows, deciding upon many things I did not want.

"Thank Heaven, I don't want that—or that—or that."

This was an amusing game I had come to play with myself as a kind of defence against Things, of which there are too many in this world. The idea had come to me first soon after we arrived in the City and I stood looking in at a shop of antiques, where there were displayed many ancient painted hat boxes, old brass bed-warmers, curious chairs, bureaus, andirons, and the like. I had at first a feeling of depression, inexplicable to me, at the sight of all these things; they gave me a kind of mental dustiness. I looked at them more narrowly, trying to understand why it was; and then suddenly it came all clear to me, and I said aloud:

"Why, I don't have to have them—not one of them!"

It may seem absurd enough, but this thought gave me such relief that I found myself laughing heartily as I walked down the street. What a nightmare—to own all those bed-warmers, candlesticks, blue and green bottles, ship models, hat boxes, spinning wheels! I had a strong temptation to go in and look at the man who did own them—and see what it had done to him.

After that, I caught myself often rejoicing, gloating, when I looked in at many a window in the City, that I didn't own *that,* or have to bother with *that.*

"I have too much now," I said, "to interrupt me. If I had fewer things I should be happier, for there would be more time to be quiet, and to think, and to try to understand."

("One grows tired of everything," said Virgil, long ago, "except understanding.")

This led me along to many amusing speculations (which I will not enlarge upon here) as to all the things I might give away, or at least hypothecate with some benevolent "uncle," and still be left with the solid essentials of life: say, ten books, a garden—trousers!

"An attic in winter," said I, "a hill-top in summer, and quietude in both!"

It was with some such grand speculations as these, which (I confide in you privately) I enjoy very much, that I was going along the street that autumn afternoon.

"If they would only put in their windows what a man really wants most!" I said.

At that it came upon me suddenly and with a power I cannot describe—how does a man's mind work anyway?—that the thing I wanted most was a sight of the folks at Hempfield. I stopped before a fine great store window, and there inside, as plain as visions ever are, I had a half-comic sight of my awkward country neighbour, Horace, with the familiar skeptical smile on his face. There he was, as natural as life, and as much out of place, among a display of rugs, curtains, and elegant chairs. I could even see his lips moving as he said, "W-all now, David," before he vanished in thin air.

I wonder, do *you* ever have suddenly a hunger for old friends, a vast unappeasable appetite for the very look of them? Do *you* ever feel that nothing will satisfy you but the look, the voice, the very way of an old friend?

It was at that exact moment that the great idea of having some of the Hempfield folk down to visit us was born; and it led up to the celebration of which I am about to tell.

From the beginning the City was harder upon Harriet than upon me, though she made little complaint about it. Harriet

58

is country bred to the bone. I knew well her deep feeling, from little stray remarks she let fall from time to time during those months. Once in the spring, not so long after we arrived, she sat looking out of our high window over that wilderness of dingy roofs they call a city. She had been quiet for some time; and then she said, wistfully:

"David, by now the cowslips will be blooming in all the marshes."

"Yes, Harriet."

"And the shad bushes will be white on Horace's hillside."

"Yes, Harriet."

"We shall miss them, David."

"Yes, Harriet."

At another time, quite without any reference to Hempfield, she said:

"David, I heard a crow crying early this morning, just as at home."

I do not at all mean to say that Harriet enjoyed nothing in the City. She did.

She enjoyed many of the meetings we had in our Tower; and some of the excursions we took. She enjoyed the plants she started, with irrepressible zeal, in our windows: the tulips and narcissus, and later, old-fashioned geraniums and a fern or two. But, most of all, of a sunny morning, I think she enjoyed going out to market with her brown armadillo basket on her arm. She had explored all the stores and markets around about and soon knew many a market man by name. Mr. Bulger was one of her favourites. He was a great, red-faced, jolly giant of a man in a white apron. He sold fish, and he had three children (as Harriet soon found out). To watch Harriet and Mr. Bulger negotiating for a pair of panfish on a Friday morning was worth something, I can tell you.

"They will eat good," says Mr. Bulger.

"But *are* they good?" says Harriet.

"I warrant 'em," says Mr. Bulger.

"Are they higher to-day?" says Harriet.

"No, they are lower," says Mr. Bulger.

"How much do they weigh?" says Harriet.

"Just short of a pound," says Mr. Bulger.

And so, by gradual stages, until Harriet has the panfish, jacketed in oil paper and stored away with three carrots, a small cabbage, and a package of tapioca, in her basket. (Nothing ever scandalised Harriet so much as the price she had to pay for a carrot or a cabbage in the City—when they were free in the country.)

But it was in the fall that both Harriet and I found our minds oftenest turning to our valley and the quiet hills of Hempfield. It would come over me sometimes with such a wave of longing as I cannot describe that the late peaches would be hanging thick on the trees, and the McIntosh apples ripening, and the hives would be full of honey.

"Contentment," I would say to Harriet at such times, thinking to cure with words things that lie deeper than words, "contentment is as possible in the City as in the country. Contentment"—and I would slip into my oracular tone—"is a quality not of place or of time, but of the spirit."

"That may be," said Harriet; "but I'd like a fresh egg or two; and think of going out into your own orchard and picking your own pears and plums. And besides, I wonder how tall the hollyhocks have grown this year."

It was thus out of Harriet's longings and my speculations that our plans for a celebration at Thanksgiving gradually formed themselves. We'd have down the Scotch Preacher and Mrs. McAlway and Horace (and his daughter), if we could get them, and enjoy an old-fashioned Thanksgiving dinner. One thing led on to another, and it was Harriet herself who proposed having in some of our newer city friends to meet our old country friends.

I never knew until then how much I loved these old friends. As the time drew nearer, it seemed to me I could scarcely wait; and when at length we heard their feet upon our stairs and the great rolling voice of the Scotch Preacher crying out, "Well, they got as near Heaven as they could," Harriet and I rushed to the doorway to let them in.

60

We had literally to unload them before we could get to them, before they seemed quite natural, for they had brought an extraordinary number of boxes and baskets filled with good things from the country.

To want one's friends near at hand—to want the old known ones nearest—is there a finer thing in this world? I grow positively hungry sometimes at the thought of some little peculiar or particular way of a friend, motion of head or hand, look of eye, smile, quick turn of body, metal or manner of speech, and long to see or hear it again; to see my friend repeat himself. And when I see him, how eagerly I check him over to see if he is all there—all, as I remember. Or, have little new things crept in? Are these new things sad?—are they strong? Have the old things changed or weakened? Has some sorrow blurred his beauty—some happiness vivified it? Is my friend all there complete?

So it was in our room, there in the Tower, as we sat about— the Scotch Preacher erect in his chair, his stiff iron-grey hair standing high on his head, slapping his knee sometimes to emphasise a point, and Mrs. McAlway by Harriet, leaning over to tell about the Barnard twins, and Horace, tall and a little awkward in his "store clothes," standing by the fireplace (the fraud of a city fireplace!) smoking his pipe.

"I told John Weaver 's long ago as last spring he was puttin' in his oats too early," Horace was drawling; "but you know John. You can't tell John nothin'——"

Often as I sat there I quite lost the talk—talk anyway is a lesser form of communication—because of the intensity with which I looked at my friends. Yes, that was exactly the Scotch Preacher; yes, I had forgotten, but that was just the way Horace always carried his head, a little to one side, skeptically.

It seemed to me that they were better than ever!

I wish you could have taken a look at our sitting room on Thanksgiving evening. It was not only the things that Horace and Doctor McAlway had brought with them; but I had written Dick Sheridan, whom we had left in charge of our

61

small acres, to send down some corn and pumpkins and other appropriate things from the country. With these, and bitter-sweet and autumn boughs, we had transformed our room into a true country bower. Horace had brought a basket of the finest McIntosh apples that ever I saw in my life; and there are no fall apples in this world, it seems to me, comparable to the McIntosh—and these we had on the table, near by, where they could be casually picked up and eaten out of hand.

"In the country there is always enough of everything," said Harriet.

Harriet had worked out the whole dinner to a nicety, even though our cramped quarters offered many difficulties. No sooner had the last guest arrived—it was Knightly, of course (who will, I think, be late to his own funeral)—than the sliding doors between our rooms were rolled back, and Horace, Doctor McAlway, Mr. Tuney and I, who had been trained beforehand, stepped out and brought in the dining table all set. The audience cheered our skill, and Doctor McAlway, who had one end, cried out:

" 'There was a sound of revelry by night.' "

The only thing that Harriet would not trust us with was the turkey. She came after us, her face glowing, with that noble brown bird upon a vast platter. There were little sprigs of green about it; and it gave off ambrosial odours which renewed a man's youth, blessed his days, restored his soul!

Harriet had insisted upon having no hired help.

"What's a dinner for ten? If I could have Elviry Moon, that would be different—but these city girls!" I wish you could have seen the look of superiority upon Harriet's face.

Just as we found our places and before we sat down, Harriet said:

"Doctor McAlway, will you say grace?"

It rather astonishes many people these days, especially in cities, to hear God spoken to, openly, as though he were real. God has become a Hypothesis, not a reality. But when the Scotch Preacher talks to God, you know and feel that God is there, actually there, to be talked to. The Scotch Preacher does not

hang his head, or whisper abject entreaties, or cringe, or apolo-
gise. He squares away his great shoulders, lifts up his fine old
face, which begins to shine with a kind of glory, and speaks out
to God as a tested, certain, deeply loved Friend.

The Scotch Preacher understands love, understands it better
than almost any man I know: that love is not something soft,
yielding, sentimental; but something strong, true, fine, upon
which one can rest as upon a rock in a weary land; that its
tenderness is not weakness, nor its joy selfish.

Something of all this he radiated there at our table that night:
braced us, liberated us, made life seem somehow a worthier
and higher thing than we had thought it.

I cannot begin to report what was said that night; but there
was something about it that was infectious, that set us all laughing at everything and nothing. All the bonds and bars of strange-
ness fell down between us, and everyone shone at his best and
keenest, because at his truest. I never heard any one tell better
stories than Doctor McAlway—or laugh harder at them himself;
or any one make wittier comments than Mr. Tuney; and in the
middle of the meal little Knightly pushed back his chair and
stood up while he recited, "The Coons of Cahoon Hollow."

In thinking of it since, I have wondered if something of this
freedom and enjoyment did not spring from the fact that the
celebration was a true reversion to the youth of all of us, the
youth, the naïve youth—indeed, of America. No holiday in all
our calendar is comparable to Thanksgiving. There is no holiday quite like it anywhere in the world. It celebrates no battle,
no fall of a Bastille, no bank or business holiday, the birthday
of no great man, no political revolution, no church ritual. It is
the great holiday of common people who have worked all the
year and now thank God humbly for good harvests. We are not
celebrating Washington or Columbus or the Declaration of
Independence—but just the true, good things, the simple bless-
ings of the soil and the common life. Most holidays are somehow pagan, and if traced back are rooted in the dull and bloody
stories of some old war; but Thanksgiving is the holiday of
peace: the celebration of work and the simple life. You must

go back to the old Greeks for anything to compare with it—a true folk festival that speaks the poetry of the turn of the seasons, the beauty of the harvest, the ripe product of the year, and the deep, deep connection of all these things with God.

Something of this came out in our talk.

"Yes," said Mr. Pitwell, "it is undoubtedly the most American of all our holidays."

"Even the food," said Mrs. McAlway.

"That is true," put in Mrs. Tuney, "there is scarcely a dish on this table that is not peculiar to America, native to our soil—and most of them can be had nowhere else in the world."

It was truly an old-fashioned Thanksgiving dinner. We had many of the things down from our own country, all the vegetables except the sweet potatoes—celery, onions, and Hubbard squash (one cannot properly give thanks without Hubbard squash)—from our own land. We also had jelly that Harriet herself made, and honey from our own hives. But the grand event of the meal was the pumpkin pie. None of your little, thin, emaciated, leather-bound pumpkin pies; but deep, thick, golden-yellow, baked in a brown crockery plate. Made of a special small variety of russeted sweet pumpkin which Harriet and I discovered years ago, perfect pumpkin! (I have told Harriet since that if she had not been born modest, the remarks about that pumpkin pie would have spoiled her!)

"I have not eaten such a dinner since I was a boy," said Mr. Pitwell.

"I have been trying to think of a really appropriate word for it," said Mr. Knightly.

"Delectable," said Mrs. Tuney.

"Salubrious," remarked her husband.

"W-all," said Horace, now breaking in—he had been pretty busy all along—"I'd call it durned good."

One feature of the talk after dinner stands out above everything else; and it came from quite an unexpected source. We never knew Horace had it in him!

Somehow, the conversation had turned on old New England traditions, of which Thanksgiving was so much a part. Mr.

Tuney observed that it was rather a pity that we had not developed here in America, perhaps because we were so young, the folk stories and songs common in other countries.

"Why," put in Knightly, "there is no body of folk stories in the world comparable to the Negro stories of the South, and no songs better than the Negro spirituals."

"But I mean in New England."

Here the Scotch Preacher broke in:

"Horace, sing us the 'Ballad of Springfield Mountain.' That's New England."

Horace looked abashed.

"Go on, Horace," I urged.

"If I could sing it," said Horace, "as well as my grandfather Horton used to do it when I was a boy——"

"Go on anyway," we cried.

So Horace, with some embarrassment, cleared his throat, sat up in his chair, and began singing in a high, nasal voice (deliciously Yankee), with now and then a slide and a quaver in it, the mournful "Ballad of Springfield Mountain":

> "On Springfield mountain there did dwell,
> A likely youth, who was known full well,
> This youth, his age was twenti-one,
> Was Leftenant Myrick's only son."

Horace paused and looked around at us. He was just warming up to the occasion.

> "On Friday morning he did go
> Into the meadow for to mow,
> And as he turned around did feel
> A pizin sarpint bite his heel."

I wish you could have heard the unctuousness of Horace's delivery of the "pizin sarpint!"

> "When he received his deadly wound,
> He dropped his sythe a pon the ground,
> Tho' all around his voys we heerd
> None of his friends to him appeered."

65

Horace was lost in the depths of sorrow.

> "This youth he soon give up the ghost,
> And up to Abraham's bosom did post—
> A cryin' all the ways he went,
> 'O crewel, oh crewel; oh crewel sarpint!' "

Horace, sober as a judge, had to wait for the explosion of laughter that here broke through.

> "So soon his careful father went
> To seek his son with discontent,
> And there his onley son he faound
> Ded as a stun a pon the ground.
> His father viewed his track with great consarn
> Where he had run acrost the corn.
> Uneven tracks, where he did go,
> Appeared to stagger to and frow."

Horace's voice now reeked with unutterable woe.

> "The seventh of August, sixty-one,
> This fatal axsident was done.
> Let this a warning be to all,
> To be prepared when God does call."

Horace certainly brought down the house.

"I told you Horace could give you a real taste of the soil," said Doctor McAlway.

But it was little Knightly who was most excited.

"Where did it come from?" he demanded. "Are there any more?"

Nothing would do but Horace must sing it again—which he did, and far better than at first, for he had lost all embarrassment and entered wholly into the spirit of the fun. If old Gran'-ther Horton could have done it better I missed one of the great things of life in never having heard him.

Since then I rarely see Horace that he does not recall that evening in our Tower: it was truly a red-letter day in his life.

Once, before I began to understand who I was and what I had to do with this world, I was sometimes distressed by the problems of the Present, and concerned over the chances of the Future; but at such times I would say to myself:

"One thing is certain—the Past. No one can rob a man of his Past, or the happiness of it."

It was one of the early solid things I held to; for one can be certain of joys he has already had. How I have lived over again and again the pleasant, simple hours of our Thanksgiving there in our Tower: and the more I wear them with thought, the brighter they grow.

And one of the most delightful of these memories is the fine enthusiasm of little Knightly. He came up to see us a few days after the celebration.

"Grayson," said he, "I want to tell you I lived the other night. I really lived."

His eyes glowed.

"Those were great men you had down from the country: that old Preacher, and Horace the Farmer. They were not like our City men: all hazy, vague, all cast in the same mould. They were as distinct and clear-cut as a mountain or a church spire. Or like a great solid oak tree that has grown for a long time in one place, and the wind has blown upon it and torn it, and the rain has drenched it and the sun has shone upon it—a tree that has plenty of room for its roots in the soil, and plenty of space in the air to spread its branches."

"That," said I, "is what I think, too."

VI

THE MAN IN THE GLASS CAGE

"Man, if thou knowest what thou dost, blessed art thou, but if thou knowest not, thou art condemned."—Passage from the "Sayings of Jesus," his remark to a shoemaker.

I REMEMBER once a man asked me what my business was, and how the truth jumped straight out of me, as truth sometimes will, before I could think. If I had stopped to consider I should probably have said, vaguely, that I was a farmer, a gardener, a writer (and he would never have thought of me again); but what I did say was this:

"I am a man trying to understand."

I consider this business the most interesting in the whole world, though it never made any man rich, except in satisfaction. I have conducted this business for many years in the country, where it is possible to have some success at it. If one is humble and works hard and loves deep, he can come to understand a few simple things about the land, and cattle, and corn, and bees—and people. But in the City——

Let me tell now of a strange experience that came to me after I had spent several months in the City. I had begun to be superficially acquainted: I had played joyfully at being a caliph, incognito, in Bagdad—and I had made some fine new friends; but, instead of growing plainer to me, the City seemed only more puzzling.

As I went about looking, smelling, feeling, listening, thinking —as any man must do who would understand—I began more and more to sense a secret about it all that I could not fathom. Something existed here that we of the country did not know or feel.

Nature in the country responds to ancient reason—the slow

logic of the soil, seed time and harvest, summer and winter, day and night. One can discern a rhythm; and it is only as we discover a rhythm in life and move to the cadence of it that we grow tranquil.

But in the City nature seems all awry. Men have been cultivating the soil for fifty thousand years—who knows, a hundred thousand!—but great cities are absolutely new. The oldest has existed only a few minutes, as it were, of the ages that men have been here hunting, fishing, farming.

I found it rather an odd thing, as I thought about it, what a variety of reports of life in the City I had from the City men I met.

Jensen, or Mrs. Jensen, said it was "too qvick."

Pitwell was bored amid all this roaring life, "just plain—damned—deadly dull."

Tuney had turned cynic, and considered all these hurrying people to be "insects." He lived in a kind of metaphysical tub and went about with a lantern, not really to find an honest man but to prove that one could not be found. Which is the way of some men with lanterns.

Little gentle Knightly had dismissed the complicated show and retired into the blessed haven of old books; from which he poked out occasionally to walk down the street "and laugh heartily at such variety of ridiculous objects which there he saw." He was the happiest—and poorest—of the men we had come to know.

Now, what was a countryman like me to make out of all these diverse reports? Why did so many of the men one met seem so unquiet, unsatisfied, apparently not knowing what they were doing or where they were going?

The more I went about the City, exploring strange parts of it, the more I began to have a new, almost uncanny, feeling about it all. It would come over me suddenly, in a street, up a stair, on a car, that the City was itself a kind of organism or machine, operating quite independently of these puny human beings that were running about its passageways or crawling into its little cells and burrows. No one of them, nor all of them, could stop it, or hasten it, or turn it aside—and yet no one of them knew where it was going or what it was all about. (I am trying here to put down honestly what I thought and felt: this writing will have no value unless I do this.)

Here it was, then, this stupendous City, roaring and growling by day like some inhuman monster, and blazing away at night from a million eyes. Traffic ran like blood in its myriad arteries, and one could see the breath of it curling out of its nostrils and drifting away in the sky. A strange beast, this! Gone wild, this beast. Entirely out of control.

"Why," said I, "it almost convinces a man at times that there is something here more important than human beings."

In the night especially would this strange impression come upon me, and I would find myself lying wide awake, listening intently. It seemed to me that the dull roar of the City rose and fell like the mighty breathing of uneasy sleep, and sometimes, toward morning, it would almost die away, as though the monster was settling down at length, with a sigh, to rest.

Then I would find my mind going out to the country around about, just such pleasant country as I knew and loved, and I would see vividly all the loaded trains rushing toward the City —with locomotives belching sparks into the night—hurrying with the food of thousands upon thousands of acres of green countryside to feed this monster of a City. I thought of the unnumbered men and women back in the valleys and on the hills ploughing, planting, harvesting, to load these trains. . . .

And on all the sea stretching away to the East and South I saw ships coming, heavily laden, driving resistlessly through wind and wave, to bring strange goods for this monster's daily use or pleasure. I could see all these things pouring in to keep the monster alive—but what for? What was being done? Where was the monster bound? Who ordered all this?

It may seem strange that these questions should have plagued me (as they have perhaps also plagued you, at times), but I was a countryman come to a strange place and overwhelmed with strange impressions.

It was in June that my walks, mostly in the evenings or on

Sunday, took me more and more into the dingy outskirts of the City. I had at first a deep interest in the people I found there, and talked often with them at street corners or in little shops; but presently the grim-walled factories there, especially a certain Mill with tall chimneys, began to have a curious fascination for me. Often as I went by I could hear from behind the walls of this Mill a kind of thudding heartbeat, as though I were listening at the breast of a living creature. One place in particular, on a little bridge over a sluggish stream, absolutely absorbed me. Here, above the fortress-like walls of the Mill, I could see a squat grey tower, or chimney, with a lazy reddish smoke curling out of it. It was curious smoke, heavy, almost oily, and at times, when the sun shone dimly through the smoky air, having a kind of opalescence. I had been watching this smoke curiously the first evening I was there, when suddenly before my eyes the whole top of the tower or chimney seemed to blow off and out gushed—vomited—an enormous eruption of flame, strange coloured and full of whirling white-hot cinders. It came roaring with an indescribable passion of force and seemed to plunge at the sky as if to pierce it. It thrilled me to the core.

And then, as suddenly, it disappeared; the roar died away leaving all the sky by contrast cloaked in gloom. It was followed a moment later by the evil-looking smoke I had seen before lifting lazily, almost feebly, skyward—the smudgy aftermath of a passion burned out.

I suppose this spectacle was familiar to commonness to the people of that neighbourhood, but I cannot describe what a thrill it gave to me. It was titanic, diabolic—and the more so when I remained into the night and all the surrounding City was lost in shadow. I could now see though windows or holes in the Mill walls the glow from within, or the light cast upward against half-seen smoke from lesser chimneys. The walls appeared to be covering, like a ragged garment, the molten life within. It was then that the mystery deepened and the Mill with its thudding heartbeat and its fiery respiration grew more and more a kind of living thing—a terrible living thing. It increased and emphasised the impression I have already described, of the

71

City itself as an organism or mechanism, created indeed by men but somehow alive on its own account, moving and acting independently of human beings.

It came to me presently that if I could somehow get at this Mill, find out what was inside of it, how it worked, who said what it was to do, and why it was doing what it did, I could perhaps understand a little better the mystery that was puzzling me.

I am a countryman to the bone; and in my own valley, or field, or orchard fear no man. It seems to me that every tree around about is an ally of mine; the tall corn in the fields is ranked like an army at my command; the wind backs me up, the waters flow for me, the sun strengthens me; I am like Anteus of old, drawing new power whenever my feet touch the soil. Everything I see opens to me; every question I ask is soberly answered. I have a proud feeling at times that if all cities were swept away, all governments demolished, all inventions destroyed, I could yet cling here to my friend the Earth, still draw nourishment from her breast. We have been here a long time on the soil—my race—and we would be hard to dislodge!

But in the City I had no such surety of feeling. I seemed not to have my roots down anywhere in firm soil. I seemed somehow overwhelmed; and yet there I was—sucked into the vortex by the war—trying to understand.

I am hoping with these observations to explain the timidity I felt before these marvels—a timidity which must, I know, seem absurd to many a seasoned city man, to whom marvels are as daily diet.

I picked my way slowly around the walls of the Mill in the darkness and came presently to an archway, through which, no one stopping me, I went into the Mill.

I found myself in an enormous room, like a great cathedral but full of rumbling noises. All the machinery was powerfully at work, beginning at one end with huge glowing ingots of metal, which were handled and rolled about as callously, as deftly, as though they were matchwood—crushed down, smoothed out, cut off with easy but terrible efficiency. It was such an exhibit of sheer power as I had never before seen; and yet it was not what impressed me most. What impressed me most was the fact that nowhere at first did I see a single man. Not one. It was uncanny. The machinery was going as if by itself—of its own volition, toiling like a gigantic slave with no master.

What a thing was that to a man whose mind was stretched to the uttermost of wonder, trying to understand!

Presently I looked up. There on the wall, high up on one side of the building, in a glass cage, sat the man I had been looking for among his levers and buttons.

"He is the god of the place," I said.

I could see him move easily, look out through his cage windows, pull a lever, touch a button, take up a telephone. He was as nonchalant as a god about it, smoking his pipe.

I stood for a long time looking at him, fascinated, and then felt as though I would rather go up there and ask him a question or so than anything else in the world. I was so intent upon this absurd project that I had actually started to pick my way across the roaring building when I heard someone shout at me; and then a hand, not too gentle, on my shoulder.

"What are you doing here?"

I looked around into a grimy face. I suppose a casual visitor in the night *was* unusual!

I groped desperately for the right thing to say, and could find nothing, at the moment, but the truth.

"I am trying," I said, "to understand what *you* are doing here: what it all means, and whether you know what you are about."

So often the plain truth appears ridiculous—at first! Moreover, could there be anything more affronting than to ask a man whether he knows what he is about? While most men don't know (this is a secret) they resent being asked.

We stood there looking at each other.

"What in hell are you talkin' about?" said this grimy man, roaring at the top of his voice to drown out the machinery.

The absurdity of the situation now came to me suddenly and

humorously: my own ridiculous position not less than the anger of my grimy friend. But I came straight back again:

"What are you doing here? What are you working for?" I roared.

This seemed to make him still angrier.

"Me?" (I will here omit certain decorative eloquencies not found in Webster's dictionary.) "Me! I'm workin' for me little five dollars a day."

I was about to roar in response that five dollars seemed no really good reason for working in such a place—it seemed a chance for an amusing argument!—when he informed me that they didn't want no blank, blank strike spies in this here Mill (I found afterward that they had just had a strike) and what, blank, blank, was I doin' anyhow——

I suppose if I had had wit enough I could have somehow got around this grimy man, found his human spot and won him over; but I didn't have, and took a roaring departure, with my host seeing me to the archway. Here no playful caliphry would get me by!

I could not, however, dismiss from my mind the Man in the Glass Cage, nor the desire I had—it was more than desire, it was passion—to talk with him and see if he could not answer some of my questions. I felt that such a man sitting supreme above the bellowing machinery and controlling its least motion with a turn of the wrist must have precious secrets to tell. He must have thought it all clear! He, if any one, would know what it was all about.

A day or two later I went in to see my friend Mr. Pitwell, who, I felt, liked me.

"Well," said he, "here is the Caliph."

"Who, powerful as he is," I replied, "cannot reach one of his subjects."

I know of almost no man who has so much of the precious gift of old urbanity as John Cross Pitwell. In no time at all I was telling him of my experience at the Mill and of the absurd encounter with the grimy man.

"And you asked him questions like that?" he laughed.

74

"Yes; because they were exactly what I wanted to know."

There is a magic circle in the City. Within it everyone belongs; without it, no one belongs. Mr. Pitwell was within it. He not only knew the Mill, but was actually a director in the company that owned it. He gave me a slip of paper—he called it, smiling, a talisman—which, he said, would get me to the Man in the Cage.

"They've been having an ugly strike out there," said he, "and it is not surprising that you had a hostile reception."

As I was leaving, he said, half earnestly:

"If you get an answer to your questions, let me hear what it it. I have a notion myself that we don't quite know what we are about down there at the Mill."

My talisman took me truly into that magic place; and the very next evening, in a little dressing room just outside the Mill, I met Himself—the Man of the Glass Cage.

His name was John Doney. I had imagined him a powerful, vital man, with an eye blazing with conscious understanding of the great work he was doing. For how could any man sit up there year after year, watching those gigantic and marvellous processes, and not think it clear, not know what he was about?

"You want to see how she works?" said he, looking up at me.

"Yes," said I gently, "very much. I am from the country and it is wonderful to me."

Methodically he changed his coat and lighted his pipe. He was a slight, rather pale man with a curiously immobile face and a tired look. My imagination, pouncing instantly upon these outer signs, interpreted it as serenity—the serenity, perhaps, of complete understanding, when all marvels are plain, each in its ordered place.

I followed him up the iron ladder to his cage, where he relieved his "side pardner," as he called him, and sat on a stool near him. From that vantage the great dimly lighted room with its enormous clashing machinery appeared still more awe-inspiring.

John Doney showed me, with faint evidences of pride, shouting at the top of his voice to make me hear, what this lever did;

the purpose of that electric button; and how, with a motion, he could stop or start a fifty-ton crane, or turn over a red-hot ingot weighing a ton or more. But it was not what he told me, amazing as it was, that impressed me most, but what I saw as I watched him.

I watched him closely; and presently began to have the uncanny impression that he was doing these things without volition, moving instinctively, like a man in a trance. His arm went out here to a lever, there to a button, now picked up the telephone, now relighted his pipe.

"Why," said I suddenly, "he is as automatic as the machinery down there on the floor."

I looked at his eyes and had, in a strange flash of understanding, the sense that he saw nothing at all with them. He was blind! Blind.

The immobility of his face, then, was not the serenity of understanding; it was sheer blankness. It came to me with a flash that it was not he that controlled the machinery, but the machinery that controlled him. He was as much a part of it as any lever, roller, pin, or cog. Instead of having his consciousness, his understanding, sharpened by the marvels of his nights in this place, his personality seemed literally effaced.

I felt such a wave of pity as I cannot describe; the shame one has in seeing the spirit of a man done out of him.

At the change of the shift, I went out with John Doney and sat on a stool at the night-luncheon place. I found him talkative enough, about his family—he had a wife and two children—the rent he had to pay, and his insurance; but when I came up to the great questions I wanted most to ask, I got answers that seemed to me curious and vague. Finally, I plumped the problem straight at him:

"Why are you doing this work, anyway?"

He looked around at me, puzzling:

"Why, I get forty a week."

"Is that all you get?" I asked.

"Yes," said he, "and it ain't really enough."

"But what do you do up there?"

"Why, you've seen it: I'm the control operator."

"I know," I said; "but haven't you any idea of what you are doing—I mean the whole big job—when you sit up there night after night? Aren't you *interested* in it?"

He looked around at me suspiciously, half alarmed.

"What do you mean? A man's got to live, ain't he? He's got to make his wages, ain't he?"

It was hopeless. And at that a wave of compassion for this man—this blind automaton!—came over me; and I thought that it would be the greatest thing in the world if I could wake him up a little, make him see what he was doing, the sheer importance and beauty of it, the bigness of it. So I said to him quietly, touching him on the arm:

"Do you know what I thought the other night when I came into the dark Mill and looked up there and saw you in the glass cage for the first time?"

"No," said he, looking curiously around at me.

"Well, I thought you were the most important man in the whole Mill. You controlled everything. I wanted to meet you. I thought you could tell me all about what was being done in the Mill, what was made there and why it was made."

The man's eyes were fixed upon me with extraordinary intensity; his lips parted.

"I had a curious thought about you," I said. "You know there are two parts of the brain: the cerebellum is the part that controls action. You are the cerebellum of this place. You control it. If anything happened to you, everything would go to pieces."

He was still looking at me with an intentness I cannot describe—but now a look of puzzled alarm came into his face. For just a moment I thought I had him, that he would come awake; but he shook himself and said roughly:

"Say—what are you drivin' at? You talk like one o' these labour agitators."

I tried further, but soon saw that I had lost out: he seemed afraid even to carry on the discussion.

"I got to go back," said he gruffly. "I got wages to earn."

I walked homeward in the night with a deep sense of depression; and in the following late afternoon went again to see my friend Pitwell.

"Look here," said he, "I've been in the office all day. Let's take a turn in the Park and talk."

This delighted me, for I had come to like Mr. Pitwell greatly; and so we set out together.

"Well, Grayson," said he, "how do you like our Mill?"

"It is one of the most wonderful places," said I, "that I ever visited. But strange."

"How, strange?"

"Can you stand a parable, a country parable?"

"A country parable best of all," said he.

"Well," said I, "you know I keep bees. I enjoy this greatly. They have come to seem like people to me. I like to stand watching them, or, better yet, lie down close to their hives, say in May when the drones are plenty and the young queens come out for their courting—and swarms are likely. It is a fine and wonderful society they have built up——"

"It must be," said Mr. Pitwell.

"But at times," said I, "there seems something positively terrifying about it: and this is what I am getting to."

"How do you mean, terrifying?"

"The bees are one of the most highly developed of living creatures," said I, "more highly developed in some ways than men; and their development is much older. I have read a good deal about bees. You know that they have been found in fossil form in the Baltic amber, showing that at least fifty million years ago—probably far longer—they existed in forms practically identical with these of to-day. Think of it!

"They have been repeating themselves, raising their queens, swarming, building comb, killing their drones, making honey, for fifty million years. Probably they have made and eaten a bulk of honey in that time half as big as the entire earth. Lying there by my hives in the sun, I have thought of this with a strange feeling of weariness: the endlessness of it, the ceaseless, terrifying repetition. . . . Fifty million years, and no change, no progress!"

"Extraordinary," exclaimed Mr. Pitwell; "it is something I never thought of before."

"Well," said I, "I had something of the same feeling last night when I sat looking into that strange hive you call a mill. I had a curious flash of wonder if men were not drifting into a blind alley of mechanism like my bees—where they would go on repeating themselves wearily for a million or fifty million years—and never come to know what it was all about or be able to change it. Among the bee people the organisation or mechanism absolutely controls the bees: not the bees the mechanism."

"Go on, go on," said Mr. Pitwell, when I paused.

"Well," said I, "I had an amusing conversation with that Man in the Glass Cage. I felt afterward as though I had tried to argue with one of my worker bees, coming in laden with pollen from a morning flight. I seemed to make as little impression upon him."

"What did you say to him?"

I told Mr. Pitwell, then, as exactly as I could, what happened in the Mill, giving the narrative a somewhat humorous turn.

"He could not see that he was the cerebellum of the establishment," laughed Mr. Pitwell—laughed, I could feel, partly at me!

To this I responded instantly, before I could reflect:

"Any more than you can see—you and your friends—that you are the cerebrum of the establishment. You do the thinking for it; and if you don't know what it is all about, or what you are trying to do, if you can't prevent outbursts that threaten the destruction of the entire mechanism—what can you expect of these lesser men?"

I was afraid at first I had hit him too hard. He stopped still for a moment there in the Park roadway, shot a swift glance at me, and then walked on again slowly, without looking around. I said nothing.

"It is odd, Mr. Grayson," he remarked presently, "how little we *have* thought about the larger meanings of what we are doing.

"What did you make out of the strike?" he asked, after an-

79

other pause. "We've tried to treat our men well—we *have* treated them well—but they strike."

"It impressed me as curious last night," said I, "as I sat there in that magic room—it really *is* magic, Mr. Pitwell—the sheer wonder and glory of human genius: that it could build such a marvel and set it to work for the benefit of mankind. It is greater than anything Plato could have imagined or Napoleon brought to pass. You have built a kind of steel giant to do your work for you. It toils night and day, summer and winter; it never gets tired, it demands no vacation, it exacts no wages, it joins no union.

"And yet, as I sat there last night in that high cage, looking down upon that toiling but willing slave, I thought how it was that you, who have done all this, are quarrelling over the management of it. Not long ago you actually had soldiers picketed around the Mill to prevent some of the men who are interested— the workers—from breaking up or crippling this willing slave which helps feed and clothe you all. You balk it, you limit it, you misuse it, so that it does not begin to do the work for you that it might do. You're wonderful when you invent and build; but how utterly you fail when it comes to controlling or using what you invent."

"It's true, Grayson, it's true. But what is there to be done about it? What will prevent these workers from breaking down the efficiency of what you call this slave of ours?"

"Well," said I, "I am only a countryman and know very little about such things. But I had the impression powerfully last night when I was talking to the Man in the Glass Cage, that if somehow I could wake him up, and make him truly feel the wonder and importance and beauty of his job—if I could be the Homer of his war!—he'd be quite a different man: happier, and a better worker. What you need is a poet connected with your Mill."

"Perhaps," said Mr. Pitwell; "but he'd only make the workers more discontented."

"Well," I said, "I had a feeling last night that if I found myself

80

becoming just a kind of cog or pin or lever of that machinery—an automaton—like the Glass Cage Man, I'd do *anything,* even smash the machine, to prove that I was really a man."

I had stopped in the road and found myself gesticulating like an orator.

I shall not forget the expression on Mr. Pitwell's face: smiling indulgence, puzzled concern. I could see that I was touching a sore spot, for Mr. Pitwell was a sensitive and thoughtful man.

"Well, Mr. Grayson," said he, "you need not think these problems have not bothered me."

We had stopped now by the side of one of the little ponds in the Park; evening was coming down, as sweet as only June can make it. I heard a catbird somewhere among the shrubbery at the pond side—strange music in such a place. Suddenly Mr. Pitwell looked at me curiously and turned the tables upon me with a question:

"Grayson, are you happy?"

This is a hard and sharp question to ask any man. But it is truly—as I thought afterward—the first question to put to the critic; for if the critic has not arrived at an understanding with himself (which is as near true "happiness" as any man ever gets) what right has he to criticise? I replied instantly (wondering since somewhat about it!):

"Yes, I am. Once I had a civil war going on in me, and I was unhappy. Now, I know who I am and what I am trying to do. I know what life is for."

It is only occasionally—once or twice in a dozen years—that two men (at least, men of mature years) get down thus into the very roots of things.

"Well, what is life for," asked Mr. Pitwell, "since you say you know?"

"It's to make better men, nobler men—and after that still nobler men. It's to throw all you are and everything you have into that one purpose. It's to understand the wonder and the truth of life—and then to make other people understand. It's to make of life a great adventure—an expedition, an enthusiasm. Not to blink sorrow, or evil, or ugliness; but never to fear them!

If I could have made that Man in the Glass Cage see what I see and feel what I feel, his whole life would be changed."

Mr. Pitwell said nothing, but stood looking off across the little lake.

"If a city produces good and noble and beautiful human beings, then it is a good city; if a mill produces good and fine men, then it is a good mill. This is true. It isn't enough to produce steel in a mill."

I have felt abashed since when I thought how I orated there; and yet, should not a man, when asked, tell what he honestly thinks true about life—the true and ultimate thing it means to him?

We walked homeward, for the most part silent; but I had the strange warm feeling around the heart (how do we get these messages—by a cadence of the voice, a look of the eye, a chance word?), the warm feeling that this man at my side was more my friend than ever before. I liked him and had the feeling that he liked me. When we parted at the foot of my street, he took my arm—or just touched it—but it was enough.

"I think," said he, "you are right. It isn't enough to produce steel in a mill."

VII

A WINTER INTERLUDE

"It is good for thee to dwell deep, that thou mayest feel and understand the spirits of people."—*From page 92 of the inimitable journal of John Woolman.*

March 1st.

DID you ever love a little place?—a little town, where there is stillness and ease of the soul? I have. I know such a place. . . .

I have had a great experience, in which I have discovered again the beauty of the near, the charm of the common. At one moment it seems to me I could relate the uneventful story of the past three days in a single sentence; but when I think of it again, warmly, deeply, and my mind pauses with an indescribable kind of love over each separate moment of it, I think of a certainty I could write an entire book about it. Nothing happened; everything happened!

I have had three great days at home in Hempfield. I left the City last Friday, the air murky, the streets full of slush, and came at evening to Hempfield. And all about it was of a whiteness and cleanness impossible to describe; and still, still! When I walked down the road the snow was heaped on every side. It tufted all the fence posts, powdered the tree-tops, lay deep and white upon the fields. My breath made a plume as I walked in the frosty air, and the snow creaked under my feet. I had my cap drawn down over my head and a muffler wrapped high around my throat—in one hand my grey bag, and in the other an awkward lumpy package containing a bottle of milk, a pat of butter, a loaf of bread, a wedge of bacon.

I cannot tell how eagerly I tramped down the road that I might come quickly to the turning where I could catch the first glimpse of our own home. It was just in the edge of evening—

you know, the time when the snow begins to look blue where the shadows fall upon it. But before I reached the corner I stopped there in the road, for it had come upon me with sudden sharpness that the house would be unlike itself—cold, still, vacant.

"It will seem an unfriendly place," I said.

But I ploughed onward again and presently the house came into view. Its eyes were indeed all closed with shutters, it lay asleep there on the hillside, no breath rose from its chimneys, and yet what a surge of feeling I had that I was come again to my own place! I made my way through a foot of unbroken snow to the doorway. A drift barred the steps; I tramped it down and came thus into the dark, cold, strangely familiar house. At first it struck a chill through me; but I shook myself, got a light in my own room, and went down on my knees at the fireplace. I built up a little live blaze among the old ashes. I ran to bring the largest stick I could find for a back-log and smaller ones to build up around it.

In a few minutes I had a noble great fire that lighted up the whole room and sent out a delicious glow of heat. I threw off my coat and got in more wood; and soon found myself whistling and presently singing, as I do when I am sure of my solitude. There is nothing like an open fire—the whole process of making it, poking it, mending it—to comfort the soul of man. There is nothing more friendly than an open fire.

Do you know the odour, the delectable odour, of bacon frying over an open fire? On a cold night, mind you, when your appetite has been whetted to a keen edge? The very look of it, sizzling there in Harriet's long-handled skillet—and oh, the sound of it—where is there anything finer?

I rigged a temporary hob by using the andirons and two pokers, and upon this I soon had a kettle of potatoes boiling over. Whenever the lid began to dance about, I swung the kettle aside until its fiery ardours had calmed down. I burned off the nose from Harriet's old coffee-pot; but the coffee!—the coffee was nectar for the gods.

Consider me now at my banquet table there by the fire, where

I could reach the skillet handle—the room glowing with comfort—full of the good odours of bacon and coffee—the lord of all I surveyed. . . .

When it was over I threw more logs upon the fire and began to look about the place, renewing my acquaintance with many an old friend: a picture here, a book there. I think of all things in this world an old book gathers about it the richest mosses of remembrance; I know well many an author of whom I can say, as the woman of Samaria said of the Master, He "told me all things that ever I did."

So it was by chance there on my shelves that I came upon a set of old green-clad volumes, gold-lettered, that I have known as long as I can remember.

"Hello!" said I, "there you are again!"

I recalled warmly all the long history of those old books. They had belonged first to my father, and bore within their covers his characteristic book-plate with the blazoned motto:

> The ungodly borroweth and payeth not again.

How well I remember seeing my father read those books—a kerosene lamp held in one hand, the book in the other. Through the long winter evenings! It was thus that he kept burning the lamp of his spirit there on the raw frontier. In my early days, when any book whatsoever that came into my hand was meat and drink to me, I read parts of those "Ancient Classics"—they had in them the Iliad, Pindar, Aristophanes, Pliny, and many others—and remember how dull I found most of them, and yet how I persisted for the joy of coming upon such marvellous stories as Pliny's adventures during the eruption of Vesuvius.

Looking at these faded old green volumes I forgot where I was, or who I was; I forgot the world, the flesh and the devil. By merest chance I opened one of them, to find my eye falling upon the rollicking chorus of women in one of Aristophanes's plays: the one beginning:

> They're always abusing the women,
> As a terrible plague to men.

85

I read it through to the end, thinking how utterly modern it was: these verses written three or four hundred years before the birth of Christ:

> They say we're the root of all evil
> And repeat it again and again;
> Of war, and quarrels, and bloodshed,
> All mischief, be what it may!
> And pray, then, why do you marry us,
> If we're all the plagues you say?

"Why," said I to myself, "that might be sung any day on any stage in twentieth-century America."

I had laid out serious work for that evening—for I had come to Hempfield on business—and forgot it all, forgot everything. I rolled my couch up to the fire and put the old green books on the floor within arm's reach, and there, stretched out in a veritable riot of solid comfort, I read and read and read.

> "Though care and strife
> Elsewhere be rife,
>   Upon my word I do not heed 'em;
> In bed I lie
> With books hard by
>   And with increasing zeal I read 'em."

When I came to myself it was late enough, I can tell you; so I stepped out of the doorway to make my bow to the wintry night, as I love to do in the country. It was clear and very still. The frosty stars seemed low and near. Far across the valley, like pinholes in the dark, I could see here and there the friendly light of a home. So I came in again to my own warm room, and it seemed strangely good to me to be there with all the ancient, familiar things about. I made me a bed upon the couch with blankets rummaged from Harriet's closet. After the lamp was out, I lay there looking into the fire for some time. . . .

"Life on any terms," said I, "is good."

And so went to sleep.

The following day, Saturday, was truly a great one. I had plenty to do. Dick Sheridan, whom we had left in charge of the place, came down early, and we walked about discussing many things that must be done, such as the pruning of the apple trees and grapevines, the repairing of fences, getting up wood, and the like. I stopped for some time to look at my bees, safely hid in their winter quarters, each shelter heaped with snow. It had come off sunny and warm that morning, and some of the bees were venturing out to explore the arctic regions of orchard and garden. They are truly a neat and orderly people and lose no opportunity for house-cleaning. They were bringing out the dead bees, a single worker sometimes lifting and flying as much as twenty yards with a dead bee before dropping it. Often before going back in they would light down on the sunny snow for a minute or more. To drink? I do not know. Every colony seemed active and in good condition, which greatly delighted me.

I soon found it so pleasant there on my own land, even though the snow was deep, that I brought out a pruning saw and shears and set to work on my favourite McIntosh tree. I worked for some time entirely absorbed, thinking only of the task in hand, but presently, as I stood high up in the tree, I looked all about me, across the snowy countryside with all the farms about, and smoke rising from many a friendly chimney—and the cattle calling in the yards—and hens cackling—and in the town road the jingle of sleigh bells—and it came over me with a sudden glow how much I loved it all! It was something also, I thought vaingloriously, to stand up thus in a sturdy apple tree which I had planted with my own hands, so short a time ago (it seemed), and cultivated and pruned and sprayed. It gives such a sense of reward and possession as nothing else I know.

But I was not to enjoy it for long. I heard a wild commotion in the dooryard, and I looked up to see old Jim Carter come puffing and wallowing down the lane. Behind him came his son, driving his home-built contraption for "buzzin'" wood. I had sent Dick to get him, but had not expected him so soon.

"Hello, Jim," said I. He seemed like an old friend.

"Hello there yourself," he responded heartily. "Where ye been all this time?"

A big, slow man is Jim, loose in his clothes, his face burned in the cutting winter air to the colour of rich old leather. He has the twang of ancient New England hills in his voice, and never fails to add a needless "r" to a word if he can possibly find a place for it.

He drives the champion long-lived motor truck known to man, so old that the engine covers long since disappeared, leaving the bowels of the creature shamelessly exposed. When he starts the engine the noise is terrific; one is alarmed lest Jim be at once blown into the heavens. But he isn't, he would never go so far up. His "buzzer," as he calls it, is not "boughten." Why should he buy a machine when he can make one? What's a Yankee for, anyway!

He explained to me—I could not leave him for the very joy I had in watching the exciting process of events—he explained how he got an old automobile engine—"Cost me less'n twenty-five dollars—" mounted "her" on his truck and hitched her up to the saw. "She" is cooled by water from a vinegar barrel which stands just behind her and slops merrily when the car runs. Never mind, once the engine starts, the heat generated soon dries everything off—such is the cleverness of genius.

He has often to patch up his contraption, both car and saw, with bits of board, wire, nails, screws, bolts, a rusty box of which he carries always near at hand. To watch this huge man down in the snow and sawdust under his machine, blowing like a porpoise as he twists a bit of mending wire, is something to see, I can tell you.

I stood laughing inwardly as I watched him—or listened to him talking as he went along, like a surgeon cutting out an appendix. But, lord, how he can saw! "Buzz" is truly the appropriate name for it. His son passes along a cordwood stick. He sets it on the carriage, drives it—zip—against the saw. The carriage flies back, and he drives it forward again—zip—and the job is done. The sawed sticks fly from under his elbow like dirt from under Bowser's paws when he digs for a woodchuck.

It is incredible that the contraption can hold together to the end of the pile. It doesn't. But genius, and Yankee genius at that, is hard to beat, and a new bolt sets her going again. Before I knew it the wood was sawed, and with vast eruptions of smoke and steam the buzzer set off up the snowy road seeking new piles of wood to devour. Done! Achieved! Money in pocket!

That afternoon I tramped over to see Horace, and then around by way of Close Valley and Barker's Mill to the town. At every turn I came upon familiar views or met men I knew. How good the flavour of the place, how pleasant the remembered scenes!

There is a kind of sturdy humour in the country that the city does not know. A humour that grows straight out of the soil. There may be wit in the city, but wit deals with words: humour with life. I was amused at Horace's observation regarding his visit to the City, when he spent Thanksgiving with us. He had enjoyed every minute of it, said he; but, "I was glad to git home agin where people understand my jokes." (Humour, when you come to think of it, is the very last thing we come to understand in a foreign place or a foreign language. Conrad, great writer as he was, could do everything in English except joke in it.)

As I tramped, it seemed to me that I never had seen such a stir of vigorous outdoor life, sharpened and vivified by the sun and the wind of winter. Stories sprang up by magic on every side.

It was the time when teamsters were drawing wood into the town from the Burnham Hills and Crewsbury. Most of them had been down in the forenoon loaded, and were now on their way back. There was something so jaunty and bold about these robust teamsters with their fine great horses swinging along the snowy roads that I could not help stopping to watch them. I liked the very sight of them.

Presently, as I tramped, I heard someone sing out my name. "Hi there!" said he.

So I turned about to see a young farmer I know, named Larkin, mounted upon his empty sled. He waved me a grand salute, which I returned. He came to a stop with jingling bells, near me, and I mounted beside him on his rack.

"Git up there!" he called to his horses, and in a moment we were whirling up the road—the sun glinting on the shining brasses of the harness and the red pompons dancing on the horses' heads. Occasionally a ball of snow cast by the horses' hoofs would come whirling back into the sled, and the sunny air was full of fine, sharp ice crystals that stung our faces or felt like pepper in our nostrils. And all about, sunshine and wide snowy fields, and a sky above as blue and clear as a man ever saw. Who can describe such a winter day! How it makes the blood race in one's veins and all the earth appear inexpressibly beautiful.

A log chain was dragging behind the sled, polished to a silvery perfection and jingling in a note lower than that of the bells of the harness. Larkin stood sturdily erect, his feet braced apart, the reins in his hands, swaying to the motion of the empty rack. His collie dog, which had come down in the morning, no doubt, walking sedately enough behind the loaded sled, was now mounted grandly upon the rack beside his master, head and tail up, nose to the wind, sharing the exhilaration of the moment. Once he barked in sheer lordly pride at a humble fellow-dog he saw afoot. It is something to be a dog on such a day!

Larkin, in his felt boots and sheepskin jacket, has made his sled a veritable travelling caravansary with all the trappings of a far journey. He comes a forenoon from Crewsbury and must want for nothing. At the top of one of the rack stakes is the battered pail for watering the horses. It gleams in the sun and gives off its own rattling music. On another stake hangs the humble necessary shovel to dig the runners out of the snow if by chance they should be caught. On two other stakes are the great woollen mittens of the driver, lifting, as it were, eager hands to the sky. Here are all the horse blankets, folded for a seat for Larkin when he has passed entirely out of the town, here the horses' nosebags, now empty of oats—like the driver's dinner pail.

We talked on the way, in shouts, exchanging news of the town. And so came to the hill above Barker's Mill.

"Got a good one on Sam Kennedy," said Larkin.

"What's that?" I asked.

"Ye see," said Larkin, "Sam's gone and got him one o' these here new motor trucks, and after the big snow the other night he couldn't get her up the hill. So he gets out early and ploughs all the snow off the road from his place down to the corners. But we're all drawin' wood these days, and so, soon's he got away, John Blair and George Broderick, and a lot of us, got out and ploughed all the snow back on again. You ought to see Sam when he comes up again with his fancy truck. Mad!"

"Well, what happened?" I asked.

"Say," said Larkin, "this is a free country, ain't it? Majority rules, don't it?"

At the upper turning I left Larkin, and within half a mile ran across Jabez Parkinson. He lives on one of the stoniest hills in all Crewsbury; and likes, I fully believe, to be joked about it. So I joked him as we walked along together. I remembered a story he once told me about old Jed Snow, and I wondered if I could not somehow touch the right trigger to set him off upon it. It took some manœuvring, but at last his eye began to twinkle.

"Stuns, ye say! Wall!"

Then he pursed up his lips, and I knew I had him!

"Ever hear tell of old Jed Snow? Talk o' stunny farms. Old Jed had the durndest stunniest farm ye ever saw. But he was a worker, Jed was. First year he built a good big stun wall clear round the place. But when he was a-ploughin' that fall, he turned up more stuns than ever; so he took an' built cross walls, so's to divide his farm into four parts. Big walls they was, too. Third year seem's if he found more stuns than ever he found before. So he just took and throwed 'em into the four fields until he'd filled 'em all up level—I jing!"

I thought, as I walked along, laughing to myself, that it was worth a trip to Hempfield to hear Old Man Parkinson wind up a yarn with "I jing."

That night I had supper with Horace and a fine evening of good talk, stumbling home late through the snow to build up again my open fire and fall into the dreamless sleep of sheer physical weariness beside it.

On Sunday morning, I walked into town and went to the church to hear the Scotch Preacher. He grows older, but never loses the fire of his spirit. I will not here attempt to tell of all the old friends I met—who inquired, to the last one of them, for Harriet—nor of the services there, nor of the Scotch Preacher's sermon. All this would take a chapter in itself. But as I walked homeward again I suddenly said aloud:

"After all, life is the thing. The greatest art of all is the art of living."

It seemed to me, and not without a momentary sense of depression, that writing and painting and carving and acting—all the arts—were poor business indeed compared with this tremendous art, set forth so nobly by the Scotch Preacher, of making something out of the hard, tough, cross-grained material of human life as it was lived among these hills.

I had a fine great visit that afternoon with the Scotch Preacher and his wife (I stayed to supper) and came back late for another delightful evening by my own fire.

In the morning—this was Monday—I packed the books I wanted and began putting the house in shape to leave. And here is where I missed Harriet terribly. As long as the clean dishes hold out I get on reasonably well, but it is not long before complications begin to arise. I run out of cups or forks. I begin to feel big and clumsy; I tip things over, spill the sugar and the flour, get things wet and can find nothing to wipe them on. All the towels degenerate mysteriously into wet wads, the coffee-pot gets lost under the table, the butter melts down, and the bacon burns!

"Harriet," said I, when I got back, "I'm mighty glad to see you."

Surely I never spent a finer three days in all my life.

VIII

COLOURED

And herein lies the tragedy of the age: not that men are poor,—all men know something of poverty; not that men are wicked,—who is good? not that men are ignorant,—what is truth? Nay, but that men know so little of men.—W. E. B. DuBois.

I HAVE in my life had much enjoyment out of Negroes; and several I know I have liked well and esteemed my friends. Something joyous, amusing, tuneful—some agreeable variety—would go out of American life if we had no Negroes in it. We are a sober folk, we white people; and look too solemnly at life. In many of my walks, these days, in the City, or when I stand to look as people go by, I have reflected upon how rare indeed it is to see a happy face (much less a tranquil one), a face that seems to suggest an enjoying spirit.

So it was that yesterday, in the noon hour, I was amused and delighted at the sight of a group of Negro teamsters who had gathered by the side of the street to eat their lunch. They had left their horses with heads comfortably ensconced in oat bags, and blankets thrown over their rumps—for the day was cool and raw—and were now gathered in a somewhat sheltered spot where there was open ground—a few vacant lots, shelving off into a ravine.

They had either brought along or gathered up a number of wooden boxes, sticks, bits of old furniture, and had built up a brightly blazing fire. Two or three of them were sitting on the ground with their dinner-pails between their knees, but most of them were standing about the fire. Just as I chanced along, one of them suddenly executed a kind of buck-and-wing dance and burst out in a clear, tuneful voice:

"She's mah Lindy, Lindy Lu——"

Two or three of the other men seemed to stir irresistibly to the harmony, and when the bit of song stopped it was followed by an infectious laugh all around. I could see white teeth gleaming; and there was a quality of real joyfulness in the tones of the voices and the look of the eyes. I couldn't help liking it, or thinking that a similar number of white teamsters would probably each be sitting by his wagon eating his lunch morosely alone. But here, by magic, these Negroes had made a little camp in the jungle of the city, built up a friendly fire, and in a moment thrown off the work and worries of the day.

"They have," said I, "one genius not sufficiently prized in this world of ours—a genius we jeer at—the genius of knowing how to enjoy themselves."

This idea pleased me so much that I stopped a little way up the street to look at them again. One of them had begun telling a story of some sort; if I could not quite get the words the gusto of the tones reached me, and from time to time all the others would burst out laughing, slap their legs, or poke one another in the ribs.

When he had finished, another, younger man broke in with an equally convulsing narrative, which he dramatised with head, eyes, hands, feet, in a way delightful to see.

"They have another secret," said I, "they know how to enjoy one another. I wonder if these are not the qualities which make the Negro, unlike the Indian, thrive and increase even in an unfriendly environment."

I began to wish I could drop in easily upon the group and talk with them, human being to human being, and was considering how it could be done without breaking the unconscious charm (I doubt whether it could be done by any white man), when the whistles blew, and the Negroes, kicking apart the embers of their fire (not too promptly), went back to their wagons. But even then they did not stop their banter. While they untied the nose-bags of the horses, drew off the blankets, and climbed into their seats, they were still shouting and laughing at one another, as though something about life was irrepressibly amusing. I walked onward again, smiling at what I had seen, and all that afternoon, at my work, had the odd, subconscious feeling that I had had an amusing experience and that the world was a gayer place than it sometimes seemed. A bit of colour and harmony in a drab street!

Where I live in the country we have quite a number of coloured people around about, and from time to time I have had certain of them helping me on my land. I am fond of talking with them; for there is scarcely a man among them who has not a gift of original humour or a touch of dramatic imagination. They are able to extract interest, amusement, and even a kind of beauty, out of the simplest incidents; to be happy with little. A Negro can do more with little, and less with much, than any man I know.

Two summers ago hay weather with us in July was extremely hot, and a teamster for one of my near neighbours—a good man, too—forced his fine team of horses a little too hard, and one of them dropped dead in the field. It was a severe loss to him. A couple of days later I met my neighbour in the town road and upon my inquiry and expression of sympathy he responded:

"Yes, Black Bill kicked off. It'll cost me all of three hundred dollars."

That was all there was to it; and I remember thinking afterward that there was not a little of admirable New England sententiousness and stoicism in this remark—real Yankee. It was a stiff loss; but why make a fuss about it?

It so happened that the next spring I had a Negro ploughman smooth-harrowing a plot of ground where we were to plant onions. One morning, when I saw him coming down the lane, I thought something was wrong with him.

"Ah'm in trouble, Mr. Grayson," said he.

"How is that?" I asked.

"Ah lost mah bes' horse las' night."

"How did that happen?"

" 'Long 'bout three o'clock in the mawnin' I heard a poundin' and a knockin' in the barn. I says to my wife, 'What's that?' She says, 'I don' know.' So I gits up and listens; and all the time I could hear that poundin' and knockin' in the night. So I says:

" 'I reckon Jake has cast hisself and got caught in his halter.'

"I ain't never dreamed there was nothin' wrong. So I gits up and goes out with mah lantern; and all the time that knockin' an' poundin' out there in the dark.

"When I opens the do' an' holds up the light, there I see mah horse Jake a-lyin' on the flo', a-kickin' and a-poundin'. When I gits in he raises up his head and looks at me.

" 'Git up,' says I to him.

"He only looks at me—sad.

" 'What's the matter with you?' I says.

"I kicks him with mah foot, and I says, 'Git up thar!'

"But he only looks at me again—sad—and then begins a-shakin' an' a-tremblin' like a leaf. Then I hears him draw a long breath in his throat—like he was sighin'—and he tries to raise his head again to look at me. But he can't.

" 'What's the matter, Jake?' says I, cryin'.

"But he only throws out his legs and shakes and shivers all over—and dies—poof—like that."

The old man shook his head sorrowfully.

"Jake was a good horse, Mr. Grayson; he was the bes' horse in this town."

I cannot convey the feeling—the sheer drama—that my Negro harrower put into his simple story; or the way in which he used his eyes and hands, nodded his head, modulated his voice, while he was telling it. The tears came into his eyes. He must also have felt keenly the monetary loss, for he is a poor man, but he never thought to mention it. I could not help thinking of the extraordinary difference between the way the white man and the Negro took their loss.

When I was a boy and lived in a town in the North we had one Negro family there. Most small towns in the North I knew had at least one. We called this man, "Negro Joe," and he was the cause of much mirth and many stories. He was a white-washer, or, if there was no whitewashing to do, he could clean a chimney—standing on the roof of the house and singing a song while he worked; or he could paint a barn, or dig a garden, or build, poorly enough, a stone wall.

He also performed a highly valuable public service in a thrifty town like ours, where poverty was unknown, of furnishing a safety valve for our pent-up benevolence. Whenever we wanted to give to the poor—as we were enjoined to do upon high authority—there was Negro Joe. We could pick on him! He had a large, comfortable wife, with a great rolling chin, rolling bosom, rolling hips (Joe was slim), and two or three children, who easily adapted themselves to the part they had to play in the town. And their small house on the edge of the village—I visited it more than once—was a true museum of antiquity, with many an ancient chair, picture, rug.

A trained eye could tell where each thing came from: this had been Old Lady Morton's, that was from the Barbours'; these pictures, "Wide Awake" and "Fast Asleep," had hung for years in the Cashmans' back parlour—until the old gentleman Cashman began to get rich and his daughter Stella came back from school with new notions of furnishing.

Negro Joe and his family were thus valuable adjuncts of the town; but, like many treasures, we did not fully appreciate them until suddenly, one day, Negro Joe announced his intention of "movin'."

"Yes," said he, "Ah'm goin' to move."

No one could make out what the reason was; but, like everything else that Joe did, it was somehow amusing and dramatic. We did not at first think it anything but talk; but Joe meant what he said, posted an auction bill on the signboard of the town hall, and put a "For Sale" notice on the little house.

I don't know quite who originated the idea, or how much of it was due to real regret, and how much to a desire to have a little more fun out of Negro Joe before he left; but one summer evening, almost spontaneously, a group of young people, led by a harum-scarum young lawyer named Cochran, started down to Negro Joe's home. They had secured somewhere an enormous wooden cane with cheap silvered bands around the handle; and this they had tied up with ribbons.

I shall never forget the scene when that little party filed into Negro Joe's front room; all by agreement as solemn as judges. I recall thinking at the time that not a man in town could have carried off the business of welcoming his visitors with more dignified hospitality than Negro Joe.

"Won't you res' your hat?" said Negro Joe. "Mister Cor'cran, you sit here in de big chair; an' you, Mister Morgan, do mah home the honour of sittin' here by de organ."

Our young lawyer began his speech in the finest mood of burlesque, expressing the profound regret of the town at the loss of its prized citizen. For ten years he had lived among us; his life an open book. We were dismayed; we could not understand; we hoped; our good-will would follow, and so on, and so on, as the orator warmed up to the occasion.

I could see Negro Joe and his family standing there, listening with a kind of dignified simplicity—taking every word in dead earnest. There they were in their little home, which, as we looked about it, seemed remarkably comfortable; as good a home as many a white family in the community lived in. They were evidently proud of it.

For some curious reason, we did not find the oration of our young lawyer so mirth-provoking as we had expected. Nor did he himself seem to find it so, although he finished with a grand peroration and presented the be-ribboned cane to "our admired fellow citizen whom we are about to lose—Mr. Joseph B. Blanton."

Some of us had never before heard his full name; he had always been "Negro Joe" or "Nigger Joe."

I shall never forget the picture of Joe standing there with the cane in his hand, or the way in which he stepped a little forward to respond.

"Gennelmen," he said, "I ain't never expect nothin' like this. I thank you, Mister Cor'cran, for yo'r fine words. I thank you, gennelmen, for yo'r kin' thoughts."

He paused: you could have heard a pin drop in the room.

"Gennelmen, I respec' yo'; an' I thank yo'. There ain't never no trouble between folks that respec's each other—white or black. I express mah special gratitude to you, Mister Cor'cran, for all the fine words you say—an' for this gif' of yours which signifies yo'r respec'."

I recall how quietly we walked back into town, and how, just as we reached the corner, one of the boys broke out:

"Gosh! I never realised before that niggers were just like anybody else."

The very next day the sale notice came down from Joe's house, and the auction bill from the town hall—and we had the whole town laughing at us; it was months before poor Cochran heard the last of it.

In Tolstoi's books there are many fine passages regarding the wisdom, and often the happiness, of simple people: men who live close to the soil; or who through their lives have had to deal with disadvantages or hard conditions. He was thinking, of course, of the Russian peasant; but I have been often reminded of it in talking with Negroes—which I greatly love to do.

Not long ago, since I have been here in the City, I had a talk by the merest chance with the Negro woman who takes care of the printer's office where I go every week. I had been detained later than usual, and she had come in to dust off the desks and chairs. I fell to talking with her. She was originally from Maryland; and she was a Roman Catholic—though most of our Negroes hereabouts are ardent Baptists or Methodists. There was something smiling and happy about her, even in the tones of her voice. She had been a servant, doing menial work, all her life.

"You appear to be happy," I said.

"Oh, Ah'm happy. Nobody ain't happier than I am."

"You've got plenty of hard work," I said.

"Ah don' min' that."

"But what is it that makes you happy?" I asked.

She laughed as though this were an odd question.

"Oh," said she, "Ise got lots o' good frien's—and it don' matter whether white or black."

I thought I would sound her a little on the problem of the colour line.

"Oh, that don't trouble me!" She laughed. "I know my place; an' I know who my frien's is."

(How many people, I thought, white and black, lack this wisdom; how few know their place!)

"An' this colour line," she continued, "don' make no trouble when people is frien's, white or black."

I remember once hearing a coloured man I know tell of an experience which well illustrates one of the differences between white and black. I speak of this man advisedly as "coloured," for no one looking at him would ever have thought him a Negro. A Spaniard, an Armenian, an Italian, perhaps, but not a Negro. And he had a good education, he had read far more widely than many a white man of his calling; and yet in Tennessee, where he had lived, he was classified, by the iron law of caste, as a Negro.

He told me of a curious expression among coloured people, which I had never heard before: "Goin' over to white." Negroes who are almost white can sometimes cut away from their Negro life, settle in a new town or state, where they are not known, and "go white."

"I tried it once, long ago," said my coloured friend.

"Didn't it work?" I asked.

His answer quite astonished me.

"No," said he, "I didn't like it. White people don't have as good a time as coloured folks. They're stiff and cold. They aren't sociable. They don't know how to laugh!"

I never before had this glimpse of my race!

Then he told me of his experience. Thinking his life as a coloured man too hard, too much restricted, it came to him one day that he was white enough to pass almost anywhere for a white man, especially in the North. So he acted upon the inspiration.

He went to Memphis and bought a first-class ticket on a Mississippi River boat to Cincinnati. No one suspected him of being coloured, or, if they suspected, gave him the benefit of the doubt. He sat at the table with white people, occupied the chairs with them on the deck. At first, he told me, he could scarcely restrain his exultation, but after a time he began to be somehow lonesome.

"It grew colder and colder," said he.

In the evening of the second day he sat on the upper deck, and as he looked over the railing he could see, down below, the Negro passengers and deckhands talking and laughing. After a time, as it grew darker, they began to sing—the inimitable Negro songs, with their lift and swing, their strange, wistful sadness.

"That finished me," said he. "I got up and went downstairs and took my place among them. I've been coloured ever since."

I have often reflected upon the curious inner problems of the Negro—especially the mulatto, who has two racial spirits at war within him. Life must have strange, deep questions for him, not known to us. I remember once hearing an eloquent coloured minister—he classified as Negro!—set forth his personal problem thus:

"My father's father was a Black Hawk Indian seven feet tall. My father's mother was an Irish woman. My mother's father was an American white man. Her mother was a full-blooded African woman. What am I?"

Once, long ago, I heard a story of Jefferson Davis, President of the Southern Confederacy, which may or may not be true: It happened at Washington before the Civil War, while Davis was a United States Senator. A young friend was walking with him down Pennsylvania Avenue. They met a number of Negroes on their way, each of whom bowed or lifted his hat to Mr. Davis—and Mr. Davis returned the bow. His young friend finally expressed his surprise that the senator from Mississippi should take such pains in returning the salutations of the Negroes.

"I cannot allow any Negro," said Senator Davis, "to outdo me in courtesy."

What a fine, high thing was this! It deserves to be worn, like a jewel, in one's thoughts.

(I went once to dinner in a rich and comfortable home. A Negro maid waited at table. The discussion turned upon Negroes, and much was said of their amusing ignorances, their pretences, even their evil. Afterward the hostess told me with surprise that she found the Negro maid crying in the pantry. This has hurt me for years whenever I have thought of it.)

I wonder sometimes if society—as we now know it—is not based upon the assumption that men will do their worst rather than their best; that they will all be beasts if they are not made afraid of instant clubbing. And this has made me dream often of some fair country where society assumed that men would do their best instead of their worst; a country in which they had learned the great truth that we all make our own people as we go along, fashion them, much as God does, after our own image.

I should like to live in such a country—

In that far country, as I have visited it, often and often, in my thought, the people are not equal any more than they are with us: neither are they of the same colour or race, or religion, or education—or anything whatsoever—but they have struck upon a marvellously simple device for making life more beautiful and happier than it is with us. It is not yet perfect, as the wisest among their inhabitants know well, but it serves.

And this is the secret of it: Those of the population of the country who are well born, or educated, or rich—knowing well that these benefits came to them by chance of birth or fortune, and that almost all the good things they have are due not to their own labour but to the vision and toil of men long dead (Jesus and Socrates and Newton and Shakespeare and Washington and Lincoln)—knowing all this, as I say, these well-born or educated or rich men, instead of demanding that all the poorer people, all those of a different race or colour or religion, be honest, courteous, virtuous, and industrious, begin by being honest, virtuous, and noble themselves; by having themselves the courtesy they demand of others. It is strange how excellently well this policy works in that country. . . .

This, of course, is a dream. . . .

IX

JONAS

"He most doth bathe in bliss
That hath a quiet mind."

I HAVE had a day of quiet enjoyment: an amusing, lazy, inconsequential, but utterly charming day. If I had tried for a year I could never have imagined such a train of oddly quiet events, or dreamed of such curious, interesting, simple human beings. When I came home and thought of it all, I said to myself:

"Here is a day in which nothing of any consequence has happened—but, lord!—how I have enjoyed it!"

But the more I thought of it, the more it seemed to me that everything of any real consequence had happened; for is there anything better in this world than to know real people, and to be able to enjoy, utterly and completely, an entire day? Stevenson says somewhere in one of his books that if one could add together all the days, hours, minutes in a lifetime that were fully worth living, the sum would be only forty. Forty days worth living out of a life! I've had many more than that already, but if only that were true I could say that in this day I have lived one fortieth of my life.

The day began quietly enough. It being Sunday morning, quite early, I went down the steps into the sunny street. In the country, at such an hour, life is as much on the go as ever; one can hear the hens cackling in their runways, and the bees humming, and the cattle calling, and the birds singing, and perhaps the whistling of some early boy in the fields! Oh, it is fine in the country of a sunny Sunday morning in May!

But in the city everything quiets down of a Sunday morning; and the streets are as deserted as those of Sidon or of Tyre; and the tall still houses have a strange look, and such sounds as there are—a boy crying a paper, the iron ring of the milk-man's wheels on the stones—echo and reëcho as in a cavern. But how sweet the sun looking over the house-tops, stealing in at the windows, warming a cat curled on the steps! How pleasant the new leaves on old fretted ivy along the walls; how charming the ailanthus trees here and there leaning out of alleys and areaways!

All this came over me as I stepped out lazily into the Sunday morning sunshine. Where is spring not lovable?

> "What in all the world, in all the world, they say,
>   Is half so sweet, so sweet, is half so sweet as May?"

It is the orioles that sing this, so the truthful poet reports—did he not hear them singing it? And they sing it well in the country I know best, where there are tall elm trees with swaying branches for orioles to nest in. But even a stranger in a far city can feel something of that delight on a sunny May morning.

It is this way with me: When I begin to enjoy a time like this I wish there were someone I could take in with me. So it was, by a perfectly natural process, that I thought of the Jensens, and of Jensen's garden, which I had not seen for some time. And that brought upon me a wave of longing for growing things, and I thought I would go in and see how Jensen's miniature garden was progressing. I had come to have a real liking for the old man.

I found him in the little areaway back of the house, and to my surprise quite dressed up—as though going away. He was resting in the sun, which was just high enough now to reach down between the buildings opposite and touch his little box of radishes and lettuce, now quite luxuriantly growing. The precious "punkins," however, which had been planted far too early and were now glassed over by Jensen's careful hands, looked lank and spindling.

There Jensen sat resting in the sun, with a calm look on his fine old face. He had seen much of life, and suffered much, and thought much, and was tranquil.

"I see, Jensen," I said, "that you are sitting, like Jonah, in the shade of your gourd."

He looked up with a smile.

"Aren't you afraid that Nineveh will be destroyed before you get there?"

He took his big pipe slowly out of his mouth to reply; but at this point Mrs. Jensen came bustling out of the door. She was also dressed up, quite astonishingly, with a bonnet that even I—who have never in my life seen of my own accord more than two bonnets—could not help seeing. She looked grand.

"Ve go for a tour," said she. "Jonas, he iss bringing soon his flivver, and ve go riding. All day ve ride."

Her excitement was fine to see; and when I began to express my interest she led me into the kitchen and showed me the blankets, sofa pillows, lunch baskets and the like—enough for an Arctic expedition. One thing rapidly led to another, and before I knew it Harriet and I had been invited to go with them.

"No, no, no!" cried out Mrs. Jensen, "ve haf plenty, plenty. You shall go with us in Jonas's flivver. Ve have plenty lunch."

I glanced around at Jensen. He was saying nothing with such a look of inviting friendliness that I could not help accepting. I went up the stairs much excited by the prospect and quite prepared to meet difficulty in overcoming Harriet's scruples. Sunday! But to my surprise, Harriet scarcely made a single objection, and in a few minutes we were at the steps, ready to go.

Jonas had just arrived with the "flivver," which now stood still, trembling a little, and barking like a tired dog, with two or three tolerably loud barks, then a little weak one. Jonas immediately leaped out, threw up the hood, and went at the machinery head first, with the result that the barking presently became quite steady, though still somewhat weary.

"I don't dare stop her," said Jonas—this flivver was apparently of the feminine gender—"for she's hard to start up again."

Jonas was a stocky young fellow, with a round head and prominent blue eyes. In honour of the occasion he wore an unaccustomed white collar and red tie. He had oil on his hands.

"Where are we going, Jonas?" I asked.

"Goin' fer a ride," said Jonas.

"But where?"

"Anywhere," said Jonas.

Mrs. Jensen came hurrying out with baskets, blankets, cushions —Jensen quite helpless.

"Hurry, Ma," said Jonas.

"Vell, do I not hurry, Jonas? What you t'ink!"

I sat up in the front seat with Jonas; Harriet with Mr. and Mrs. Jensen behind. The flivver shuddered a few times under us, barked desperately, and then with a leap started off down the street, Mrs. Jensen crying out, "Ve go; ve are off!"

It was something to see Jonas sitting up there at the wheel, eyes sternly fixed upon the road and hands grasping the steering gear as though he himself were pushing the car. We darted around a corner, dodged a silent policeman, passed a truck at thirty miles an hour and swung finally into a broad boulevard.

"Gee," said Jonas, "she runs fine to-day!"

I glanced around to see Harriet holding on her hat—and all smiling broadly.

"It's a fine day for a trip like this," said I, trying to start up a conversation.

"You bet," said Jonas.

"Everyone seems to be going out into the country," I continued.

"Sure," said Jonas.

"Do you like the city, Jonas?"

"Yep," said Jonas.

"When I was a young man," I said, "we used to want to go West and take up new land or look for a mine."

"Nix fer me," said Jonas.

So we rolled along gaily upon that broad, smooth city pavement, the wind in our faces, and all about spring sunshine and more and more trees, grass, open spaces. It was most exhilarating.

We stopped presently at a roadside station for gas, Jonas stepping out like one of the lords of creation.

"Fill 'er up, Bill."

While Bill was fillin' 'er up she coughed asthmatically under us, shook as though with a chill, and then suddenly stopped.

"Ve stop," cried out Mrs. Jensen excitedly.

Like one accustomed to the mishaps of life, Jonas seized the crank and turned it vigorously. She wheezed. She snorted. Jonas ran around to choke her. She gave a despairing flop and swooned away. Again Jonas went at the crank, again running around to set the throttle. The perspiration started upon his face.

"Ve do not go!" cried out Mrs. Jensen.

"Hey there," said Bill, the gasman, "ye ain't goin' to take all day startin'. Other people want to get gas."

With that Jonas and Bill, on each side, ran "her" down the street some distance, out of the way of traffic.

"Ve are stopped," remarked Mrs. Jensen.

I looked around at Jensen, and saw that philosopher getting out his china pipe, the solace of many a misery; and presently he was blowing off puffs of smoke, and looking about upon the spring morning with the utter placidity of contentment.

Jonas was now quite in his element. He stripped off his good coat, slipped on a jumper, spread a rug on the pavement, got out a package of instruments, threw up the hood, crawled under the car—and generally enjoyed himself.

Mrs. Jensen, who had at first observed these proceedings with some anxiety, now followed the motions of Jonas with upsurging pride.

"Jonas, he knows," she assured us, "he vill fix 'er."

So we sat there in the fine spring sunshine. The automobiles in the road had now become numerous and there was a jolly, almost holiday, air about the people in them. One or two shouted jokingly at Jonas as they passed, or smiled at our predicament.

"David," said Harriet excitedly, "there's a rose-breasted grosbeak."

"What, here in the City!"

Sure enough, there he was in an open lot near by. It seemed quite like home.

"And look at the dandelions blooming!"

"And there are actually lilacs not gone yet."

I had not seen Harriet so much excited before since we came to the City. These were old country friends she was greeting; and this bird was a country bird; and this grass country grass; and this sunshine country sunshine. A pleasant glow came in her face. Jensen's eyes looked at her and then at me. There was a kind of blessing in that look. Presently he took his pipe slowly out of his mouth and said:

"Ah, ve lofe the spring."

Jonas was a long time at his fixing, but now that we had begun to look about us at the glory of the day—and to see the fine people rolling by in their cars—we minded it not at all. Presently Jonas arose from the bowels of the flivver, a broad grin on his face, and smut on his nose.

"I got her," he remarked.

He turned triumphantly at the crank, and, sure enough, she responded instantly with a loud snort. It was as though some obstruction had suddenly come up out of her throat. She snorted again and again, with a kind of vainglorious excitement. She shook all over; she seemed about to blow up and be done with it. Jonas ran around to the throttle; and then she settled down suddenly to a steady snort-snort-snort.

I wish you could have seen Jonas at that moment. There he stood, well blacked, both face and hands, hair sticking every way for Sunday, perspiration pouring down his face—but with such a look of pride and satisfaction as cannot be depicted.

"Ah, Jonas," said Mrs. Jensen, "he iss good vit engines. He knows engines. Every engine he can start."

So now we were on our way again, headed for the open country. We rolled along as easily as you please, twenty, twenty-five, thirty miles an hour. We skirted around a great limousine as though it were standing still, we darted over crossings, we swung around corners, holding on for our lives.

"Gee," said Jonas, "she runs fine."

"Jonas, Jonas," cried Mrs. Jensen, "you vill kill us; you go too fast."

"This ain't nothin'," responded Jonas, out of the corner of his mouth without looking around—and straightway speeded up.

"She can make fifty easy," said he.

I glanced around to see Jensen drawn down in his seat, hanging on with both hands, his hair flying in the wind——

At that there was a loud explosion, and Jonas, with his feet braced on the brakes, came to such a sudden stop as nearly to throw us out. He swung out of his seat and looked down.

"Yep, she's blowed out," he observed.

Sure enough, a rear tire, which had been old when Germany first declared war, was now flat. Jonas was not in the least irritated. Off came the coat again, on the jumper, and he began changing the tire. He seemed actually to enjoy these opportunities to exhibit his skill.

Well, as a result of several incidents of this sort, noon found us not in the country, where we were bound, but near the corner of a park already occupied by a good many people. A bandstand was there under the trees, but the band had not yet arrived.

"Ve stop here," exclaimed Jensen, in great delight. "Ve haf music."

"Ah, Jensen, he lofes music," said Mrs. Jensen. "Vell, ve vill stop."

It was well said, for the "flivver" had again swooned away; and Jonas, now looking like a blacksmith at the end of a hard day's labour, was again changing into his jumper. So we all got out and carried the blankets, cushions, and baskets to a pleasant spot under a tree some distance back in the park. It was not near enough to the bandstand to suit Mrs. Jensen, but it was none the less a charming place. Above were wide-spreading maple boughs with little openings to the sunny sky. As we looked about we could see many people sitting or lying on the grass, some reading the Sunday papers, some eating their lunch, some stretched out in utter comfort, sleeping.

Mrs. Jensen's ceremony of preparation was something to see. First she spread down newspapers on the grass; over these she put down her blankets, then in the middle a red tablecloth with a fringed border. The baskets she disposed at two corners where she herself was presently to sit like a Queen between them. She moved so fast that Harriet, who tried to help, was quite useless. Jensen went for a pail of water at the public fountain.

"Jonas, come now," she called presently, "lunch is ready."

Jonas, lying head first under the car, did not reply.

"Jonas, *Jonas*. Sooch a boy!"

After much further calling, Jonas proceeded to the fountain, washed his face and arms, while his mother stood waiting to hand him a towel, and came presently with hair sticking straight up and face exactly the colour of a ripe tomato.

"Gee," said he, "I got 'er goin'."

His mind was still on the flivver.

What a luncheon was that! I think I have rarely seen Harriet more interested as one after another of the strange things came out of the basket. The strangest of all were a blood sausage and a round red-coloured cheese—such as no inhabitant of Hempfield had ever seen from the beginning of time. When Harriet expressed her wonder, Mrs. Jensen at once became volubly explanatory as to how in her youth, in Denmark, she had herself made cheeses and blood sausage.

So, vividly explaining, she cut the great sausage and the cheese and passed the pickled cabbage and the rye bread. It had been a long time since breakfast in our Tower, and riding in the open air, especially exposed to the terrors and alarums of Jonas's flivver, was sharpening to the appetite. It was downright good, Mrs. Jensen's lunch (although I observed that Harriet somehow avoided the blood sausage). We had hot coffee poured out of thermos bottles; and, finally, at the end, the veritable surprise of the day, ice cream from a little pail packed in ice.

"Jonas," said Mrs. Jensen, "he lofes ice cream."

Jonas not only loved ice cream but everything else. I began soon to understand why Mrs. Jensen's baskets were so capacious. Dishes started in both directions toward Jonas and stopped there. If there was anything left, Jonas ate it. It was a spectacle, a performance, a work of art, to see Jonas eating his lunch. Jonas had nothing to say, scarcely anything to think; his whole being was focussed upon the business of lunching. I had a brilliant idea as I sat there (which I think worth at least ten thousand dollars); and this was to put Jonas on the stage each evening at eight o'clock and let him have his dinner there. It would bring down the house! And as he ate, Jonas grew redder and redder —if that were possible—looked more and more comfortably stuffed.

Jonas was second man on a truck owned by a wholesale grocery house. His father had tried to teach him his own beautiful art of bookbinding.

"Why should a feller spend years learnin' to be a bookbinder," said Jonas, "when he can git as much right off? I can pull down more'n any bookbinder in the trade, an' I ain't got to work more'n eight hours a day."

It was incomprehensible to Jonas how his father sometimes forgot himself and worked overtime on a binding—and so was late to his dinner.

"He ain't on to Amurrica," said Jonas.

I had often talked with Jensen about his earlier life; and he told me how, as a boy, he had learned to repeat part of the Norse Sagas; the stories of Frithiof, of Thor and Wodin and the Frost Giants. He was full of old poetry; and yet with a kind of humour, too.

"I remember ven I came on the ship to New York," said he, "I stood on the deck tinkin' I vas Columbus; and the first ting I looked for in Broadvay vas Indians."

The heroes of Jonas were quite different: Ty Cobb and Dempsey; and instead of the lore of Thor and Wodin he had Mutt and Jeff and the movies.

He had also an apt and ready pragmatic philosophy. I once asked him how he dared drive a great new truck the company had bought when he had not yet learned how:

"Oh, you ain't got to know," said he, "you've only got to put it over."

Toward the close of our meal the band began to play, the music coming pleasantly to us through the trees. Jensen drew back against the maple trunk, lighted his pipe, and sat there placidly smoking. Jonas returned to his blessed car, and although it stood on the roaring and dusty street he drew himself together and went to sleep on the back seat.

But it was Mrs. Jensen who most attracted my attention. She sat there on the grass, legs straight before her, and busy worn hands resting at last palm upward in her lap. As the music stole across the sunny spaces, a curious rapt look came over her face; and a kind of absorbed gaze of the eyes as though they were turned in upon the vague but deep memories of the peasantry of a hundred generations. I had a curious sense that here was no Mrs. Jensen; here was Woman dreaming of the deep things of life. . . .

So we all sat there in delightful restfulness and contentment, each thinking the thoughts that came up to him out of his own past.

This love of getting out into the open fields and woods in the spring, the delicious warm days, is truly one of the deepest instincts of humankind. Deep, deep in the race it stirs; deeper than civilisation, deeper far than any superficial memory or experience. For what endless generations before man was really man, before he knew himself, has our race crept out of the miserable caves, hovels, and burrows of our winter hiding places to the warm and sunny hillsides of spring—and with what nameless joy. It is deep in us, this love in spring of the open woods, the trees, the fields, the marshes. It is native to our family! Congenial to our blood!

So we sat there for a long time, saying little, listening to the music, resting, in utter comfort. Occasionally Jensen would take his pipe out of his mouth to make an observation, which usually required no response. Once, after his eyes had followed with lazy fascination the swiftly rolling traffic in the road, he remarked:

"In the old country ve know where ve go; but in deese country dey go joost the same vidout knowing."

After a time Mrs. Jensen began to stir and presently looked around to see if Jonas was still sleeping in the car. He was; and would continue to do so, as we discovered, until well shaken. Suddenly, without any preface whatever, Mrs. Jensen remarked:

"Jonas, he should marry. I say to him, 'Jonas, why do you not marry?' 'Who shall I marry, Ma?' says he. 'Vell,' says I, 'there is Mary Sorenson; she iss a good von; a good vorker.' 'Talk sense, Ma,' says he, 'she makes more'n I do. She pulls down her little forty-five a veek,' says he."

Jensen remarked:

"It iss America!"

At this Mrs. Jensen fully waked up and with indignation exclaimed:

"Do they not marry in America? Why do you say to ever'ting, 'It iss America'? I say Jonas, he should marry. He iss grown up, he should marry."

"Vell, you tell him," responded Jensen indulgently.

"I do tell him; but he laughs. He laughs. It iss the same when I tell him about religion and God. He says, 'They ain't no God.' Sooch a boy!"

"It iss America," said Jensen placidly.

"Ach!" exclaimed Mrs. Jensen indignantly, and started up to her feet.

The music had now stopped and the shadows had begun to lengthen, but the park still echoed with pleasant voices. We could see young lovers, groups of children, boyish friends, families, drifting along the walks or across the wide green spaces.

"Isn't it a fine thing," said Harriet, "that these people who cannot live in the country have a chance to come to a park like this?"

Mrs. Jensen now began to gather up the baskets and blankets and carry them down to the car. Upon each visit she gave Jonas a poke.

"Jonas, get up. Ve go."

But Jonas, his head crooked down on the seat, continued to snore. To the last Jensen remained sitting calmly by the tree, until the excited Mrs. Jensen, like a frantic hen with contrary chickens, succeeded in getting Jonas awake and Jensen up.

At length we were all loaded in and Jonas sitting bareheaded at the wheel, quite triumphant at the ready way in which "she" had started off for home.

"I think she smells her oats," said I.

I shall not soon forget the fine ride home we had in the cool of the evening, rolling easily along with a light breeze in our faces and exhilaration in our hearts. The entire city seemed homeward bound and many a car was loaded with the spoil of the woods. For some reason Jonas's flivver seemed content, like old balky horses I have known, to make the return journey without a single protest, landing us quite safe at the foot of our Tower.

"Here ve are," said Mrs. Jensen.

Harriet and I tried to express our great appreciation, but Mrs. Jensen would scarcely let us.

"Ve haf a good day!" said she. "Ve do what ve like."

When I thanked Jonas, he said:

"You bet."

So it was that I thought to myself, that evening:

"Here is a day in which nothing of any consequence has happened—but, lord!—how I have enjoyed it."

As I copy out this account of our expedition with Jonas, now two years afterward, my mind goes back still warmly to that day in May. I like well to think of the Jensens and their garden— hopeful every spring, hopeless every fall. I think sometimes our gardens, like our poems, our books, our true noble deeds, are best in the dreaming. Jensen's "punkins" were. He saw them with an April imagination climbing far up the brick walls, to the glory and astonishment of the neighbourhood; the great yellow globes pendant from the vines and supported by his own cunning invention in little woven string hammocks. But in August! I remember the straggling, dusty vine, the pale, half-wilted blossoms which no bees came to fertilise, and one long green accidental nubbin of a pumpkin through which some boy among those windowed cliff dwellings had, with sling shot, driven a hole. But Jensen loved it and watered it and nursed it and trained it to the last. The City, after all, will have its way. And yet men are interesting, not because they succeed—either as poets or pumpkin raisers—but by virtue of the bravery of their vision, the power of their intent.

X

THE ADVENTURE OF THE SHABBY MAN

ONE morning, I remember vividly, in that City, as I was walking down to the print-shop of my misery, I saw a shabby-looking man standing on the corner near a cigar store. It came to me with a warm thrill of amused excitement—how do such things come to a man?—that if I liked, if I had enough imagination and ingenuity, I could come to know that shabby man, know all about him, know him in such a way that he would like me and be glad to help me in whatever I was trying to do.

I stopped at the curb some distance away to turn this amusing thought over in my mind.

"No doubt," said I to myself, "if I wanted to get to the President of the United States, or the Emperor of Japan, or Henry Ford, I could start with him as well as any one. For we get to great people only by way of little ones."

I glanced again at my Shabby Man. He seemed gloriously at leisure and was entirely unconscious of the designs I had upon him. I thought he would not be irritated if I interrupted his meditations.

"No doubt," said I to myself, pursuing my project with new amusement, "he would know the boss of the street gang, or the corner policeman, or perhaps even the local political leader, and would introduce me:

" 'Boss, this is Mr. Grayson, a friend o' mine.' "

Then, if I had the imagination and ingenuity I could so interest the Boss or the Leader (he might think I had a vote or two to turn his way) that he would introduce me to the Congressman of his district ("Jim"—he would call him Jim to let me know he was on the best of terms with him—"Jim, this is Grayson, a good feller and a friend o' mine"), and the Congressman, being under obligations to the Boss, and he under obligations to the Shabby Man, and the Shabby Man to me, what would be easier, if I went down to Washington (and still had enough imagination and ingenuity!), than to persuade the Congressman to take me to the White House and introduce me to the President? And if I could meet the President——

At this I turned to look again, quite hopefully, at the Shabby Man—and he had totally disappeared, probably stepped into the cigar store or slipped around the corner while I wasn't looking and so, just as I was there in the White House, about to shake hands with the President—"How are you, Mr. President?"—down fell my beautiful project in complete ruin. I felt as though I had lost a great opportunity. I had been cheated of my just prey.

Well, I went down the street laughing heartily at myself, and yet somehow enjoying this little unimportant incident. When I told Mr. Pitwell about it afterward, he roared with laughter.

"I still think," said I, "it is a good way to get to the Emperor or Henry Ford, and one of these days, you'll see! I'll try it."

I should not describe this absurd incident at all if it were not for the further adventure it soon led me into, the results of which I truly prize. For it was only a few days later that I again met the Shabby Man.

Not far from our Tower in the City, we are blessed with an open square or common, which sometimes at evening, when failing light has blurred the hard angularity of the buildings all about and dimmed the evidences of human use, has a sweetness that reminds me of the country.

It is cooler there than in hot city streets, for little breezes adventuring in from the sea of an evening, being off duty, stop to play in the tree-tops. At the centre of it there is a pool of water, which, if you look at it from the right angle (as one must often look at sorry things), will sometimes give you back the sky or the stars. It is fed from a fountain at one side with water spurting from the uplifted bronze beak of a swan held fast in the arms of a fat, naked, rusty bronze Cupid. Sometimes, just at evening, three Italians, two with violins and one with a piccolo, come there to play funny lively music, and afterward go about smiling broadly to collect a tariff of pennies. In the daytime this charming spot swarms with children; but in the evening lovers meet there, and old men sit in the seats to rest, and sometimes an orator comes to the street-side to tell the populace how the evils of this crooked universe of ours can be quickly cured by taking his particular pill.

I have loved to walk in this small common and look at all the people who are there, all the strange, poor, fascinating, valuable people. I had also another secret purpose which, now that the danger is past, I may openly disclose. I discovered to my amazement one day that a pair of our own familiar song-sparrows— that cheerfulest of birds—was actually nesting in a low thicket of viburnum and hemlocks near one corner of the common.

All about, day by day, played the children, the City clanged and roared, and all night long blazed the lights of the streets— and yet these birds tranquilly nested there. I cannot tell the delight I had in finding their nest, nor the curious sense of kinship I felt for other wild things caught in the City (and making the best of it). I made many an anxious, tiptoeing visit to see how the family progressed—I had to be shy, I can tell you, with sharp-eyed boys about; or with my back turned as innocent as you please, I listened to the exquisite low music of the male bird as he hid near the nest.

I suppose I ought not to interrupt the current of my story for so long a description of the little common; but somehow I love it, and cannot let it go by without a word or two. For how can any little pleasant place be all it should to us unless we say truly what we feel about it?

It was here, one evening, that I saw again the Shabby Man who had set me on my absurd imaginings. He was taking his ease, as it were, in his own pleasant garden, looking about him quite tranquilly. No millionaire in his own private park could have seemed more complacent. I saw him some distance away and decided with a thrill that this time he should not escape me.

Yet I was in no hurry. I even stopped a moment to consider, with eager amusement, how I should go about capturing him. I had an idea that I should like to find out why he was shabby.

As I have already related, I have had much joy in certain amusing adventures, playing country Caliph visiting incognito this dim Bagdad of a City. Should I try being Caliph with the Shabby Man?

I decided instantly in the negative. In fact, I had begun to grow rather tired of that method. While I had had a thundering success with it—or so I considered it—when I met Mr. Pitwell, the later adventures had been checkered. The business decidedly had its ups and downs.

You see, while I was thinking of myself as a Caliph, other people, looking me over, did not, somehow, get any such idea. I knew well what I was inside, but they didn't. They were conscious only of a rather awkward country-looking man interrupting them while they were busy with pick and shovel digging for gold; and since he could contribute no practical hints to help them with their digging, and because they were always a little suspicious lest, while he fixed them with his glittering eye, he would cunningly make away with some of the nuggets they turned up, they sometimes made short work of him.

It came over me, then, in a flash of amusement, how I would do it.

"I will be a kind of Socrates of this Athens," I said, "and floor him with questions."

I liked the idea tremendously. As to the method itself, it was old enough—had I not asked Yankee questions, recklessly and gloriously for years in the country? But the sudden feeling that I could myself be the veritable Socrates of this task (I actually felt of my nose to see whether it would qualify in socratic stubbiness), was boundlessly delightful. Socrates immediately and completely elbowed the Caliph off the scene (being no doubt a stronger character).

So it was that Socrates strolled along the street of Athens. Over there was the Parthenon; and this, though the identification was not complete, was the agora. It was evening in Athens.

"How are you?" said Socrates to the Shabby Man.

"How are *you?*" said the Shabby Man to Socrates.

He moved along a little in an inviting way—being no doubt glad of any interruption—and Socrates sat down on the bench beside him.

"I see," said Socrates, "that you are taking your ease in your garden."

It is the way of Socrates to begin anywhere.

"*My* garden," said the Shabby Man somewhat indignantly; "where did you git that idee?"

"Are you not sitting here freely, of your own will?"

"Why, yes," said the Shabby Man; "they ain't nobody compellin' me."

"And can any one, by any law, make you move?"

"No," said the Shabby Man.

"Do you think any millionaire who sat here could have any pleasanter views or cooler airs than you have now?"

"Why, no," said the Shabby Man; "but dang it, what are ye drivin' at?"

"Well, then," said Socrates calmly, "I have proved, haven't I, that this is your garden—at least, as much yours as any one's?"

I wish you could have seen the expression on the Shabby Man's face. Socrates in his own day must have had no end of inner amusement. But the Shabby Man, lingering on corners or sitting on park benches, had also seen something of human nature.

"Say, neighbour," said he, "I ain't particular, but are you all straight?" And he tapped his forehead with one finger.

"You have not answered my question," said Socrates—you will remember that Socrates never allowed his victims to wriggle away from him. "Isn't this your garden you are sitting in?"

"Say, this here is a public park."

So literalism, like an incubus, sits upon the soul of man!

"I see plainly," said Socrates, "that you do not know how rich you really are. Did you ever think that whatever you can enjoy belongs to you?"

The question missed the Shabby Man entirely, but he pounced like a hawk upon the assumption that he was rich without knowing it.

"Me—rich!" he exclaimed, showing at last some real heat. "Rich!"

"I feel certain," remarked Socrates, "that you didn't know it, else you would be a happy man to-night."

(I liked being Socrates better the further I got along with it.)

The Shabby Man edged a little away, and glanced down as though he expected to find his pockets suddenly full of money:

"Say, neighbour, what do you mean?"

"Isn't this open space here in the crowded city valuable?"

"Why, yes," said the Shabby Man; "course it is."

"And these trees—and fine walks and seats—and that fountain playing there, aren't they precious? Aren't they costly? Aren't they beautiful?"

The Shabby Man was beginning plainly to be angry; but Socrates did not wait, this time, for an answer, but, leaning over a little nearer, put another question.

"Did you ever think of the men who are at work the year round, or of the money that citizens contribute, to make a pleasant place like this where you and I can come and sit in the evening and enjoy ourselves?"

"Huh!" said the Shabby Man. "You mean these here lazy white-wings that rake up the leaves in the park! A lot o' grafters, I say! I know 'em. And I know the man that bosses 'em. He couldn't make a livin' poundin' sand in a rat hole. I *know* 'em."

"That's the very trouble!" said Socrates. "Isn't it odd how much annoyance we rich ones, we aristocrats, have with our servants? We can't sit at ease of an evening in our own garden and enjoy the beauty or the quiet of it, can we? without thinking of the indecent neglect of those who work for us?"

I don't know that I blame the Shabby Man for being restless and even angry; no one likes to be driven into a hole with questions. I don't wonder that Socrates, back there in old

Greece, had finally to drink the hemlock. He must have been a truly uncomfortable character. Down with him! And I don't know what might have happened next if there had not been an interruption which provided an easy way for the Shabby Man to escape.

This interruption was the orator I have already mentioned, who came of pleasant evenings to discourse to the multitudes (he had often as many as twenty or thirty people to listen to him) upon the state of the nation and the world. He had a curious wooden chair which he brought with him. It had a straight high back with a box attached to it, wherein he kept pamphlets for sale. He would plant this chair upon the pavement, mount upon the seat, take off his hat and run his fingers through his sleek black hair, and begin with a voice that would put to shame the bull of Bashan:

"Fellow citizens."

It was he who interrupted our Socratic dialogue there in the park. The Shabby Man drifted into his audience. I had myself seen him a number of times and had even stopped to listen to him; but I had never looked upon him save as a picturesque feature of the life of the City.

But that night I was stirred by my adventure with the Shabby Man, and wondered what it was in this orator that drew him away. So I also joined in the audience. I felt far from being satisfied with my pursuit of the Shabby Man which I had begun so jauntily. I had not captured him, much less found out why he was shabby. I hated to let him get away from me.

Well, I listened intently to the orator until he had finished this speech, and I listened to the discussion that followed.

It was a remarkable talk. The man had the passionate sincerity of one who had himself suffered. He had been a journeyman printer, and in the course of a hard life had learned not only to read his galleys upside down, as printers do, but everything else under the sun. Half the world judges the other half by its hurts.

Well, he gave appealing or humorous glimpses of his experiences, so that I thought I should like to know much more about him, and I felt envious of the power he had of stirring up the men who gathered around him.

His whole message could be boiled down into a few sentences: He told his hearers that they were poor and having a hard time of it, that they were not getting half what was rightly theirs, and that the fault lay in the Government, in the laws, in society as it was organised. His advice to these men was to demand their rights and step up and take what was their own.

I think this a fair statement of the essence of his message; and one hearing it honestly could not deny that there was much truth in what the man said. When has power ever been just with weakness? His hearers literally drank up his words. They were flattered to learn that they were having a hard time and were not getting enough pay—and that the trouble was not with them but with other people or with a distant government.

These thoughts came whirling upon me as I walked away after the orator had finished, and I was so absorbed that I forgot the existence of the Shabby Man and the playful mood of the earlier evening. For when a man gets a glimpse of even a partial truth passionately expressed, he must make a place for it in his thinking, or it will continue to plague him.

"I expect," I said to myself, "I have too much of the countryman in me to wish to be pitied for anything whatsoever; and, so far from having a hard time of it, it seems to me I have had, always, far more out of life than I myself earned. And when I think of my troubles, it seems to me I have caused most of them myself."

It came over me suddenly and humorously and I said to myself:

"One of these nights I will bring *my* soap box and get up there by that orator, and every time that he tells the people how poor they are and how much society owes them, I'll tell 'em how rich they are, and how much they owe society."

This picture immensely struck my fancy.

"Between us," I said, "we'll manage to get out the whole truth; but"—and I saw the consequences with startling vividness,

—"I'll be the one to be knocked on the head. No one in these days wants to be reminded that he owes anything."

I was so absorbed in these amusing speculations that I was startled when I felt someone touch me on the arm. I glanced around. It was the Shabby Man walking beside me. An indescribable change had come over his face. Earlier in the evening he had seemed cowed and on the defensive. Now he looked bold.

"Say, neighbour," said he, "what did you think o' the speech? Had the goods, eh!"

I could see that the Shabby Man had been stirred.

"Well," said I, "there was much truth in what he said."

"I'm tellin' ye," said the Shabby Man enthusiastically.

"He made a pretty good story about what society owes men like you and me now, didn't he?"

"You bet he did," said the Shabby Man.

(I did not recall until afterward that in all the conversation that followed I never once thought of being Socrates!)

"If I had all that was comin' to me," continued the Shabby Man before I could reply, "I wouldn't be here."

"Where would you be?" I asked.

"Well, I'd be—I don't know exactly where I'd be, only, I wouldn't be here."

"What's wrong with it here?" I asked.

"A man can't be a man in this hole of a place. It's a prison, that's what it is."

"That's curious," said I, "I knew a man once who was in prison, but he had that in him which made him happy there. Whenever I went to see him he made it seem better to be in prison than it was outside."

The Shabby Man looked puzzled; his face fell.

"There you go again," said he, "arguin'."

I laughed.

"Let's sit down a moment," said I, "it isn't late. We were both interested in that speech——"

"You bet!" he interrupted.

"And we can talk about it."

So we sat down on a nearby bench.

"Did you ever," said I, "look at that library over on the corner?"

"Sure; been in it, too."

"And see the names they've got up there cut in the stone?"

"Sure."

"Newton and Franklin and Lincoln and Shakespeare and Cervantes and Milton, and so on?"

"Sure, I've seen 'em."

"How do they make you feel?"

"Why, I don't know's I feel anything in particular. How do you feel?"

I laughed.

"You'll smile when I tell you," I said, "but I never go along there without wanting to take off my hat to them. Thank you, Ben Franklin, for flying a kite in a thunderstorm; it has meant a lot to me since. Thank you, Edison, for the electric lamp; I could hardly live without it. And I always make an especially low bow to Abe Lincoln, for I don't know of any man in this world who did more good without getting in his own way than Abe Lincoln. When I consider sometimes what has been done for me by the great men of the past—often done with much sorrow and suffering—I feel as though I were a deeply indebted man. I have been surrounded by incalculable benefits and luxuries, like this pleasant park, which I did nothing to earn and can never hope to pay for."

I'll have to be honest; my Shabby Man looked dazed, as though he did not at all understand what I was driving at.

"Say," he said after a pause, "I thought we was goin' to talk about that speech."

"All right," said I, "let's talk about it. That orator made us feel that we were pretty badly treated, that we weren't getting what was coming to us."

"Sure, and it's right too."

"I suppose a large part of the people in this city feel that they are being abused and not getting all they ought to."

"You bet there's a lot o' discontent, and, what's more, we're goin' to do something about it."

"Should you say that there were as many as ninety out of every hundred people who feel that way?"

"Ninety-nine anyway," said the Shabby Man.

"You might," said I, "call it a kind of universal creditor frame of mind. Everybody believes that other people owe him and he owes nobody."

The Shabby Man looked still more puzzled and began to appear uneasy.

"Now you're arguin' again," said he.

"But," said I, "it's an intensely interesting problem to me. If ninety-nine men feel themselves creditors and only one recognises that he owes anything, how is the one going to satisfy the ninety-nine?"

I could see now that I had entirely lost the Shabby Man. The exhilaration he had shown after the speech had gradually faded away and he was back where he was when I found him. You can easily steer a ship that is going somewhere, but how steer a ship that is shoaled?

After we parted I walked the dark streets of the city for an hour, thinking hotly of all I had seen and heard that night. As I was going up the dim stairway to our Tower the whole affair seemed to come suddenly clear to me, so that I stopped there on the landing and laughed aloud.

"Human beings are curious," I said, "curious and contradictory, but amazingly interesting."

"Where *have* you been?" asked Harriet when I came in.

"Harriet," said I, "I have made a great discovery about this world."

Harriet said nothing. I expect she is accustomed by now to my great discoveries.

"All times are great," I said, "exactly in proportion as men feel, profoundly, their indebtedness to something or other; to the gods with the Greeks; to Jehovah with the Jews; to Jesus with Christians; to science with many a modern. A feeling of immeasurable obligation puts life into a man, and fight into him, and joy into him. A sense of profound indebtedness makes a man beautiful."

I paused.

"And," said I, "when a man thinks everybody owes him and he owes nobody, he soon grows—well, shabby."

In the night I woke up with the somewhat uncomfortable feeling that I had been orating again, when I keep saying to myself that it is enough to understand. (No one ought to orate!) But presently I turned over:

"It's what I actually thought. It's the kind of man I am. If I tried being anything different, or saying anything different, I'd fail."

So I turned over and went comfortably to sleep again.

XI

THE MAN AFRAID

ONE of the greatest pleasures I have had since I began writing these "Adventures," now many years ago, has been the letters I have received. But some have had in them, so it seemed to me, a strange background of tragedy; for these writers, contrary to the common report concerning what men want most, seek something that no money, no position in life, no law, not even any institution, can satisfy. They cannot find rest in dollars.

So it is that I have concluded from these letters, and from much other experience of life, that the chief thing desired in this world by human beings is a working agreement of a man with himself; that is, unity or peace within. If a man have that —if he can live upon friendly terms with himself—nothing else seems to matter.

For lack of this agreement within, the place of which is taken by tumultuous civil war, each man fighting himself, most human beings are sad.

I was thinking some such things as these the other day when walking the streets of the City, where there is much strife and little tranquillity, and came home to my Tower to find a letter addressed to me from a stranger. It was a curious letter, which made me feel at once that it was written by a man who was afraid of life. It was not that he said in so many words, "I am afraid," but he put in fear as he would put in a comma at each pause in the sentences, and fear lurked, like a period, at the end of it.

I read over this letter several times, for there was true feeling in it, and finally looked up and said to Harriet:

"There is nothing that comes to a man so dreadful as fear."

"That," said Harriet, "is true."

"And fear of life," said I, "is worse than fear of death."

"That is also true," said Harriet.

The man's name was Thorpe; and I could not get him out of my mind.

"This man Thorpe," said I to myself, "feels strongly and suffers deeply."

Two or three times I sat down to answer his letter, thinking I would put courage, like commas, in my reply, and hope, like a period, at the end of it. But I have been long a writer and know well the poverty of the written word. Language, at best, is a poor method of conveying what one truly feels. There will perhaps come a time when thought, leaping clear of the slow wires of language, will cross boundless space when one soul tunes to the wave-length of another.

I could not make my letter to this man Thorpe convey what I felt. As I read again what he said it seemed to me that he had much fineness of spirit—hidden fineness, easily hurt—covered and concealed by the kind of whistling which is supposed to keep the courage up. He would be a man who would shrink from rough contacts, and by virtue of the gentleness of his nature would suffer not only for himself but even more keenly for those he loved. For to love—if a man have not come to understanding—is to suffer; and the deeper the love the sharper the suffering. I know this.

His letter gave little evidence of his outward circumstances, save that it indicated a good background of cultivation.

"He is probably a poor man," said I to myself, "say, an unsuccessful professional man, or a teacher, or an artist, who is afraid for himself and his family because he is poor. Poverty is a skilful intimidator."

This was the way I pictured him: a harried and worn human being living in some teeming hive of an apartment, cut off from pleasant and comforting scenes and being crowded slowly to death by the cares of life. (A mere leaf of grass will hold up a cobweb.)

"Why," asked Harriet, "do you talk so much about this Mr. Thorpe—whom you have never seen?"

Harriet is a sensible person.

"Harriet," said I, "human beings are inconceivably interesting, and how can you know them without thinking about them?"

"Well," said Harriet, "you can easily satisfy your interest; you can go and see this Mr. Thorpe. He lives in this city."

This suggestion came to me with the shock of discovery.

"So I can."

I suppose I am stupid, but I had been so absorbed in picturing this Mr. Thorpe as a kind of abstraction—the man afraid—that I had not thought of going any farther. And he might be living in the next street or so. It came upon me with a warm glow.

"I'll go now," said I, jumping up and reaching for my hat.

"David!"

When Harriet speaks in that tone I know something is wrong.

"It's ten o'clock at night," said she.

"So it is," I said. "I'll go to-morrow."

I expect you will think me ridiculous to become so excited over a matter like this, but so it was. It seemed to me such a chance as I had never had before to test out my thoughts regarding such a character as I conceived this Mr. Thorpe to be, with the man Thorpe himself, the reality. I lay awake that night picturing to myself all the various strange, unexpected, amusing, even shocking things that might happen. I soon had two or three first-class stories about Mr. Thorpe growing like mushrooms in my imagination—each leading away to a different conclusion but all strung upon the red thread of fear. (The difference between a story and true life is that the first must have an ending, while the second goes straight on to the stars.)

The quite simple rush of sympathy I had felt when I first read this man Thorpe's letter was losing itself in a maze of speculation. I could feel myself rapidly becoming a mere story-smith, forgetting that this was a live man, loving, suffering and afraid.

There is something cold and hard about daylight in a city, and great bare stone buildings, and cars pounding through the streets, and boys crying the afternoon papers; and when I turned in at the address given upon Mr. Thorpe's letter—it was an office building of the older sort, yet prosperous-looking— I had a strange shrinking feeling. I hesitated inside the door and for an instant the whole project seemed absurdly quixotic. Why should I bother this man Thorpe? I would probably be disappointed in him and he in me, for we would see only the outsides of each other. And then the thought of the man himself as he had wonderfully expressed himself in his letter came over me warmly, and I said aloud:

"I must see this Mr. Thorpe."

I suppose surprise is of the essence of adventure, and what, after all, is more surprising than reality? I had to laugh at myself, so feeble did all my imaginings appear. Instead of the shabby apartments I had so vividly pictured in my mind—where the worn Mr. Thorpe ate out his heart with fear—I stepped into a roomy office which exhaled the veritable aroma of prosperity. I can think of no one word that conveys the essential impression it gave as well as "metallic." All the furniture seemed made of hard metal, sharp corners, and glittering surfaces. The typewriters had a biting metallic click and the heels of the hurrying clerks upon the hard floor sent out a metallic echo. The voice of the girl at the telephone seemed to be made out of the wires of her instrument, so hard, sharp, cut-off, it was. Everything was running like a perfectly oiled machine, so that I thought that if a man were to live long in such a place his brain would begin to tick like a clock.

At first I said to myself, "Mr. Thorpe is undoubtedly a poor bookkeeper, or a stockman, or some little caged secretary, afraid of his life." But I discovered immediately that Mr. Thorpe was none other than the manager, the superior, the veritable king of the place. It was *his* office. His name in large letters was there on an inner door.

"It is going to be more exciting than I thought," I said to myself.

I cannot describe the eagerness I now felt to see, actually see, the kind of outer man who would cover such a spirit as I had found in Mr. Thorpe's letter.

It appeared immediately that Mr. Thorpe was hard to get at, very much engaged and so forth. The Cerberus at the gate was delightful enough—she had indeed, only one head, and a very pretty one it was, but it served as well as three.

"Is your business urgent?" she asked.

"Most urgent," said I.

"Are you—selling something?"

You can see what skepticism prevails among the young!

"No," said I, "I am giving it away."

I looked at her and smiled.

"Oh," said she.

"But," I said, "what I give away many people would be glad to buy."

This remark seemed to confirm her worst suspicions. I could see exactly what was going on behind her bright eyes.

"You think I am odd, don't you?"

"Well——"

"And you think I am trying to get to Mr. Thorpe to sell him some bonds, or books, or a patent warming pad?"

"Well——" she was smiling broadly.

"You tell Mr. Thorpe that there is an odd sort of man out here—you can describe me with as much humour as you like, it won't hurt me—and that he wants to see me. Tell him he wrote this man a fine letter—a personal letter—on June 16th. Tell him this man's name is Grayson."

Human nature is curious. I had thought that after writing me such an appealing letter Mr. Thorpe would receive me with open arms. But, as I reflected afterward, I should have known better, for the essence of the man was fear. He could impulsively pour out his harried soul in a letter to an unknown writer who had touched him; but when that writer appeared upon the scene, an actual, common person (probably quite different from what he expected), he scurried away within himself and shrank from the contact. The shells of human beings cause most of the trouble in this world! They not only keep other people out but they keep the man himself in.

I found him standing quite forbiddingly behind his desk—a rather large, though active man, with dark eyes. He was immaculately dressed and wore to perfection the easy mask of One Weary with Large Concerns. He seemed at first sight positively repelling.

For an instant I would have given half I possessed if I had not come: the difficulty of reaching any simple human relationship—and that was all I cared for—seemed insuperable. I groped for the right word to say, but it would not come. I heard the door close behind me, as the secretary went out, and had a momentary feeling of panic, as though I were caught there, in a trap. I looked helplessly at Mr. Thorpe and he looked helplessly at me. If there had not been that strange letter, that spark of the spirit, between us, he would probably have given me a business-like "Bow-wow," and I should have replied "Bow, wow, wow," and we would have parted upon the open road of the world.

Suddenly, like a flash, I seemed to come around a corner and catch a glimpse of the ridiculous picture we made. There I stood awkwardly, hat in hand, in the middle of this chilly office, on the absurdest, most quixotic errand one could imagine—and with nothing whatever to say. What a fool was I!

Well, I burst out laughing. I could not help it. At which Mr. Thorpe seemed still more to shrink into himself, grow more erect and repellent. But I was now determined to carry it through.

"I hope you will pardon me for laughing," I said, "but it came over me all at once what a terribly dangerous thing it is to write a book. It gets a man into the most ridiculous situations."

Mr. Thorpe stirred restlessly, but still said nothing.

"I write a book," said I, "and aim it at no one in particular. I shoot it off with my eyes closed. It hits you. You write me a letter which, in return, hits me. I think a good deal about that letter, and try to answer it and cannot; but I say to myself, 'This Mr. Thorpe is a man I should like to know.' So I begin to consider what kind of a man you are, what you do and how you live. And by a kind of magic we are together! You can easily see what a dangerous thing it is to write a book."

In my eagerness I had stepped up close to his desk and found myself leaning over it toward him. I was tremendously excited, and yet somehow amused. I thought I could see his countenance changing, and went on eagerly:

"You'd laugh too if you could know how I pictured you."

With that I gave him a graphic and humorous description of some of my absurd speculations about him, based upon his own letter.

"And there you were, living miserably in a crowded tenement, cut off from pleasant and comforting things—and poor, oh, very poor."

I could see all along that Mr. Thorpe was having difficulty in maintaining his composure, and at this last remark he laughed outright.

"And you got all that out of my letter!" he exclaimed.

"Oh, that was only the bare beginning of it. I could a tale unfold——"

"And I was poor?"

"Very poor."

"Why did my letter make you think I was poor?"

"Because you were so afraid of life."

This remark had the most surprising effect upon Mr. Thorpe. I have thought since that if I had been trying to imagine such a scene I should never have conceived a transformation so swift. He started, and the blood quite left his face. He dropped down into his chair, all the imposing dignity of his former pose suddenly disappearing. Leaning over the corner of his desk toward me, he said sharply:

"I never said I was afraid of any one or anything."

His voice had taken on a new intensity.

"No, you did not actually say it in so many words," I replied; "but you made me feel it. I knew it as well as though you had spent a week telling me."

"I made you feel that! I never thought I'd admit such a thing to any man; I hardly admit it to myself."

He paused. If ever the bare suffering soul of any man came into his eyes, Thorpe's came at that moment.

"But it's true," said he, "it's true. I happened on something in your book that somehow made me think you would understand, and on the spur of the moment I wrote you that letter."

"And regretted it afterward," I said.

"How did you know that?"

"Don't think I haven't been all through it myself."

"You have!" he exclaimed eagerly.

We had unconsciously been drawing closer and closer together until we were now sitting opposite each other. I could put my hand on his knee.

"Afraid!" said I. "I've been afraid of more ridiculous things than you ever have—I'll bet. One of the things I was once afraid to do was to let out all that I was—my ignorance, envy, ingenuousness, egotism, to say nothing of far worse follies. You see, we all want to appear something other than we are. We'd rather appear worse than we are (there is a kind of superiority in a reputation for devilishness) than actually what we are. But one day I found out what a joke I was playing on myself."

"What do you mean—a joke?"

"Why, I saw all at once that a man cannot possibly conceal himself or appear either better or worse than he is, not for long! for the secret leaks out at every look. There is no style, no art, no lie, that can long cover up what a man is. It discloses itself in every word he says, every line he writes—whether he will or no—and gets itself soon published abroad. This may be clear enough to many men; but long ago it came to me as a kind of discovery. It made me laugh at myself and that ended my fear."

"It did!" he exclaimed eagerly.

"Yes," said I, "to be able to laugh at one's self is the beginning of peace—and you cannot imagine the comfort I began to feel.

The sense of wishing to be known only for what one really is is like putting on an old, easy, comfortable garment. You are no longer afraid of anybody or anything. You say to yourself, 'Here I am—just so ugly, dull, poor, beautiful, rich, interesting, amusing, ridiculous—take me or leave me.'

"And how absolutely beautiful it is to be doing only what lies within your own capacities and is part of your own nature. It is like a great burden rolled off a man's back when he comes to want to appear nothing that he is not, to take out of life only what is truly his own, and to wait for something strong and deep within him or behind him to work through him."

Afterward, when I thought of it, I was ashamed that I should have said so much, and in such a way, at the very start, but so it was. But it is possible that my own frankness stimulated his. At any rate, the next hour was truly one of the most remarkable I ever spent. I think the man was literally starving in his spirit to talk with someone who could, in some degree, understand. (We have no institution in our roaring modern life that quite fills the place of the old confessional.) He had been fighting a civil war within himself until he was exhausted.

Well, the man literally poured himself out, struggling for words with which the more mercilessly to expose himself. The telephone rang, but he did not hear it. The door opened and a secretary tiptoed in. He looked up and said:

"I'm not to be called up. I cannot see anybody."

"It isn't that I'm afraid of death," he went on, "I think sometimes death would be an easy way out. Life is what has been too much for me."

I shall not attempt here to put down the entire story he told, it would make a small book, but I think I can give the essence of it in a few paragraphs.

He said that what he wanted was to feel safe, secure, and he could not. It was not for himself alone that he wanted to feel secure, but still more for his wife and his children. He said that he tried to reason about it but continued to worry. It was plain that he was a man of deep affections, especially for his children, and curiously for his old father. All that he wanted, he

135

said, was money enough to meet the contingencies of life; but he could not be sure either that he had it or could ever get it.

"You'll probably smile when I tell you," said he, "but I'm positively obsessed about insurance. I suppose it's an indication of my state of mind. I've insured against everything I can think of: fire, accidents, disease, robbery, death—but the more I insure the more fearful I seem to grow that something will happen, some scurvy trick, that will wipe me out."

It was strange to me how clearly he saw his own condition and yet could not deal with it.

It was the same regarding his health and that of his family. He had sought out the best doctors in the country and even in Europe: doctors, hygienists, posturists, food specialists, and even those strange, new men who pretend to cure the mind—hoping by science to reduce the hazards of life; but the more doctors he had, the more fearful he grew that some unsuspected weakness or disease would leap out upon him.

He told me that he had had the best possible sort of upbringing. His father was a preacher, "a great preacher," he said, "of the old sort." What his father preached was fear. He frightened people with the terrors both of life and of death, and so tried to drive them to thoughts of God. He succeeded in thoroughly frightening his own son, for the son accepted the idea of the danger of life without adopting the dogma that was to relieve it. The old man, still himself living, mourned over his son, whose sufferings he blindly felt but did not understand.

Thorpe's wife! He told me also about her, for, once started, he would stop at nothing. She was brought up accustomed to every sort of material convenience and comfort. She was evidently the kind that could be satisfied only with ample means. She did not fear life—only poverty. Thorpe loved her deeply and, when unirritated by not having everything she wanted, she was plainly an agreeable and lovable woman. But how she added to Thorpe's fears, how she crucified him with daily alarms lest he be unable to satisfy her requirements of house, clothing, position. And his fear was not content with dwelling upon present difficulties and dangers, but raced wildly into the future, and pictured the cruelty of life a year, ten years, even two generations away.

All this may seem extravagant, but it is what he told me.

Thorpe's children!

"Well," said he, "you might think I could feel sure about them; but I see clearly that what we are doing is to train them, also, daily and hourly, in being afraid of everything under the sun: physical, intellectual, social, moral. What chance have they of not finding life too much for them?"

Of course Thorpe was an intense conservative in all things: politics, religion, business, education (for fear is the backbone of conservatism). There seemed greater safety in that which was settled, tried out, established! All change, experiment, adventure, was a terror to him, a leap in the dark. He loathed books or plays that bit down on life; he sought diversion and anodynes.

It seemed to me as the man talked, and I listened, never interrupting, that one who thus fears life dies a thousand deaths. The wise accept the chances of life and go forward joyfully.

He finished with a helpless wave of his hand and sat back in his chair. I had been trying for some time to think what I could say that would help, but in the presence of such a catastrophe what *can* one say?

I must have been silent longer than I supposed, for Mr. Thorpe said finally:

"What do you make out of a miserable story like that? It makes you smile, doesn't it?"

"Was I smiling?" I said. "It wasn't at that; it wasn't at anything you said. But while you were talking, especially there at the last, I could not help thinking of a man I knew when I was a boy. He was one of the great unknown men—to me, at least. As you were talking he seemed trying to get out of me and say something: that is one of the ways he has of taking his immortality—talking through me—and he is urgent about it. Would you care to hear about him?"

Mr. Thorpe waved his hand in the way of the man whose troubles are so great that nothing any more matters.

"I never think of him," said I, "without a peculiar feeling of comfort. To this day the picture of him I have in my mind makes me smile. He was a German, an old German. There was always something of a mystery about him, in the gossipy Western town where I grew up. He came to America just after the Franco-Prussian War and lived in a garden by a little lake.

"He was an old man with a white beard when I, a boy, tiptoeing in his garden paths, first knew him. He wore, I remember, a velvet skullcap and smoked a large pipe with a white bowl. I can see him yet, moving about at his work, sometimes humming a tune, and bending over with a kind of love to the care of his flowers. Or I think of him sitting at evening in a home-made rustic chair in his own doorway looking out across the garden to the quiet waters of the lake. I never knew any one who could sit so still for so long a time; and as he sat, a great look of peace would come upon his face. He was not married. He wore carpet slippers.

"I never knew, being a boy, why he should be considered mysterious, unless it was that though he had few dishes, few chairs, few dollars, he had books. In that day in the West books were enough to make any man mysterious. And such strange, worn, leather-covered books, all in a foreign language! One, the only one I can remember, was 'Werther' by Goethe.

"He made a poor enough living by selling flowers, aster and pansy plants, and in spring such garden plants as strawberries, tomatoes, cabbages, and peppers. He kept a few hives of bees and a few hens, and trained a grapevine upon the sunny side of his house. He had his flowers in old-fashioned boarded beds with narrow walks between, and in late summer, when the hollyhocks, asters, and zinnias had grown tall, you would see him almost hidden among them, his benignant countenance springing out of a mass of bloom. Well, I am long, Mr. Thorpe, in getting to the point——"

Mr. Thorpe nodded.

"But once the thought of him came to me I wanted to tell you about him. At first I was somewhat afraid of him; but as time passed I began to like to go into his garden. He exercised a strange fascination that I could not then understand. He would sometimes pick a sprig of geranium, pinch it between his thumb and finger, smell of it himself, and then put it in my buttonhole. He would sometimes speak to me in broken English, but soon lapse into German, not one word of which could I understand. But there was something about his voice—something rich, beautiful, comforting—that made me like to listen to him. And one sentence or motto he said over so many times that one day, quite to his astonishment, I repeated it after him:

"*'Wenn ihr stille bliebt so würde euch geholfen.'*

"When I said it after him, he looked at me keenly.

"'Ach!' he said, 'you haf learnt a great t'ing.'

"He paused.

"'Do you know what dis means?'

"'No,' said I.

"*'Wenn ihr stille bliebt,* dot means "if you vere qviet"; *so würde euch geholfen,* "so voold help come."'"

As I look back and think now of that old German gardener I am convinced that there *was* some mystery about him; some reason why he left his Fatherland and came to that wild new country and made him a garden to live in. Possibly it was only the ancient mystery of a bruised spirit or a broken heart, possibly it was something more startling, but, be that as it may, one shy boy, tiptoeing in his garden paths, knew that he was a good man, and that he lived at last tranquilly; and that boy was never to forget the motto he had from the old man's lips:

"When you are quiet, help comes."

There isn't really anything more to tell—yet. This is one of the incidents out of life which has not "turned out," but is on its way to the stars. Mr. Thorpe and I parted friends; we have since kept up that friendship. That's the conclusion, if there is any. And how better could any story end than in a friendship?

XII

THE RETURN

In thy home is the truth. Go where thou wilt, to Benares or
    Mathura;
If thy soul is a stranger to thee, the whole world is unhomely.
    —*From* KABIR, *the Weaver Mystic of Northern India.*

IT was in summer that we came home again. I shall never
forget the little turning beyond the hill when we came home
again. It was early morning, and there was the smoke of breakfast fires in many a friendly chimney as we passed; and I saw
the crows lifting and calling from many a dewy field. Dear quiet
Hempfield. The wide valley, the trees and the hills. *My hills.*
I stopped to look at them again, all clear in the morning sun.

"There is old Ransome's barn. . . . There is Darth's tumble-
down fence and his Jersey cows. . . . Dold has built a new
shed. . . . And there is our own great elm."

It came to me with such a rush of feeling as I cannot describe,
how much I loved it all. Dear town; sweet loophole of retreat.

Suddenly, something within me that had long been knotted
hard, strained and twisted down in dull, unhappy endurance,
began to unknit and loosen away. I came newly alive there at
the turning, at the sight of the smoke in my own chimney, and
when I next looked up at the hills I could not see them. . . .

I do not intend to relate every step in that recovery. After
one stops whirling, he remains for a time still a little dizzy. It
seemed to me I wanted to get hold of the firmest, simplest,
realest things I could anywhere find. I wanted to be slow and
quiet.

"Harriet," I said, "I am not so much in a hurry as I was to
write a great book."

She did not answer.

"But one thing I am sure of."

"What is that?" asked Harriet.

"Why, that one can begin living a little book anywhere, at any time."

Most of my notes of that time, I find, are of common work and common, simple people: men driving teams, cutting hay, spraying their orchards, cultivating their corn.

It was, indeed, just at hay-cutting time that I came home again. We had a fine crop in our own meadow; half alfalfa it was, and heavy. I helped at the pitching on until I dripped in the hot sun. I followed the great loads down to the barn. I watched them going in at the gaping doorway. I smelled the cattle in the stanchions below.

I waited for the man on the load to drive down his barbed hayfork, and watched the old horse pull away on the hoisting rope. "Gid-ap there, Moll; gid-ap!"

I heard the squeak of the pulley and saw the great fork full of hay lift upward and shift over the gaping bay.

"Whoa!" cries the man in the dusty mow, and down comes the load upon us.

There are little dusty golden shafts of sunlight coming through holes in the roof; there are startled pigeons in the dim eaves.

The man on the load is bare-headed, bare-armed, bare-chested, and black as an Indian with dust and sunburn.

"Gee, but it's hot," says he, looking down at us.

Walking back to the field with every sense clean, sharp, naked —hungry and thirsty as I had not been before in months—*good* hunger, *honest* thirst—I caught an odour that I did not at first recognise, but that somehow gave me an old thrill. I followed it across a little ravine full of wild blackberry bushes and came to a neglected field-side where there was a world of milkweed in bloom. Do you know the odour of milkweed blossoms on a hot day? Man, if you do not, you have a life yet to live!

"So, it's *you,*" said I, "after all these years."

I cannot tell in words what a renewed grip this utterly trivial moment gave me upon the earth. For it bridged suddenly the years backward to my boyhood, and the deep, deep realities I knew then. I recalled vividly a certain hillside covered like this hillside with blossoming milkweeds—where I went with a sword of whittled lath, to slay them where they stood. What blood I shed! What bold thoughts filled me then!

They brought water to the field in a small milk can—with the return from the barn of the empty hayrack. And we all stopped there to drink and look at one another and joke the Polish man on the wagon and laugh at the boy on the hay rake, whose bare legs were too short to reach the release, so that he had to hitch forward from his seat each time he dropped his load.

Drink! How we poured down the blessed cool water there in the hot field. Our Irishman with a fine gesture flung the can on his shoulder and, turning his head to one side, with his mouth twisted awry, drank gloriously, we jeering him.

"It minds me o' the good old days," says he, smacking his lips, "whin hayin' was hayin'."

He drew his bare sweaty arm across his mouth.

"Thim times," said he, "we hayed with a jug—and something in it."

This caused the Pole on the load, who understood this remark perfectly, to laugh immoderately.

"We no get him now," he said.

"That's the true word," responded the Irishman, "or whatever ye do git, it's plain poison."

Next to men at work I love well to see men at rest. I watched to-day one of the boys on a load of hay which he had driven up to the barn. He had to wait a few minutes while another load, then in the barn, was emptied. He was a sturdy young fellow, with great powerful arms and a face burned quite black in the sun; a good worker, as we knew well, for we had pitched to him on the load.

I saw him drop down on the hay while he waited and fling his arms wide there in perfect comfort. I saw him looking up at the sky, half drowsily, at the hens running about in the yard, and presently at the barelegged girl who was now leading the pulley horse. There was a half smile of complete contentment upon his youthful face. It was good to look at him. And when at length the other rack was backed out of the barn and the man in the mow called out, "All right there, come ahead," he sprang up with alacrity, seized the reins and, with legs widely parted, cried out:

"Git up there, Jim; now, Kate——" And he drove gloriously, like a young god, into the great doorway of the barn.

It was by such homely incidents as these—and there were many of them in those first months after I came home again—it was by such incidents, and the attempt to realise them more deeply by setting them down afterward in my notes, that I seemed to get hold again upon reality—the true, normal things of the earth. It is true: we travel in circles and if left to ourselves, return again upon ourselves. . . .

"Harriet," I said, "look there at the cloud on the horizon. Do you not see the cloud on the horizon?"

"I see no cloud," said Harriet.

"It is there," I said, "it is the cloud the City makes. The City is a great invention. It is a wonderful place, the City. But it is no place for a man to live."

I knew presently that I was coming truly alive again by the reviving appetite I had for everything that happened all about: on my land, in the country roads, or in the town. For we may truly test the health of our spirit by the appetite we have for the common, simple food of living. And finally one day—this was early the next spring—I had an adventure with a peach-tree man which seemed to me to cap my life with a full recovery, for I could again laugh at life, as well as look at it.

I had been much pestered that spring with interruptions of all kinds. It is a curious subject upon which I have done some reflecting—this matter of interruptions. Although I pretend to be much provoked and disgusted with interruptions, I have a kind of fondness for them. (This is a secret.) Often and often when I have set myself to a hard task—grim-jawed, determined—I can't prevent a little imp somewhere in the back of my mind jumping up and down and literally yelping for some kind of an interruption, anything—a man coming down the lane, or the postman, or a voice from the doorway, "Telephone, David."

And at the very moment I feel sternest toward all interrupters I know in my heart that I like nothing better in this world than to pounce upon some neighbour who is contentedly at work and surprise, and steal his secret of contentment. One gets little from an idle man; much from a busy, happy man; and how can one get to a busy, happy man, I'd like to know, without interrupting him?

Nevertheless, I do like variety in interrupters, and the Peach-Tree Man I speak of was the third or fourth nursery-stock salesman who had come smiling down my lane within two weeks. When I saw him with his picture book under one arm, and a couple of sample peach trees, their roots wonderfully wrapped in burlap, under the other, I hastily scrabbled around in my mind for just the phrase which would send him back up the hill—not exactly bleeding or badly hurt, but finished! I was getting my bees out of winter quarters and was very busy. It is one of the disadvantages of the farmer that his office is all outdoors; there is no polite stenographer at the gate to say, "I'm sorry, but Mr. Grayson is engaged."

But this salesman was a downright good one. I feel certain he must have been graduated somewhere with the degree of D.P.P. (Doctor of Practical Psychology). For he caught me while I was figuratively reaching for my gun, and there I was, looking at his wonderful coloured pictures of the rosiest, yellowest, biggest peaches ever grown this side the Garden of Eden; I was hearing his dulcet explanations of how his trees were selected and budded and pruned and root-pruned; and I could see for myself, as he deftly turned over his sample, how well his great, reliable, sincere, honest, earnest, patriotic, one-hundred-per-cent-American company packed its trees for shipment.

Oh, he was a smart one! I resisted with all my might, looked cold and distant, was sententious in my utterances, even two or three times made as if to return to my work, but I felt myself slipping, slipping.

I had a wild idea of opening one of the hives near at hand—casually and absent-mindedly as it were—and letting come what would. The thought of that agent retreating up the hill and trying to be dignified with twenty angry honey-bees at each ear was a picture of some attraction.

Suddenly a great idea recurred to me. It had served me once before; and it has been good for more than one crisis since. It is also now in use, with great success, by several of my neighbours. It is a simple and delightful idea; and I give it here free to all the world, without patent, trade-mark, or copyright.

"Excuse me," I said to the Peach-Tree Man, "excuse me for just a moment. I've got something I want to show you."

He let go without enthusiasm, and I went to the house and came back with a copy of my last book. (A cake of honey or a bushel of potatoes will do as well.)

I opened my book there before the somewhat perplexed Peach-Tree Man and told him with what care I had selected and budded the ideas I put into it, how afterward I had both pruned and root-pruned them.

"And you will see finally," I said, talking fast, "how perfectly my company has covered and packed my production so that it won't dry out, or die—so, in fact, that it will start an interesting growth in any soil whatsoever in which it is planted, and finally produce the most beautiful, gorgeous, delicious fruit known to man."

I enlarged upon the profit he would secure if he took my book at only a dollar and seventy-five cents, treated it well, fertilised and cultivated it; and what happiness he would presently have at the harvest.

"And," said I when I was beginning to get out of breath, "it will last long and bear well after every peach tree in your packet has been planted, grown, harvested, and died."

I shall not soon forget the look of amazement that slowly grew in his eye; amazement and irritation. It was something plainly unexpected and wholly new to him—this interruption of the interrupter. (That's my slogan: "Interrupt the interrupter.")

"Say, mister," said he, "I don't want to buy books. I'm sellin' trees."

"Well, mister," I responded, "I don't want to buy trees. I'm selling books."

145

For once in his life this excellent Peach-Tree Man, D.P.P., was plainly dazed and did not know what to say. We looked at each other solemnly a moment—and rather helplessly, too, and then suddenly we both began to laugh—irresistibly.

As soon as I could get a chance I said to him:

"Did you ever hear of the Roman augurs?"

"I've heard of carpenters' augers," said he doubtfully, "and ship's augers, but I ain't never, zi know of, heard of Roman augers."

"Well," said I, "they were an interesting lot. They were a kind of fortune-teller, you know, clairvoyants——"

"Them fakers," said the cheerful Peach-Tree Man.

"Exactly," said I.

"And they called 'em augurs?"

"In Rome, yes. . . . Well, they got so they could fool the people perfectly—but of course they couldn't fool one another. You'll understand that."

"Sure—I know—sure."

"So it was said that when one augur met another in Rome he couldn't help winking at him."

I stopped a moment and waited. The Peach-Tree Man turned this curious and unexpected bit of historical information over in his mind—I could literally see him turning it! But I awaited the exact moment when he should look up with puzzled understanding.

I was on tenterhooks, I can tell you, but at last it came; and then and not till then, exactly at the right instant, I winked at him solemnly. I was sure enough of him as a Yankee, a trader, and a D.P.P. to feel that he would not miss the point.

He did not. The smile which had begun to come disappeared, and, with a face as solemn as my own, he also winked.

This was again followed by a somewhat awkward pause. There just didn't seem anything more to be said—by augurs who completely understood each other. It was the Peach-Tree Man who broke the silence.

"Good-morning, mister," said he in a kind of husky voice, and before I could respond he hurried up the hill and turned into the town road.

"Good-by, augur," I called after him, but he did not look around.

A few minutes later my neighbour B—— came along and said to me that he had just met a man coming out of my lane with something the matter with him, terribly red in the face. Mad? What had I done to him?

With that I walked slowly up the hill and came to the road, and there on a little embankment sat my Peach-Tree Man. He seemed to be in pain.

"What's the trouble?" I asked.

"Mister," said he, "I ain't laughed so much in a dog's life. Say, where did you get that line of talk? That's a dang good one."

With that his face sobered down suddenly and, although there were tears in his eyes, he winked at me solemnly and I as solemnly returned it. Then he took my arm and said:

"See here, mister, you an' me ought not to part this way. You and me ought to trade."

I said he was a good one!

"Look here," he continued, "I'll buy your book, if you'll buy some o' my trees. I'd just like to see what a feller like you would put in a book."

"And I," said I, "would like to see how near your peaches come to your pictures."

And so, on the spot, we settled it. I took the trees and he took my book.

"Come back in three or four years," I said to him, "and tell me how you like my book and I'll tell you how I like your peaches."

"You bet," said he, "you bet—I'll come back before that."

(I'll bet he will too!)

So he went off up the road with my book close clasped under his arm along with his gorgeous peach-tree catalogue.

"Harriet," said I when I got back to the house, "now I am prepared for anything. Bring on your wonders."

So I am at home again, and think it will take an earthquake in addition to a war to get me away again. Here I live. After wandering, this valley is my home, this very hillside, these green acres. Here all about me are friends I love; friends living and friends in old books. This is my progress, the process of the seasons; this is my reward, the product of the earth and the work of my own hand and brain. I want no other. Here may I be quiet, and think and love and work. Here, when I lift up my eyes, I can see the fire smouldering in the Bush; I can hear from the clouds a Voice.

ADVENTURES
IN
SOLITUDE

TO
MY FRIEND
John S. Phillips

INTRODUCTION

S OLITUDE is not the exceptional state of man: it is the normal. Every man spends most of his time alone with himself: how much more in periods of illness or of sorrow. A whole world, invisible without, a man creates within his own personality. There he lives; there he adventures; there he is happy, if he is happy; there he suffers. If he cannot command this world of his own making he is miserable indeed.

This little book deals with a fortunate, if enforced, solitude, and the effort of a man to make or find his own felicity.

I

ILLNESS

> ". . . Prisoner, tell me who was it that wrought this un-
> breakable chain?"
>
> "It was I," said the prisoner, "who forged this chain very
> carefully."
>
> TAGORE: *"Gitanjali."*

WEEKS I lay there. When I first lay down in that little
room the sun was setting every evening well to the
northward of the spire I could see from my window, far across
rolling hills, laden then with the gorgeous foliage of autumn.
I saw it creep daily southward. In illness one treasures the mi-
nutest details of the changing day. An evening came—I had
feared lest it be cloudy—when the slim spire, at sunset, pierced
the golden globe itself, and the buttressed shoulders of the church
stood out dark and sharp against a burning background, a picture unforgettably etched in gold. After that, day by day, the
sun set among hills that grew barren and drearier, among trees
that had shed their autumn glory, and presently held up to the
sky the gaunt tracery of approaching winter.

Illness, like its elder brother, death, is a cessation. Life stops.
Identity blurs. One hangs up his personality with his clothes
in the closet and becomes a case—the patient in No. 12. No
longer quite a man, but a condition, a problem, stretched out
there for daily examination, looked down upon, peered into,
charted on paper with graphs like the rise and fall in the price
of wheat. It is this indignity even more than the pain and the
weakness and the boredom that makes the experience, for a man
with any imagination, difficult to bear. To be something, and
then to be nothing! It is no doubt one of the commonest of
human experiences—since I myself have known it, it seems as
though all the world had been ill—and yet no one can ever

know, for himself, until it has come to him, what it means to be set aside, lifted arrogantly out of his active labour, and put down horizontal and helpless in bed. With whisperers tiptoeing about, queer distant clocks striking the hours through the long night, the weary reiteration of the processes of medication, a hot and restless pillow. Everything minutely ordered, taken ruthlessly out of one's own habitual and accustomed hands —what to eat, what to drink, when to sleep, when to sit up, when to turn over—sad business! Even though one may have the assurances of those who should know, that he will ultimately recover, yet it seems somehow, in the beginning at least, that everything is lost. What value have such easy and optimistic prophecies? Does anyone *know*? Does anyone ever tell the truth to a man in bed?

All my life, except for a time in my youth, I had had robust health, and the kind of contentment that goes with it. Minor disabilities, a day or so here, a week there, though sometimes irritating, had never shaken an underlying and abiding sense of well-being. To-morrow I shall be well again! Such interruptions were even to be cherished: one could go to bed with a book.

Having health a man can enjoy everything.

> . . . the mere fact, consciousness—these forms—the power of
>   motion,
> The least insect or animal—the senses—eyesight—love.

I had never known what it meant to be too weary to look up to the hills at evening for a sure benediction, or to find, in the shorn meadows, peace. As to safety, the desire of the fragile and the vulnerable, I had never even paused to consider it. I had within me, however deeply hidden, "a certain jollity of mind, pickled in the scorn of fortune." I did whatever offered itself strongly to my taste, sometimes adventuring in the country where I have lived so many years—it is beautiful enough, most of the time, for gods to dwell in—and sometimes employing myself in grubbing labour that brought me friends I liked or money I needed. It seems to me now, as I look back, that I wanted nothing I did not have. I enjoyed a kind of busy contentment of oblivion, like that of a child, of which, when one asked me seriously: "Will it endure through the hard time coming?" I made believe I did not hear, glanced at the long shadows that lay across my garden, and turned another page in the labour of the day. What did it matter? I was content.

Life is a process which gradually jolts our self-sufficiency into understanding—possibly even serenity—if we can endure long enough to complete the process.

How well I remember now the onset of my illness. At first sly hints and warnings, to which I paid slight attention. I waked up heavy and weary instead of bounding out of bed. Twinges! Burning in the eyes and behind the eyes. There were mornings when I had no joy in what I saw, nor cared for what I heard. At first I kept quiet and made a joke of it—only weaklings went to doctors! There were moments of anger; moments of surprise; moments of downright fear. I had somehow offended nature, and would make my offering in humility, praying that the fire might descend and the earth smile again.

On the day that I went away from home I remember vividly Harriet standing there in the doorway. We are Northern, our race is Northern; we do not easily express all we feel. But I knew! I knew something of what she felt by the curve at the corner of her lips and the curious withdrawn expression in her eyes. When we are well we take so much for granted. This too, this painful parting, was an uncalculated element of a new experience. One is singled out for suffering. He goes alone; he takes no one with him.

I remember the dismal railroad journey, noisy, close, hot. Now that the mind had surrendered—it was not all a joke!—it seemed impossible to keep from thinking of each different symptom, wondering, calculating, dreading. Health is self-forgetfulness: to be ill is to be self-centred. One's mind is like a burning glass: it can literally blister any part of the body by the intensity of its concentration.

Eight doctors there were with their "diagnostic indications," and beyond them, a foreordained and predestined terror, awaited the surgeon. I found the examination itself difficult to endure. It was humiliatingly familiar, a challenge to one's dignity and personality: something positively obscene. I knew better, at a later time, the understanding, yes, and the sympathy, that lay back of those painful probings; but at the moment it was hard to bear. It seemed somehow the end of everything! I remember trying to find some comfort in two lines of a bitter philosophy of resignation that clung dimly to my mind:

> We have lived, we have loved, we have suffered . . . even so.
> Shall we not take the ebb who had the flow?

Worst of all I dreaded the uncertainty. How ignorant, after all, we are of ourselves that we must await the decision of strangers to know whether we are to live or die. Would it be two weeks, or four, or eight? Who could tell? One's whens elicit only ifs. I was to rest under observation in a quiet small hospital until the doctors made sure of what to do; after that I was to go to the great hospital and the surgeon. I had revelled in times past in well ordered certainties. To-morrow morning I would work at such and such a task; at noon meet my friend Darrow; at three drive to town with many errands to do; at five perhaps a tramp by the back road to North Hadley—but this was a place where one could have no certainties of his own whatsoever: no decisions; nothing. In the meantime—quiet! Not the teeming quiet I love, of country roads with friendly people going by, or the thoughtful quiet of my own garden, or the beautiful quiet of the still banks of hill streams in Pelham or Shutesbury—but inanition of body that whetted without satisfying the appetite of the mind. Quiet. No visitors, no letters, no books (at first)—nothing! Vacuity. To one who loved life!

In the beginning I thought I could not bear it. I would get up in broad daylight, put on my clothes, lift up my head, and walk out. Anything was better than this. A man, even in illness, is a free agent, is he not? It is his own life he is risking? How could one lie watching forever the angle of light that came through the half-open door? How listen with straining ears to sounds of distant pain or lonely weariness? How pretend to a hopefulness one could not feel? It was all wrong. They could ensure, indeed, quiet for the body, but what man among them all possessed the genius to "still the beating mind"? Who could minister to that part of me—the hot core of me—they did not find indicated after the last X-ray plate had been taken; which even the cunning pathologist, with his delicate instruments, laying me apart after I am dead, will not discover?

Yes, this was the end. This was the irretrievable experience. Strange it should come in this way.

II

THE LITTLE ROOM

*A man of understanding hath lost nothing,
if he yet have himselfe.*

I DID not get up and walk out. I could not. But I was nevertheless in hot revolt. I hated this abnormal concentration
upon the ills and defects of human life, my own and others'.
It offended every hard-won principle of my life. I hated the
atmosphere of studied cheerfulness—the doctor marching in of
a morning, a flower in his buttonhole, his face glowing ruddily
after a walk in the crisp autumn air, his ready joke, his jaunty
laughter! Oh, I played up to him, but I was secretly and bit-
terly envious—I who loved nothing in this world better than a
tramp on a glorious morning. At the same time I hated myself
for the puerility of my envy. And the nurses, also glowing with
health—offensively glowing—bustling, cheerful—that starched
tyranny! I had afterwards a different view of nurses—one of
them could whistle like a starling—but in those early days, in
cheerfully condemning me to helplessness, they incited me to
revolt, to skepticism, to pessimism.

"This," said I to myself, "is not a man's world at all. It is a
kind of matriarchy!"

This led me to think, not without a kind of humour, of a
queer old book among my treasures, published not long after
Shakespeare's death, called "The Feminine Monarchie"—a treatise on honeybees, "shewing Their Admirable Nature and Properties, together with the Right Ordering of them from time to
time." It bore a flattering dedication, I remembered, to Queen
Elizabeth.

Well, this was truly a "feminine monarchie" I lived in. Except

for the distant, glowing, planetary doctor, one's day was dominated from early morning until late at night by feminine auto-
crats. Dominated to embarrassment. A man, I maintain, does not
easily submit to the indignity of being told when his hair is to
be brushed, his face washed, his pajamas changed!

"If ever I escape from this tyranny," I said to myself, "I will
consider writing a new Feminine Monarchie, and do it, as old
Charles Butler did it, 'out of experience.'"

So I began studying, not without some sly amusement, which
I sternly repressed, their Admirable Nature and Properties,
though I have never dared to write down my observations, since
I could not be sure, even after months of experience, that I
understood "the right ordering of them from time to time."

Miserable days they were, those earlier ones, far more difficult
to bear than the pain, the weakness, even the sleepless or opiated
nights that came later in the great hospital. For misery, after all,
is not physical—pain can be borne, helplessness somehow en-
dured—misery is always mental. Tragedy is mental. It is what
we think, not what we suffer, that destroys us. It is the dis-
turbance of ordered life, the sense of inadequacy, the conviction
of failure that crush the soul. All men, ill or well, lead frus-
trated lives, all of us fall short of our hopes and ideals. Human
strength is never enough to meet problems and difficulties that
are infinite. Human life is never long enough! We suffer because
we are finite among infinite realities; because the universe is too
great for us.

Yes, we are all alike: we all fail. The difference between men
lies in the way they face disaster, meet the tragic facts of their
existence. That man is successful who has learned to live triumphantly within his limitations. I had not only never met the
real problem adequately—I can see it now—I had never even
faced it squarely until I reached the experience which I am here
describing, when everything I loved, all I hoped for, seemed
suddenly snatched away from me.

In the long hours of night when I could not sleep—sleep is
often the denied anodyne of suffering—I drove my mind in a

weary round of self-recrimination, probing the causes of my downfall, seeking some other than myself to blame, some chance incident of five or ten or twenty years ago that might if—and if—and if. And always I came out of these weary excursions exactly where I went in, with a sense of utter futility and failure. I destroyed the present, of which I was sure, with remorse for the past, which I could not change, and apprehension of the future, which I might never know.

I think of those days now with wonder and with shame.

This mood of utter wretchedness continued for many days. One night, as I lay quite still but intolerably awake in my half-darkened room, I heard the sound of a man sighing, or groaning, as though his very soul were in torment. I began to listen with a hushed intensity of interest. There it was again! What weariness, pain, hopeless longing! I knew nothing whatever about the patient next door—I had been too much wrapped up in my own misery even to inquire. I had heard from time to time the rumble of his voice through the wall, and occasionally a word or two as of someone speaking at his door. It came to me now with a strange sense of discovery that this was a human being, a person, suffering as I was, possibly far worse than I was. No doubt he had left friends and work and comfort he prized as much as I did. No doubt the future looked black also to him. My mind at once began conjecturing, a thousand ways, the unknown life and problems of the man lying there so close to me, yet entirely unknown. What was he like, where was he from, what was the train of events that had brought him, also, to this sad place? For a moment, in the sharpness of my interest, my strained listening, I forgot my own illness.

There it was again: the weary sighing, a few low words that sounded like a melancholy prayer. I cannot tell how deeply it affected me. At the very moment when I was beginning to realize that I was not the only sufferer in the world, that here was a man who might be even more sadly afflicted than I, it came to me with inexpressible power and poignancy that both of us, lying there side by side, unknown to each other, were as nothing compared with the hundreds, the thousands, of men and women in the hospitals of that great city, each with his own burden of suffering, each turning and twisting in the maze of his own discomforting thoughts. What a stupendous weight of illness, weakness, suffering, misery, in an entire state!

I am trying to put down these thoughts just as they came upon me, tumultuously, in the dark intensity of that night. It may be that my own straining weakness accounted in part for the extraordinary sharpness and force of the impression I had: it was what I felt. I had known before, certainly, that there was an immense burden of illness and suffering in the world, but I had known it only as knowledge, not as experience, not as *feeling*. Sometimes in the past, when friends had been ill or sad or discouraged, I, from my haven of security, had been able to help them—or thought I helped—with assurances of strength or courage. But here was the stark reality! I was myself a part of an inconceivable sink of human misery: I could help no one else; no one could help me.

For a day or so my mind struggled feverishly, if fruitlessly, with these new thoughts of the universality of human suffering. In one way I found my own situation somewhat relieved. There was a kind of comfort and satisfaction—yes, satisfaction—in knowing that I was no worse than hundreds of other men and women; and I had also a curious and recurrent sense of a new understanding, an entirely new relationship, between human beings, not one based upon common enjoyment, but upon common misery. These new thoughts, however, proved no permanent abatement of my own ills. After a day or so they seemed even to increase my weariness and hopelessness. My own chances, the chances of any individual in such a chaos of suffering, seemed even less encouraging. I was not an exception: I was the rule. I thought of all the vast paraphernalia of hospitals, medical faculties, highly trained physicians and nurses, and how impotent they were to cope with the appalling human disability that afflicted the world.

Misery may love company, but company does not cure misery. In illness one is, after all, terribly alone.

I will not enlarge further upon the wretchedness of those unhappy days. One morning, some two weeks after I lay down in that bed, I had a curious and deep inner experience. I do not know what caused it, save that I seem to have explored every other passage in the mazes of a weary mind, but suddenly I roused up and turned fiercely upon myself:

"What a ridiculous creature you are," I said, "bowled over with scarcely a struggle by one of the oldest, commonest, simplest difficulties that beset human beings. Even your inner fortress taken!"

Had I, then, lived a busy life for so many years, had I made good friends, had I visited strange and interesting places, had I read many books with delight—and out of all these overflowing experiences, a life's entire accumulation, was there nothing left to carry me through a few weeks or even months in bed? Had I in reality been wholly dependent upon the external interests which had filled my hours? Had I come to such a pass that I had no resources of the spirit? Was I on such terms with myself, after long and close association, that it was hopeless misery to live alone with myself?

I cannot tell with what burning urgency these questions assailed me. Though I did not stir in my bed, nor break the calm monotony with which my nurse, sitting there by the window, stitched at the bit of fancy work she held in her hand, my mind was in the fiercest turmoil. It seemed to me that I had come to the crucial test of my whole life—and at a time when I was, because of my physical weakness, least able to bear it.

The nurse, looking at me, the outer shell of me, shook her head dubiously.

"You have something on your mind," said she, examining the thermometer she had taken from between my lips.

I said nothing.

"You are disturbed," said she.

"Yes," said I, "I am disturbed. It is time that I was disturbed."

"You must be quiet," said she. "Everything depends upon your being quiet."

"Quiet," said I, "is what I most desire."

An immense weariness came down upon me. I could not think longer or with clarity. I had been stripped bare; I had no defenses left. I felt as though my life had amounted to nothing whatsoever: opinions and beliefs upon which I had rested with oblivious content furnished no refuge in the storm. For it so often happens that when a man has reached the point where he feels that he is beginning to know how to command his life and the tools of his employment, to reap the harvest of his labour, tragedy of one sort or another touches him on the shoulder.

"Can you bear it?" Or, if he winces, "Where now is your vaunted philosophy?"

When the mind is deeply stirred it seems to go on with its work in its own subterranean caverns, even when the physical husk of the body is unconscious with suffering or with sleep. Hours later, in the night, when I awakened, the tumultuous thoughts of the previous day, returning powerfully, presented an entirely new aspect of my situation—one that had not occurred to me before. While it was true that everything that had constituted a pleasant and satisfying life for me—my robust physical health, my habitual and interesting work, and all my books, my letters, my friends—while all these had been stripped away, I was still possessed of my own mind and my own thoughts. I had, after all, my own inner life. I had my life!

In the telling, in cold words, this may seem no remarkable conclusion, still less a discovery. Of course! It was axiomatic: a child would know as much. But to me, lying there in bed, restless and miserable, it came with a wave of feeling that flooded my whole being. It was true: I had in reality, however helpless, vast inner possessions upon which I had not counted. Of all that I really was I had so much left!

A couplet that had long lain concealed in my memory came to me with fresh significance:

> Still to ourselves in every place consigned
> Our own felicity we make or find.

It was true—it was true! I was consigned to myself here in this gabled room—after the manner of all prisoners, all sick men, all those fortunately banished or outcast. I was condemned to enforced quiet, to an utter vacuity of outward possessions and ordinary interests. I was consigned to myself: and no one but myself could make or find my felicity. No doctor, however cunning, no nurse, however skilful; no prophet, or preacher, or book; not riches; not friends: it was only this strange something that was within me that could find me peace or comfort.

Yes, words are poor things: they express inadequately the power and the beauty of thoughts which shake or mould our lives.

This was the beginning: it is with the tests and explorations of this idea, coming so powerfully into my mind, that I shall now write, basing what I have to say upon notes that I soon began to scrawl, a few a day, as I was able, in a little book I kept in the drawer of the desk that stood near the head of my bed.

III

THE QUIET COUNTRY OF THE MIND

He most doth dwell in bliss
That hath a quiet mind.

M Y ROOM was in the top of the house, not large, large
enough. Part of the ceiling was cut away by the roof,
but there was a fine gable window opening to the west where
I could see, looking along the white ridge of the counterpane,
which was *me,* the hills and the distant spire of which I have
already spoken. At my right, only a few feet distant, if I turned
my head, I could see through the other window the fretwork
branches of a lordly beech tree, upon which still clung a remnant
of the painted foliage of autumn. They reached so close that I
could have leaned out—if I could have leaned out!—and touched
fingers with them. Each morning, about sunrise—time meant
nothing to one in my case—two or three starlings came to sit
on the branches of the beech. They began talking to one another
quite intimately, in their own language, which at that time I did
not understand, much less care to hear.

I did not like starlings.

I did not like to have reminders of the free world I could
not enjoy.

"Quiet," I had said to the nurse, "is what I most desire."

I had said it somewhat ironically. For years I had been secretly
longing for quiet, for retirement, for a chance to think—or I
said I had. I had thought of the joy of "going into the silence"
described by the old religionists, where one could "lift off
thought after thought, passion after passion," until one reached
the inmost depth of all. Well, I now had my desires involun-

tarily fulfilled: here in this high gabled room both quiet and retirement, such as they were, had been conferred upon me, and I was not content. It was not an easy matter, even after I had discovered the true secret and place of my possessions, that they were inward, to enter upon their enjoyment or use them as a sure way to tranquillity. I know I stumbled horribly, slipping back again and again to the weary suffering, the self-recrimination, of the early days of my imprisonment.

My first deliberate effort to get at my hoarded possessions and thus turn my mind away from the misery of my situation, was prompted, I think, by the extraordinary power with which the couplet I have already repeated—"Still to ourselves in every place consigned"—had come back to me. It had been like the precipitate which the chemist pours into a cloudy mixture to make it suddenly clear. It had convinced me that I and none other was the architect of my felicity. This set me to wondering if there were not other life-saving passages tucked away in my memory: and I began at once to try to recapture old poetry, even old prose, that I had committed to memory in my youth and thought I had forgotten. At first, like a lost sailor in a heavy sea, I seized upon any chance spar—a line of any old poem or ballad, any flotsam of prose cast up by a driven memory, and found it surprising, once I had fixed my mind upon it, how I could recover entire stanzas, even whole poems that I had not thought about for many years. In my boyhood I memorized easily—a gift which, I am sad to say, has left me—especially galloping or romantic verse like "The Lady of the Lake," "The Prisoner of Chillon," Bürger's "Ballad of William and Helen," and Tennyson's "Locksley Hall." I loved the sonorous roll of "Thanatopsis," and the splendid imagery in passages from Isaiah, Ecclesiastes, and the Psalms which, though I was constrained to learn them, often gave me a strange thrill of pleasure.

In the long hours of night when I could not sleep, I now began to reclaim these lost treasures, catching up a phrase here, a rhyme or rhythm there, and piecing them together with an increasing delight that ate up the weary hours. Time was nothing to me. I must have worked several days trying to recapture certain of William Blake's lines which I have long loved for their wild ecstasy of beauty. The third stanza came to me first:

> Bring me my Bow of burning gold
> Bring me my Arrows of desire
> Bring me my Spear! O clouds, unfold!
> Bring me my Chariot of fire.

To a man in my situation there was something challenging, something incalculably inspiriting, in these bold words.

> I will not cease from Mental Fight,
> Nor shall my Sword sleep in my hand,
> Till we have built Jerusalem
> In England's green and pleasant land.

How these lines rolled under my tongue as I lay there silent, in my bed, a trumpet of new courage, fashioned in beauty. So it was also that I found comfort in repeating the 38th chapter of Job:

> Who is this that darkeneth counsel by words without knowledge? . . .
> Canst thou bind the sweet influences of Pleiades, or loose the bands of Orion?
> Canst thou bring forth Mazzaroth in his season? or canst thou guide Arcturus with his sons?

I recalled also the 12th of Ecclesiastes, the one beginning "Remember now thy Creator," as fine a poem as there is in the language.

This eager pursuit of stored treasure continued for some time, easing my weariness, occupying my mind, giving me, indeed, a kind of satisfaction entirely apart from the content of the lines remembered, for it was a delight in itself to recover out of the mustiness of things forgotten, thoughts, impressions, beauties, that had once interested or thrilled me. I found that I could have my triumphs even as I lay in bed, silent, with the curious tiptoeing life of the hospital flowing around me; and I had a sense that I was somehow getting the better of doctors and nurses who, with all their daily tests, their elaborate records, never once probed the real secret of my life, what I had going on deep down within me—the struggles there, the voyages of discovery, the rich treasures I was now finding in forgotten caverns. While I was often too ill and weary to carry even this engaging occupation as far as I should have liked—there were moments when no effort of mine could lift me out of the slough of despond—still I had begun to find a place of comfort in a weary land.

Soon I found myself thinking of the books I had read, especially those of my early years. I tried to follow them through, and by recalling the names of characters and places, strove to make the incidents live again. I made an especial effort to see if I could remember with any exactness lines or passages that had impressed me. So it was that my mind went back to *Gulliver's Travels, Don Quixote, Ivanhoe,* and others of Scott's novels; *David Copperfield, Pilgrim's Progress,* and many not so well known. It was astonishing to me, after a certain amount of success with the poems, how little beyond an atmosphere, a general impression, remained to me out of most of these books. Certain characters and incidents in each of them were, indeed, vivid enough—quite as much alive as many of the characters and incidents of my own early life—and there were bits of observation or philosophy which could not be forgotten, like the lines from *Moby Dick*—"From without no wonderful effect is wrought within ourselves, unless some interior responding wonder meets it"—but a great part even of the books I liked best had entirely disappeared. And that, I have found in recent years, especially during the later period of my illness, is one of the reasons why one likes to reread old books: it is like visiting places once familiar; meeting friends once well known but half forgotten. What we remember best, it seems, are those moments caught by the true poet in times of high emotion and expressed in words that are immortal because inevitable. A line of poetry will stick in a man's mind like a burr.

Of all this effort to recall the books I had read I soon grew weary: it was, after all, a kind of game, far less interesting than the poetry which had often in itself been inspiriting. It was only an anodyne: what I wanted was a cure. It took my attention away temporarily from the discomforts of the day: it did not fill my mind with such thoughts as I "need only regard attentively to be at perfect ease."

IV

FRUITS OF SOLITUDE

. . . then wilt thou not be loth
To leave this Paradise, but shalt possess
A Paradise within thee, happier far.

IT WAS from trying to recreate in some orderly manner the
old, great, childish story of *Pilgrim's Progress* with the doings
of Christian and Hopeful and that delightful dragon of my boyhood, Apollyon, that I suddenly began to think of the experiences of John Bunyan himself. He, too, was imprisoned; it was
in Bedford Gaol that he began to delight himself with the story
that has come down through the years. He turned, not without
an apology, from the tracts and sermons he had written so vo-
luminously, and profiting by his solitude, looked into his own
spirit, sought out his own felicity. He says of his book—though
at that time I could recover only the substance, not the exact
wording, of his apology:

I only thought to make
I knew not what: nor did I undertake
Thereby to please my neighbour; no, not I;
I did it my own self to gratify.

There is evidence that the staid old puritan had the gravest
doubts, because his work really gave him happiness, whether
or not he should print the chapters he had written. Was it
right to use "feigned words" or to speak in allegories and
metaphors when his communication should be "yea, yea" and
"nay, nay"?

But he was probably happier in Bedford Gaol, alone with
himself, despite the discomforts, the weariness, the constraint—
what, indeed, must a jail of the sixteen hundreds have been!—

than he ever was before in his life. For he was sojourning in the quiet country of his own mind.

These meditations led me to recall other men of the past who had profited by solitude. I thought of the famous portrait of Robert Louis Stevenson, propped up in bed—you will remember —with the counterpane drawn up over his shrunken knees, playing the flute. I liked to think of that picture. He was not only ill, but banished from old scenes and friends, and yet no one can read his books and his letters without feeling that he was somehow a man who had found his own felicity. He could even cheer his more fortunate but despairing friends! He could do what he loved best of all to do—live richly in his own mind. As one of his friends said of him, he had the "determination to win an honourable discharge in the bankrupt business of human life."

With that I began to reflect that so many men have owed their lasting contributions to the wealth of the race to some unhappy adventure of health or of fortune, some catastrophe of imprisonment or banishment, wherein, having mastered their own spirits, they were at length able to live a complete life. I think it was in prison that Cervantes wrote *Don Quixote;* and Paul addressed some of the best of his letters from Roman jails. Old Chinese poetry, released to us now by Arthur Waley and others, was often written while the authors were in banishment. It is a pity that the fashion of putting poets and prophets in jail should have waned: we might now be producing masterpieces!

A book I have included for many years upon my most intimate shelf is one that is all too little known. It is called *Some Fruits of Solitude* and was written by William Penn, the Quaker, during the time that he was banished from the court. A useful man, William Penn, a figure in American history, but he will live longest I think for the writings of those months or years of fruitful solitude when he had been forcibly banished from the world and had leisure to look into his own thoughts. In his introduction to this masterpiece of courage and common sense, he speaks of solitude as "a School few care to learn in, tho' None instructs us better." His various imprisonments and his banishment do not crush him: he "blesseth God for his Retirement, and kisses the Gentle Hand which led him into it: For though it prove Barren to the World, it can never do so to him."

He goes on to tell of some of the advantages of enforced solitude:

"He has now had some Time he could call his own; a Property he was never so much Master of before: In which he has taken a View of himself and the World; and observed wherein he hath hit and mist the mark."

And what does he find? He is so far from being overborne or cast down by his experiences that he is sometimes close to exultation that he is able to be quiet, remarking quaintly:

"But after we have made the just Reckonings which Retirement will help us to we shall begin to think the World in great measure Mad, and that we have been in a sort of Bedlam, all this while."

A little later, when I was able to get this book again into my hands, I remember the good laugh I had over this passage. Is it possible to reach a higher point of satisfied comfort, especially in jail, than to think one's self quite sane and all the world else in a "great measure Mad"?

So it was that I considered, as I lay there through the long days and nights—and not without satisfaction—that so much of the great and good work in the world has been done by men in trouble, themselves full of suffering and sorrow.

Two or three times I caught myself positively enjoying these meditations, my illness for the moment quite forgotten. I could sometimes continue for an hour or so, wholly absorbed, before weariness and weakness overcame me. When I awakened in the night it was no longer to the bored misery of the earlier days, but to a new interest, a fresh hope. There seemed something now to live for: something even to be achieved, for was not my felicity still to be made or found? If I had to lie there in bed, there must be a way to do it with a tranquil if not triumphant mind.

After a time the Tyrant of that place decreed that I might have Books—not too many, I was warned, but Books. I think I had never been so long before in my life without a book or books within reach of my outstretched hand. I am one of those who loves to carry a little book in his pocket: and there is always a book or so on the stand at the head of my bed at night, or by the couch where I so easily sit down to read by day. It was a great moment for me, then, when I could look forward to having a favourite book in my hand.

"I am," I said to myself, "like the man condemned to live on a lonely isle, with only two or five or ten books to comfort him. What a difficult but beautiful time he would have in selecting them."

I began at once, and with a pleasure I cannot describe, to think what books I should send for. No books by sickly men: no books by little, whining men: no invented books. Such vast libraries there were, I did not want! What I longed for, there in my imprisonment, were robust, courageous books, books that would stay the soul of a man. Old, strong, brave books! Books that were the true "life blood of a master spirit," written out of the travail of living, full of the experience of one brave in spite of pain and certain failure. There are not too many of them in the world: a modest shelf or so, I think, would hold them all. There are harmless lesser books enough to beguile a man's hours, books to dally over, to relieve the tedium of a journey, but when one is face to face with the stark reality of life it is not such that one hungers for.

The book I thought of first, since it appealed to the need of the moment, has for years been one of my closest companions. I had now a longing for it that was as intense as any primitive appetite, and, oddly enough, not alone for its contents, but for the book itself—the look of it, the feel of it in my hand as it slid into my pocket. A good appetite is one of the rewards of hunger: and my deprivation had aroused such a sharpness of desire as I had never before felt for any book. This was my small, thin pocket edition, printed on India paper, of *The Thoughts of the Emperor M. Aurelius Antoninus*. I remember well when and where I got it; it was in the year 1902, at a bookshop in Charing Cross Road in London. A long time ago! I had never read it before that time, but extracts or aphorisms, cast out as the skilled angler casts a fly, upon the wide and turbulent waters of the daily press, or in the quieter pools of books or magazines, I had sometimes snapped at, since they seemed food agreeable to my taste. One or two such passages lay warm in my mind and had stayed me in times of perplexity.

"Live as on a mountain."

"If any man has done wrong, the harm is his own. But perhaps he has not done wrong."

"Dost thou wish to be praised by a man who curses himself thrice every hour?"

It was a charming small book bound in dark red cloth with the name *Marcus Aurelius Antoninus* in gilded Roman letters on the cover. It cost me, as I remember, three shillings, as good a value for the money as ever I had of a purchase. It contained an essay on the life and philosophy of the noble emperor by George Long, who was also the translator of the text.

Other books for other needs or other moods, but no book I know contains more powerfully set forth the philosophy of endurance. It is a great and beautiful thing to enjoy life—and I, in my time, have had much enjoyment of life. It is still a greater thing to endure life—endure it not fiercely, not grievously, but with equanimity. This small book, written while the Emperor was far away from Rome, in a kind of kingly slavery to his responsibilities, fighting the wild Quadi, I have read when hard pressed with labour, when I was hurt or sad or ill or lonely. It served well, a pocket companion, in the miserable months I spent in Europe during the Great War. Of all the noble books of the world none I know seems so clearly written by the author not to instruct, still less to enthrall others, but for himself and to himself. He addresses himself, admonishes himself, reassures himself: it is his way of fortifying his own soul. Much reading of both Marcus Aurelius and Epictetus, whose philosophy is practically identical, inclines me always to the Emperor rather than to the slave: for Epictetus was discoursing for the improve-

174

ment of his followers, but Marcus Aurelius for the discipline of his own spirit. It is not a book to bow down before and worship—what book is?—but a book to use when there is the deep need of it; and it is the spirit of the man, not the letter of his philosophy, which heals.

It was this small book, then, that I put at the top of my list. To that I added William Penn's book, which I have already mentioned, and an anthology containing much of the noblest thought in the world—*The Spirit of Man,* edited by Robert Bridges, recently poet laureate of England. All these were books that I could read a little at a time, as I had strength. I also asked for Shakespeare's *Tempest,* and for a quaint book of travel, because I had long loved the author in other books, *The Bible in Spain,* by George Borrow. There were still others in the list I may mention later: and from another source I had several books by Dr. William Osler which had in them not only the true quality I required, but subjects treated which, being now myself in a hospital, I found enormously interesting. One of them was called *An Alabama Student.* A Bible I wanted also, for I had the appetite to read the Book of Job straight through.

"Have you by any chance," I asked my nurse, "among the many valuable medicines in your cabinet—have you a Bible?"

"A Bible!"

"Yes," said I, "a Bible."

So she brought me next morning her own Bible, and in the days following—slowly, slowly—I read the Book of Job, and some of the Psalms, and certain chapters of Isaiah, and Ecclesiastes, and the first book of the Corinthians.

What a book it is! Full of wisdom and beauty, ripe with human nature—if only one does not use it for a fetish or look into it for magic.

From this time onward, and with these weapons, I began to have oases in the desert of my illness.

V

THE STARLINGS

I could not think so plain a bird
Could sing so fine a song.

ONE morning early, after I had been in that place for some time, I heard through the open window the sweet, familiar whistle of a quail. Bob-*white:* bob-*white*. At first I could not believe my ears. There in that city! What place or part had a shy meadow bird like the quail in such a maze of city streets and rumbling car lines and close-built houses? It could not be possible. I listened intently and with a curious warmth around the heart. There it was again, thrillingly wild and sweet: bob-*white,* bob-*white*. It brought back to me with vivid pain the memory of the long sloping meadows I have known so well, and my own lanes and wooded hills where in spring one may start the nesting quail running as though wounded in the grass, or in autumn flush a new covey.

When I had heard the starlings at my window a week or so earlier I had closed my ears and eyes. I did not like starlings: I did not like to have reminders of the free world I could not enjoy. But the song of the quail, rich with old memories and warm associations, was quite another matter.

A little later on the same morning—before the day nurse came in and everything was quiet—I was further amazed to hear another and dearly familiar bird note: Pee-a-wee, pee-a-wee!—the plaintive call of the modest little flycatcher I had so often watched flitting about in the brushy edges of old fields. But what could the pee-wee be doing here? And why her song, so full of lazy melancholy, at this time of the year? And how was it possible that I, through my open window, among the treetops, could catch it all so clearly?

It was one of those delightful country queries that I had, in times past, so often found alluring. For a time, that morning, I not only forgot my discomforts, but I forgot also the books with which I had begun to occupy my mind.

"This morning," I said to my nurse, "I heard a quail whistling through the open window. Are there quail among these houses?"

I asked the same question of the knowing doctor, and the efficient head nurse, and the broadly smiling Negro janitor: but not one of them had ever seen or heard of any quail in that neighbourhood. There was something about their responses, something indulgent and yet faintly skeptical, that a sick man learns to know.

"Nevertheless," said I, "I heard a quail whistling."

That day I did not read much out of *Lavengro,* nor consider, as I had intended, the saying of Marcus Aurelius which seemed to speak so aptly to my present condition. I was not indeed able to read much, so I read deeply, keeping each choice morsel long in my mind that I might extract its last savour. In times past I had been accustomed to take a book as it were by storm, tearing the heart out of it, and scattering the tattered remains wherever they might chance to fall. Many books, most books, deserve no better attention: but it is no way to treat any book that is really worth the reading. For when a truly great spirit, with labour, and with pain, and with joy, has put his life blood into his work, it is only with labour and with pain and with joy that the reader may recover it again. Great things are never to be had without paying for them.

So it is that one may read for three minutes in, say, Marcus Aurelius, and have something to stay him for an hour or a day. The passage to which I have referred was this:

"Wretch, are you not content with what you see daily? Have you anything better or greater to see than the sun, the moon, the stars, the whole earth, the sea?"

It was true; it was true. I had been lying here these weeks, wretch that I was, consumed by my own ills, allowing my own miserable past and my own anxious future to blot out the sun, the moon, the stars, the whole earth, the sea. I was not content with what I could see daily. The present moment, this burning instant of time, was all that I or any man could ever really possess or command—and I was allowing it to be ruined by anxieties that were of my own making. It had come to me, powerfully, that if I could be content at *this* moment, I could be content.

It was in the atmosphere of these reflections that I heard, in the early morning, the bird notes I have described, as they came to me through the open window. They came to me sweetly, thrillingly. "Have you anything," I asked myself, "better or greater to see or to hear than this? Why not, man, enjoy it? Can you not be content with what you see daily?"

All that forenoon it seemed to me that something pleasant had, at length, come to me. A touch of my old enthusiasm! Something rare and fine. So little there is to occupy the attention of a man who is ill in bed.

I had a restless night—"You are too intense," said the nurse; "you are under some strain"—but the following morning—she did not know!—as soon as it was fairly light I propped up my pillows so that I could the better look out of the open window into the treetops. I was eager with an eagerness I cannot describe to hear again the whistling of the quail and the plaintive cry of the wood pee-wee. It seemed somehow to me then a way out of my distress.

I waited impatiently for some time, and then, to my distaste, I saw that the English starlings had come to sit on the boughs of the beech tree which reached so near my window. I was thoroughly disappointed—when I had expected so much. As I have said, I did not like starlings. I considered them alien invaders. They had come only recently to my own neighbourhood, and I had found them boisterous and unmannerly. They had driven out a friendly pair of bluebirds that nested in a hollow apple tree not far from my doorway; they had stolen my cherries, pecked into my grapes, and one cold winter morning, I remember, I found a large flock of them in my hen house, perched in every conceivable spot, even on the roosts among the fowls. When I opened the door they rose with a tremendous whirr and dove straight through the meshes of the wire netting that screened the front of the building, meshes that, it would have seemed, no bird could creep through, much less fly through. It was a feat to see! Nor did I like the raucous cry of warning or alarm with which they filled the very air. How much more modest and charming, I thought, are our own bluebirds and orioles and catbirds and song sparrows, to say nothing of that golden songster the wood thrush.

And yet here they were this morning on the bough by the window. "Wretch," I said to myself, "are you not content with what you see daily? Are there no beauties or interests in this world that you have not already discovered?"

With that I began to observe the starlings more closely. The sun was just coming up, filtering through the lacy fretwork of beech twigs, and I caught the glint of colour on their wings and back. I had always thought of them as a kind of rusty black— so they had appeared in the spring and summer flocks I had seen oftenest—but they were not so at all upon close observation. Quite otherwise, indeed, for they were clad in shimmering garments of iridescent blue, steel green, purple, with here and there, especially when they moved, the glint of a buff-tipped wing feather. The breasts were mottled with splashes of white or buff. In all these discoveries I was vastly surprised and interested.

I began to watch them still more closely. What active, sprightly fellows they were, anyway! There was something jaunty, almost humorous, in the way they sidled about, cocked their heads, preened their feathers. I had thought them unmannerly and raucous-voiced, but there was something positively charming in the little intimate, almost affectionate airs they put on as they sat together exchanging the gossip of a fine autumn morning. And so far from the harsh cries I knew them by I now heard, from my highly privileged place, their deliciously intimate conversation. They too, like our own native catbirds and thrushes, had their low whisper songs, though with them it was scarcely song at all, but low, musical ejaculations and gurgling notes, and from time to time, as though some of the gossip had passed utterly beyond the pale of credibility or propriety, some bird would break in with a kind of ironical whistle, high, clear, and sweet, and as it seemed to me that morning, full of laughter. They reminded me exactly of a group of lively old ladies, all by themselves, at a tea party.

I have been interested all my life in birds—as an amateur enjoyer rather than a careful student—and it seemed to me that morning that no birds I had known before gave such an impression of distinct and vigorous *personality* as these. They had such a gift of being entirely alive and joyous in a world that I had begun to think unhealthy and abnormal. They seemed actually to have a kind of humour!

These impressions came to me with something of a shock considering the contempt in which I had previously held them: but it was as nothing compared with the shock that I had a little later.

While I was thus observing the starlings as closely as I could I heard again the note of our meadow quail: bob-*white,* bob-*white*. It was perfectly clear and distinct. I was greatly excited.

"There," said I, "I knew perfectly well I heard it."

And a little later, to my surprise, came the song of my old friend the wood pee-wee. Pee-a-wee, pee-a-wee!

They seemed close at hand, as though the birds were under or near my window. Just at that moment one of the starlings ruffled the feathers of its throat in song, and though at first I could scarcely credit my senses, it seemed evident that my bob-white was in reality a starling! It was a thrilling moment. Was it possible? Was my pee-wee also a starling? I listened and watched again with great intentness and soon assured myself that the starlings, in addition to many other gifts, were also mocking-birds.

I don't wonder that my nurse shook her head over me that morning—though I lay there as quietly and innocently as though I did not feel like Byrd and Peary and Edison all rolled into one.

"Quiet," she cautioned, "quiet."

"No one," said I, "could have been quieter than I, and it has brought me great things."

"Great things?" she asked.

"Very great things," said I, but I did not then tell her what they were.

The next morning I was again awake at dawn, but doomed to sharp disappointment, for the starlings, which I began now to think of as old friends, did not appear. A drizzling rain fell all day long. On the second morning, however, I was delighted to find the plump little old ladies gathering for their tea party. It may seem ridiculous, but my heart beat more quickly, and I had a delightful sense of anticipation, for I had begun to love them. What busybodies they were! It was not the mating season, nor yet the gala time of year when the happy business of feeding the young birds is afoot: but the starlings, apparently without a care or responsibility in the world, were nevertheless enjoying themselves prodigiously, exchanging the most delicious bits of gossip, mimicking their neighbours and whistling ironically to one another when the conversation became too incredible —or scandalous—for belief. Lines from a poem on the starling I have since discovered express exactly my wonder:

> All this April rollicking
> In the last month of the year
> Has no logic I can see.

How pleasant and yet how rare it is, whether among birds or men, to find such a mood of easy enjoyment where there is neither love-making nor business in hand! Enjoyment of the delightful little daily things of life: a fine morning, good companions, the sound of one's own songs!

VI

ADVENTURES ABROAD IN BED

*It is by studying little things that we attain the great art of
having as little misery and as much happiness as possible.*
            Samuel Johnson, BOSWELL, Vol. I, p. 288.

MY INTEREST in the starlings grew rapidly, and because I felt that I had so wronged them in my early
judgment I wanted to know much more about them—as we do
about friends we are coming to love. Were they really mockers?
And what other birds did they mimic? Were they the destroyers
and pests I had always thought them? And where did they
come from and how?

"Will you do me an especial favour?" I asked my excellent
and obliging nurse.

"I will indeed," said she.

So I asked her to write to the ornithologist at Washington
and see if there was not some bulletin or pamphlet on the
starling which we could obtain. It was long in coming—a sick
man grows impatient—but it arrived at last, and it had a portrait
of my friend on the cover. It was an excellent and expansive
study of the bird, some thirty pages, which my nurse read
aloud to me, a little at a time. It seems that the bird has been
a native of America only since 1890, when it settled, an en-
couraged immigrant, in Central Park, New York. Like many
another alien, it had a struggle for years to live, but presently
it began to spread into other Eastern states, and it is now increasing even beyond the Allegheny Mountains. In time it will
no doubt become one of our commonest American birds. I
was pleased to find that, despite certain harmful and unmannerly
habits—don't we all have them?—it is economically a most use-

ful citizen of the country, destroying innumerable insects that infest our farms and gardens.

In one way this excellent biography of my friend the starling did not satisfy me. It resembled some other lives of the poets I have sadly read, like one Shelley from which I emerged, dripping with facts, but unable to understand how any such person could possibly have written the ode "To a Skylark." I was not unmindful of the patience of the investigators in counting the number of weevils, grubs, and millipeds that my hero had for breakfast, but it no more explained to me some of the things I wanted to know than an accurate count of the yards of spaghetti Caruso ate for supper would have accounted for his singing, not long afterwards, of an aria from *Aïda*.

But it was a fine and interesting book, and so aroused our enthusiasm that it was not long before my gifted nurse, sitting at the window, could mimic the ironical whistle of the starlings so accurately that she was accepted as an honorary member of their tea parties: at least, her notes were promptly answered. Soon our book was in circulation through other rooms in the hospital, and more than one patient began to listen to the morning meetings of the starlings.

A most interesting and surprising characteristic of the starlings I have observed more closely since I left the hospital—and that is the evolutions of large flocks of the birds in the air. The precision and discipline are truly extraordinary—the way in which they will suddenly change direction, open ranks, close ranks, wheel, rise, fall, all in perfect unison, and so far as I have been able to observe, without any one leader and without any note or cry of command. No flocking birds I know have greater gifts in this respect: and nothing except the extraordinary social discipline of bees and ants is more inexplicable. There is a secret of mass movement, a guidance of mass opinion, that is as yet unknown to man. I wonder if some social philosopher, one day, will not wish to study faithfully the gregarious habits —the "mob psychology!"—of such birds as the starling and of the bees and ants.

My morning experiences were not only a source of comfort and delight to me in that sorrowy place, but they opened the way to new adventures. Adventures abroad in bed! The nurse did not see me, nor the doctors know of it, nor was it written down in the sober sheets of my daily record, but I was going out again! Though covered to the chin with a white counterpane, apparently quite helpless, I was in reality often abroad among my own hills, or in my garden, or walking the pleasant elm-shaded streets of the little town I love best of all. I don't mean by this any mere darting memories, full of sadness or regret, I mean that I was *there*. I was there to complete absorption, so that I was not conscious for the time being of the gabled room where I lay, nor of the hospital, nor of my own illness.

It was all simple enough. I would, in my imagination, step out of my doorway, and there—oh, vividly!—was the garden, and the orchard, and the meadow, and far beyond, the everlasting hills. The steps and the path being open before me, what could I do but walk down it? And walking down it, what could I do but look at, or smell, or touch, the various shrubs, flowers, trees, I love?—or the corn, or the blackberry bushes, or the nut trees, dear with the familiarity of many years of intimate association.

Such moments—most of all in May—watching the young bees playing in front of the hives, and the catbirds in the apple trees, singing like angels in heaven—and stealing the bees!—and the tulips in bloom, and the new corn pushing up through the brown earth, and the newly sowed grassland coming green with clover and timothy and red-top—and all still and sweet. Such moments in a sunny forenoon.

Sometimes as I lay there a past experience or adventure would return to me with such intensity of remembrance that it seemed to me I was living it again. One in particular, since it was so charged with emotion, I tried to put down in the notebook I had begun to keep in the little desk at the head of my bed.

A certain old barn I love well. A great, gray old barn, reaching out its sheds like wings on either side to hover the cattle when they come in at evening with swinging udders, smelling of new milk. I love the cavernous open doorway where the barn swallows fly chittering in and out. I love the dusty smell of hay as I step inside. . . .

I can hear the horses stirring in their stanchions below—and the cows coming in to their stalls. . . .

Up there toward the west a finger of sunlight reaches through a crack and lies bright upon the hills of hay. These are hewn beams: you can see each stroke of the broad-axe, or adz. . . .

A flood of sunshine comes through the farther doorway. From within, looking out, I can see the pleasant rolling country, fine fields, and verdure-clad hills, with the sun upon them. The wind runs sweet in the grass, the crows are flying. There is no frame made by man that can equal the doorway of this barn, and no picture anywhere so well worth the framing. . . .

Here in the barn I stand looking, remembering. There is the well worn farm wagon with the hayrack still upon it; there the buggy covered with cloth to keep the dust away. . . .

Upon the wooden door of the storeroom generations of Dwights have marked the score of corn in baskets or rye in bags, four straight tallies and a cross tally to make five. Here they have added up the totals and sometimes cast them into the sure measure of dollars and cents. . . .

On the left, here, is the ancient harness room where, upon great wooden pegs worn brown and smooth with years of usage, hang the collared harnesses, the horse blankets, a girl's saddle. . . .

(It was Nanette's—I remember well Nanette, with the wind in her hair, and the high look in her eyes as she rode.)

And here is all that remains of a pony cart. (It was Lauriston's.) It was gay once with paint, and there was a fancy name on the back, but now the padded seat is torn, and one of the thills is gone. (Lauriston lies in a hillside grave in France.)

I could not go on. . . .

All these things, and many others, came back to me as I lay there in bed, charged with emotion, tinged with strange sadness—moments in which nothing of any importance had hap-

pened, and yet so intensely lived that they returned with a
warmth and clarity I can scarcely express.

So it was, now that I had found the way, that I began adventuring abroad in bed.

VII

THE AUTOBIOGRAPHY OF MY HEART

Call to recollection both how many things thou hast passed
through, and how many things thou hast been able to endure
. . . and how many beautiful things thou hast seen. . . .

I COME now to one of my choicest adventures while I lay
there ill in that high-gabled room. For adventure is not outside a man; it is within. It is a strange thing, once the mind
goes free, what may happen to any man. Space and time are
both forgot. Lying close in bed a man can in an instant be walking in his own distant garden, or, stripping away the crowded
years, find himself the boy he knew so long ago.

What one sees in a hospital—men lying there inert, waiting to
live again or to die—is as nothing compared with what goes
on there. What adventures all unrecorded, what dramas unacted
or tragedies unwept, what secret laughter, what bitter curses,
what remorse, what fear, what hope, what hot tears under
smarting eyelids—and all covered and concealed from the
probings of even the skilfulest of physicians, withheld from the
most sympathetic of nurses. To some men the experience of
being thus driven in upon themselves is one of bitterness, even
of terror; to others it comes as a fruitful opportunity, for "nowhere either with more quiet or more freedom from trouble
does a man retire than into his own soul." And some to whom
the experience is at first bitter to the point of being unbearable,
are able, presently, to direct their minds so that they have "such
thoughts that by looking into them" they are "immediately in
perfect tranquillity" for as this philosopher further remarks,
"tranquillity is nothing else than the good ordering of the
mind."

And the renewal comes not alone from reflection upon "principles brief and fundamental," but upon free excursions of the mind in all directions, particularly in that strange and vivid reliving, possible to any man, of the most interesting or happiest incidents of his own life, those moments, let us say, that he himself, in his inmost thoughts, considers best.

In my own case I found it delightful to go back to my youth. I came, indeed, upon the train of the adventure I am about to narrate, while I was endeavouring, as I have already related, to recapture the poetry I had known in my boyhood. It had led me naturally to the thought of the tall, dark old bookcase standing atop a "secretary" that stood in my father's house. It had a carved head of Shakespeare looking down from the pediment above the glass doors. My father was a sturdy old Presbyterian, and there were shelves devoted to Kitto's Commentaries on the Bible, Cruden's Concordance, and a volume of Fox's Martyrs, that had belonged, I think, to his father—in the horrors of which I thoroughly delighted—and I know not how many volumes of other religious books. But there was also a shelf of Scott's novels, in green cloth binding with a globe on the cover, and Dickens and Shakespeare, and stray volumes of Bulwer Lytton and George Eliot and other Victorian writers. There was a close-print Plutarch bound in leather, which I now have, a prized book, on my own shelves, and *Pilgrim's Progress,* and *Don Quixote,* and *Twenty Thousand Leagues Under the Sea,* and Plato's *Republic* and a set of Ancient Classics in English translations, and Byron and Felicia Hemans and Martin Tupper. How vividly I remember my father reading in bed: his leonine head propped up on the pillows, a kerosene lamp, shaded from his eyes, placed upon his breast, and the book held strongly in one hand—the other steadying the lamp—while he read far along into the night.

How eagerly, lying there in that hospital room, I revisited the old black bookcase. I could go there with my eyes shut, open the glass doors, and put my hand on any book in it that I cared for—not Cruden's Concordance, nor Kitto's Commentaries! I opened them now and from the third shelf, in the corner, for it was a shabby book, I took out the volume I was seeking. One of the corners of the binding was bent over and worn down until the brown board within was plainly visible. It looked as though it had been gnawed. In this old book I found, beginning exactly where I knew it would on the page, a poem by an author now known not at all as a poet but as the biographer of Sir Walter Scott. I mean John Gibson Lockhart. In those days I knew nothing and cared less for the names or accomplishments of authors. Smith was as full of significance for me as Shakespeare. I was intent upon the thing itself. I knew what I wanted, that was literature, all the world of writing else was trash. I have wondered sometimes if I was not a better judge then than I am now.

The poem I speak of was from the Spanish Ballads, and at the first lines of it all my years dropped suddenly away, and I was fourteen years old, thrilling again with an experience I shall never forget.

> My ornaments are arms,
>   My pastime is in war;
> My bed is cold upon the wold,
>   My lamp yon star.

It was in the evening, I remembered, that I first came upon it, and it went straight to my head, like some divine intoxicant. After finishing the entire poem in one delicious draught I shut the book with a snap, seized my cap, and dashed out of the house. A young moon hung in the clear autumn sky; the silence of evening lay deep upon the world; cool airs had followed the heat of the day. So I walked, or ran, chanting to myself:

> "My ornaments are arms,
>   My pastime is in war;
> My bed is cold upon the wold,
>   My lamp yon star."

I don't think I knew what "wold" meant, but it is one of the charms of poetry—at fourteen—that you do not understand it all. Worlds thus open to a word! And as I ran, the last verse also I chanted:

> "I ride from land to land,
> I sail from sea to sea;
> Some day more kind I fate may find,
> Some night kiss thee!"

And is not that the beautiful end of adventure—at fourteen!

Some night kiss thee!

I had not thought of this incident before in years and it came over me now with a delight that was also full of sadness:

> Ah those days beyond renewing
> Days the prime of love and lovely——

It was this incident, and especially the thought of the charm I had found so long ago in the word "wold," as it appeared in the verse I have mentioned, that set me thinking one night of the strange love affairs one may have with beautiful or desirable words. So many incidents crowded at once upon me that I began to consider the writing of Confessions, like Rousseau, or better yet, a kind of Sentimental Journey among words, in which, with a total disregard for all the proprieties, and flinging reticence quite to the winds, I should set down my love affairs—how it was that in my travels through the world I met this charmer or that, what it was that caught my wandering fancy and how it was held.

"It must," I said to myself with keen joy in the idea, "be a new kind of autobiography of the heart."

VIII

MANY THINGS I PASSED THROUGH

Take my hand quick and tell me,
What have you in your heart?

I BEGAN to think, as I lay there in bed, and with a delight impossible to convey, how I had thrown my heart away, in years past, upon one darling word after another. Nearly always it had been a case of love at first sight, and it came with such inexpressible charm that I could scarcely let the loved one a moment from my presence. How I contrived beautiful sentences wherein to mount it like a jewel, or spacious paragraphs to house it in. Age, I had learned in these chance meetings, quite contrary to the more prosaic love affairs of ordinary life, counted for nothing whatever. I had fallen desperately to the charm of a word that was a good five hundred years old, one that Chaucer knew when he rode to Canterbury with his quaint pilgrims; and a day or so later, perhaps in the rebound, I had been hopelessly enslaved by a kind of modern flapper word, as young as the twentieth century, met on the streets of New York—an impudent hussy who winked at me scandalously in broad daylight as I passed. And sometimes, and these are half-guilty meetings, had I stolen at the very wedding, like some young Lochinvar, the bride of another writer, knowing her for mine, as she knew me, upon sight.

Upon this I began to think of one of my more recent infatuations and the amusing outcome of it. I had been reading some verses which had in them, for me, a bewitching music when the fatal meeting took place. The word literally leaped at me out of the printed page, bringing with it a strange air of

dark-winged mystery—full of low music. This was the verse
I read:

> Ah! Strange were the dim, wide meadows,
> And strange was the cloud-strewn sky,
> And strange in the meadows the corncrakes
> And they making cry!

Of course, the word was "corncrakes," which never in my life
had I heard before. It was not that the word itself was charming
or even comely—but it carried such a wild, free, mysterious air!
Crying strangely, it was, in dim, wide meadows, with the sky
above cloud-strewn! Why had I never before met this beguiling
word? I loved it for its mystery, and at first went about with it
often upon my tongue, or in my thoughts, for the thrill it
gave me. Nor did I care at first for closer knowledge. Too
intimate acquaintance, I have found, often dissipates the mystery
of words not less than that of human beings. Some words are
best left free in the place where they live—say in a stanza of
poetry—for the complete impression, or feeling, they give us.
Let them go on living, strange in the dim, wide meadows . . .
and they making cry!

But human nature is perverse, and if left with the key will
be forever peeping in at Bluebeard's secret door. And so it was
that finally, my curiosity getting the better of the thrill, I opened
my unimpeachable dictionary—that enemy of mystery, that
destroyer of charm, that matter-of-fact abolisher of all half lights
and strange, dim meadows. (I say abolish all dictionaries: and
will myself head an organized movement to do it!)

Well, I laughed—a little ruefully—when I found that my corn-
crake was only "a common European bird, the land rail"—but
that's the way of life. Our corncrakes are forever turning common birds. And so it was that my sudden infatuation vanished:
and though, as I thought of it, I loved still the music of the verse,
I could not get the same thrill of it now that I saw only common
birds in those strange, dim meadows.

But if some of the love affairs I remembered had been swift,
passionate, and too brief, like this one—soon in love, soon out

of it!—I recalled others that had lasted all my life, and will, I think truly, when I am still older and grayer, touch my lips and stir my heart.

The story of one of them was truly a story of early love: a word I grew up with, knew and worshipped in school, walked with through many a starry night of my dreamy youth, and have with me yet, a dear companion. A word may sometimes be knit into the very soul of a man, and mean to him a whole life of wonder and adventure. I have heard people tell of "acquiring a language." It cannot be done: a language must be lived.

I came of pioneer stock. Each generation of my family stepped one long step westward, following the receding frontier. The appetite for going on, the far look to the setting sun, is deep in my race. You can see it in the eyes of my race. When I was a boy there was always talk in my home of the great things that lay just beyond—beyond the horizon, beyond this troubled life! (The promises of their religion bound the pioneers to its tenets.) Here life was hard; men toiled wearily in the new land; they fought poverty and isolation with grim-jawed courage —and fed their starving souls upon deferred joy. But one could always go on to the West, where the land would be richer than it was here, where men would be freer and bolder, where wealth could be had for the taking. All this lay beyond the horizon, and the name given to this joyous, far Utopia, this land of promise, was "the Plains." The Plains beyond: one could go on to the Plains.

When I was a boy we had many a vivid and surprising demonstration of the wonders of the Plains. Our men went there to hunt the wild buffalo, and sometimes met still wilder Indians. They brought back robes and mounted heads and horns as trophies, and still more marvellous tales of adventure they brought back. On the Plains men had not to hew their way through heavy forests or toil upon the bitter hills: one had only to stake out the open land and turn wide the waiting soil!

Once a wonderful covered wagon, which to a boy's fancy was a caravan of pure joy, crept across the hills from the East, and swaying and tacking like a ship at sea, held its course into the

West and went down with the sun. I remember the dusty, bronzed, and silent skipper of this desert ship; and the women in their sunbonnets and calico dresses. I suspect the hardened eye of manhood would see them bedraggled and sad-looking, but they had for me at that time a kind of prophetic beauty. They were headed into the sunset: they were going on to the Plains.

It is easy to see what beauty and mystery came to be bound up, for an imaginative boy, in that beautiful word. It was a symbol of adventure, of free open spaces, clear air, and blue heavens, boundlessly high; it was the sign of the noble and spacious life. Here at home one was bound down to the trivial and ugly—one had to carry water daily in a tin pail from a distant spring at the foot of the hill; one had to feed the pigs and bed down the horses—but there, where the wind blew in the grass, and there were no hills anywhere to hem one in, but only space and thought, one could run and sing! And somehow, and I speak of this as diffidently as men speak of the deeper things in their lives—but it is true—I thought God must be there more than here. For where everything is free and beautiful and noble—is not God there? It seemed the only place I knew where there was enough room for God.

I wondered as I lay there in my bed why some of our American poets had not seized more often upon this beautiful word which represents, with its associations, so much of the true genius and inspiration of our own people. I remembered one such stanza—a single stanza, the author of which I never knew, nor could find out—which had lain for years like a jewel in my mind:

> I am the Plain, virgin since Time began,
> Yet do I dream of Motherhood, when Man
> One day at last shall look upon my charms,
> And give me Towns like children to my arms.

All these things, then, were tied up in that single word "Plains"—the Plain—which I had never heard without the kind of thrill which comes at the stirring of an old love—an old, old love. And, indeed, it had acquired values that it never had before: because love, if it is true love, lifts, as the years pass, from the literal and physical which early charm us, to other, finer, sweeter, deeper beauty. My Plains had now lost their buffalo, the last Indian had shot his arrow and vanished beyond the rolling horizon, the blowing grass had been turned under with chilled-iron ploughs—but still I had my Plains. I had my Plains: but they were Plains now of the spirit, that the spirit would be yearning for, where all was spacious and free, and men were noble, and the wind of great thought blew through the sunny grass, and God dwelt.

So it was that I spent not a little time, during those days and nights of my illness, calling to recollection many things I had passed through. Often I found myself so completely absorbed as to be quite unconscious of my condition. Especially was this true after I began to be able to write down a few notes regarding my experiences. At times I wearied of these excursions and found myself slipping back into the depressed consciousness of my weakness and discomfort, but as the weeks passed I found it easier and easier to bridge the gaps. I found myself better prepared to meet the ordeal that was to come.

IX

THE GREAT HOSPITAL

Where a man can live, there he can also live well.

I T SEEMED a strange, vast, grim place, my hospital, when at
length I came to meet the supreme test for which I had been
so long preparing. It was at first incredibly forbidding to me—
the very cleanness of it, the bright efficiency, the ceremonial
smile it wore. One instinctively shrinks from pain, yet pain, perhaps even more the fear of it, is here the badge of the initiate,
the ritual of proficiency. I had the sense of being irresistibly
drawn into a process that was inimical and yet inevitable. I
had no longer any volition so far as my body was concerned: it
was moved about like so much inert material by forces pre-
sumably intelligent but wholly outside myself. I was no longer
asked whether I wanted this or would do that: I was not talked
to, I was talked about.

"At five you may give him the drops; after that he is to have
nothing."

The narrow white bed I lay upon was a symbol of the ex-
tremity I had reached, for my head was lifted or my legs ad-
justed not by any will of my own but by an iron crank at the
foot of it, turned by the white-clad nurse. When the time came,
I would be lifted from my bed, still more inert, laid upon a
table—and the surgeon would be there.

My reaction to these indignities was somewhat surprising to
me. Why was I not angry or terrified or crushed? I had been
far more nearly overborne when I had lain down, weeks before,
in the room with the gabled window. No doubt I had gained
something of self-possession in those weeks, some added power

of living with equanimity in my own mind, and yet, much as I should like to take the credit, I do not think my attitude was due to self-discipline. One rises to an emergency; he does what he must; a soldier will rush into battle with colours flying who has suffered all the pangs of fear in waiting for the battle to begin.

It was a strange thing to me indeed—I am trying to set forth my exact thoughts—that I found myself, the inner core of me, taking very much the position that the doctors themselves took. This body of mine, this poor defective body that I carried about with me, was something separate, something inert though living, that could be observed dispassionately, treated objectively. *Me*—I was something apart, a detached identity, curled up in my own place—where *is* that place?—peering out at the doctors, the nurses, the little room, and my own body lying there on the queer, cranked bed. *I* was perfectly well: it was my body that was suffering. I was living and thinking with a power and vividness they could know nothing about.

Such a welter of swift thoughts! At the same moment that I was reassuring myself of my own independence and sufficiency, I was also pitying myself, even calculating quite coldly upon the chances of the operation. If I was afraid, I was also thinking ironically of the absurdity of the entire process. These serious doctors, interested in my "case," believing they could cure my body without knowing me! These smiling nurses to whom my situation, so vastly important to my life, was all in the routine of the day! At times I was miles away from the hospital, and all of its sights and sounds and odours and discomforts: I was in my own garden, walking there, and there were tall hollyhocks in bloom, and flaming zinnias, and delphiniums still in flower—and, oh, the blue of the distant hills! Or I was talking familiarly with my friends and referring to the hospital as though it were something quite distant and wholly immaterial. But always I came back to the little room, and the queer bed, and the nurses smiling there; always I came back.

Above everything else in those days I was full of a kind of still confidence that I can only call faith—an immense faith.

197

Without it, how could any man live through such an experience, how trust the most precious of his possessions out of his own control? To surrender voluntarily one's consciousness, to go down and down and down into the abysmal nothingness of anæsthesia, not knowing *certainly* whether it would be for hours or forever—what is that but an act of faith? Or, if a man goes down involuntarily, by terror and force, how is he better than a horse or a dog? I thought much in the long days of my illness how impossible it was for any human being to live without faith—faith somewhere, in something, in somebody. All that makes a man a man and not an animal is suffused with faith. Without it the individual is insane and society a chaos. With it, and in proportion to the vitality of it, there can be nobility, and peace, and serenity.

The day of supreme trial came at length. The doctor was unusually benign; the nurse, unusually cheerful. I knew! I was to have the ether early in the morning. . . .

I had a swift sense of a world that was incalculably dear to me somehow slipping out of my grasp. I was conscious of a swift procession of familiar figures, Harriet there, my old friend Dr. M——, and my father, strangely the *essence* of my father, saying as he once said, long ago, when I was in danger—I could hear the very tones of his voice—"Steady now, boy, steady." Moments of joy turned to exquisite pain! Somehow the mind, knowing how short the time is, and keyed to an intolerable clarity of emotion, selects only essentials. At such moments every man is an artist. I tried afterwards to jot down all the things that raced through my mind in that instant between consciousness and unconsciousness, but could not: a teeming world of them, a universe lived in a moment of time.

A day or so after I came out of the ether, having thought much of that strange experience, I said to my nurse:

"Did I speak to you—did I say anything—on my way to the operating room?"

"Oh, yes," said she indulgently.

I paused: but finally asked the question.

"What did I say?"

She was smiling, I thought ironically—a little superior!

"You said: 'You will not leave me: you will stay close by?' "

It was what I had felt; but I could not remember whether I had really said it. I was strongly moved: thinking how instinctively, when we feel ourselves drifting out, we reach for some human contact.

I had gone down into the oblivion at nine in the morning and came struggling out sometime after five in the afternoon. Someone was apparently lifting or twisting my head aside by main force, and I was unspeakably miserable, faint, weary. The place was too warm. It seemed as if someone were holding me down. It made me indignant, and I began to kick. A voice that seemed infinitely distant was saying:

"He is coming out."

At that a wave of intense irritation swept through me. I was being disgracefully treated! It was a terrific effort, but I said as angrily as I could manage:

"Why don't they go on with it? Why all this delay?"

"It's all over. You came through beautifully."

"All over!" I said incredulously.

"Yes, you're through. Everything is all right."

It was unbelievable. All through! And I had felt, or heard, or seen nothing. I was at the moment unspeakably wretched, nauseated, but there was balm in those words. In the miserable half-opiated hours that followed, when there seemed nothing that I could do, no position that I could take, that was not exquisitely painful or uncomfortable, I kept saying to myself: "All over. I'm through." I clung fatuously to the words, "You came through beautifully." In spite of everything there was hope! I did not know at the time that I had been on the operating table, under the hands of that masterly surgeon, for two hours and a half, and that one does not recover too speedily from such an experience. Nevertheless, the worst had come and gone.

I had also a scarcely definable sensation that gave me the greatest comfort. I had found myself again! A kind of warm welcome swept over me at recognizing the familiar personality I had felt slipping away from me, that I had trusted so fearfully out of my own control. It had come back! What if it had not come back?

A little later I had another and wholly unexpected source of comfort. One day when the assistant surgeon was bending over me, attending to the dressings, I noted a small white scar across his face. I asked him about it.

"Well," said he, "I have been through it, too."

"You have been operated on?" I exclaimed in the greatest astonishment.

"Indeed I have," said he.

It had actually never occurred to me before that a surgeon, pursuing his bloody career, might himself have to undergo the same sort of ordeal. There had been an element of the super-human about the confident master of his art that was now dis-sipated. The tables had been turned on him: he was, after all, a man of flesh and blood. I had quite a new feeling toward the profession!

"Are you entirely well again?" I asked.

"Perfectly," he responded.

"Are you as strong as ever?" I asked.

"Stronger! I'm better than I ever was before in my life."

It was like a draught of wine to me! It may seem absurd, but the surgeon leaning over me, hurting me cruelly, appeared at that moment a kind of angel—I have laughed since when I thought of his beaming young face—but he had given me new hope. *He* had been through it: *he* was better than ever!

Hope, I thought, is like love: it is there all the time, oceans of it, but someone must touch it off, awaken it.

I may have "come through beautifully"; I did not know how slowly nature moves in mending man's ills.

X

A SHIP OF SOULS

Nay, in thy own mean perplexities, do thou thyself but
hold thy tongue for one day. . . .
Sartor Resartus, Chapter III.

M Y OPERATION produced a subtle change in my attitude
toward this grim hostelry of pain. It seemed no longer
quite so forbidding: I was not alien, I was initiate, sealed to the
order by suffering. It was not that I liked it better, but that I
had begun, curiously, to feel myself a part of it, constrained to
share its fortunes, whatever they might be. One night, I recall
vividly awakening in the warm darkness, looking at the dim
light on the narrow wall, listening to the wind that crept and
called and whistled at my window—for it was now the dead of
winter. I had suddenly the feeling that I was in the cabin of
some great ship. It was like a great ship; and I outward bound,
with a thousand other souls, for some far port. Were we safe?
Were we safe?

Outside I could hear feet pacing the muffled deck and from
time to time the signal that called the captain to some part of
the great ship. The orderlies, they would be the stewards, and
the nurses, the stewardesses: and there were the robust young
officers who came to reassure the suffering or fearful passengers.
There on the stand by my side stood the veritable flowers my
friends had brought, a *bon voyage.* for my journey.

It was an idea that grew upon my imagination. After I had
recovered sufficiently to be wrapped up in warm blankets it was
down the gangway they trundled me, and I was placed in a
steamer chair on the lee deck. Even the incongruity of snow on
the ground, the roar in the streets, the sun gleaming palely
through the murk of the city, and a sparrow perched on the

rail, did not shake my feeling that it was a ship I was travelling in.

There is loneliness on a long voyage, even to one who has learned in some measure to live in the house of his own spirit—and one turns with eagerness to his fellow passengers. Strange men and women whom he has never seen before, nor heard of, and yet they are somehow bound to him and he to them by the common experiences and dangers of the voyage. Who are they, then? What is their port? It is like that greater and sometimes painful voyage on the good ship Earth, where, whether we like it or not, we are fellow passengers with many a strange human being.

It is singular, in a ship, how much one can come to know of his fellow voyagers by mere propinquity, by chance meetings on the deck, by random talk in the saloons. When one hears a man groaning piteously in an adjoining cabin, how can he avoid coming presently to know something about him? Without ever having seen him I came to know quite well a fine young officer who had had his leg amputated three times and was tossing in a wild delirium of fever. How I watched for news of his progress as it came daily by way of the attendants; and what relief when at length he won the doubtful struggle! I had been easily comfortable, I thought, compared with him.

"When you go out," I said one day to my nurse, "set the screen a little aside so that I can look through the door."

With my head properly bolstered up I watched the people going by in the broad corridor, and it made me think of the road in my own town, and all the curious people that ride or drive or walk in it. And many of them I thought I should like well if I could come to know them better. One in particular I watched for every day, a blind man, walking quickly, chin up, a woman, I thought a nurse, guiding him, with her arm locked firmly through his. Blind he was, and yet there was something confident and courageous about him. Possibly, I thought, he is going on to the eye clinic: he is bracing himself for an operation.

"Who is the blind man who goes by every day?" I asked finally.

"Why, that," replied my nurse, "is Dr. ——, and that is not a nurse but his wife who guides him."

"A doctor!"

"Yes, Dr. ——."

Something, a very little, I uncurled of his story: the courage of it, the toil of it, the devotion of it—and indeed the success of it. He might well have excused himself in facing life—"Doth God exact day-labour, light deny'd?"—but he had gone onward, centring all the powers that remained to him in the touch of his strong and delicate fingers. He had found a calling fitted to his gifts. He was a kind of sculptor in living tissues, nerves, bones. A story one liked to enlarge upon: to tell himself!

As I began to creep out in my long gown, like some preposterously old man, I could look in as I passed at many a half-screened doorway. If one could but capture it, I thought, there was a story in every room. Not petty stories either, dealing with inconsequential things, but going down deep where life turns upon the stark realities of pain and sorrow and death. I came during the days of my slow recovery to know a little of some of them. One of the voyagers was a mere lad, suffering the aftermath of infantile paralysis, lying with his legs painfully strapped and weighted. He had been on a long, long voyage, and upon reaching port he would probably have to limp ashore: and yet a cheerier lad I never saw—the slow Southern humour in the turn of his voice, the glint in his eye. I liked to have him wheeled into my room for a visit—he in his chair and I in my bed. No lugubrious conversation did we indulge in, never a word of commiseration, but gusts of laughter that there should be so many ridiculous and humorous things in a hospital.

One passenger I came to know had been long on his voyage: a seasoned traveller compared with me. He had many books on his cabinet, symbols of his permanence, and framed pictures near him on his stand, one of a splendid boy who was, I learned, his son. He read me a poem he had written—"in the nights when I find it hard to sleep"—and it was for this son he wrote it. The refrain alone I recall because it contained, bound up in a few words, what he himself had learned during his hard voyage. This was it:

Plough on, my son, plough on.

Another man I chanced to meet during these days of my own slow recovery had an indescribable fascination for me. *He was going to die and did not know it.* Everyone about seemed aware of it. It was the bandied news of the corridor. A significant look of the eye, a nod of the head as one went by his door—there in that room is a man who is going to die.

It gave me the strangest sense of tense awareness. I had, in the past, seen men die; I had known the sorrow of the death of dear friends; but death—it is curious when I think of it—had never for me, previous to my experience in the hospital, seemed at all a reality. It was something terrible that happened to other people, and though it may appear shocking in the telling, but it is so, I thought of it somehow as their own fault. Here it had come close to me in many forms as a stark reality: something that might even happen to *me*. In this place it was no longer a phenomenon, but a measurable and daily expectancy. It was this new congeries of observation and intense feeling that so stirred my interest in this man who was going to die—and did not know it!

One day I met him. He had read something I had once written and asked if I would come to see him. I went with the greatest hesitation and reluctance, and yet with an overpowering curiosity. How must a man feel who was about to die? What would he think? How would he look? What would he say? As I walked down the corridor with the nurse who brought the message, these questions came upon me with a vividness and power I cannot describe. In my imagination I saw the poor fellow in bed, emaciated, slow of breath, feebly reaching out his hand to touch mine. I could scarcely control the beating of my heart or the trembling of my knees when I stepped around the screen.

"How are you, sir?" said a steady voice. "Come in. I'm glad to see you."

There he sat in his chair, a stout, rather florid man, in a gay-coloured dressing gown. There were flowers on his table—a world of flowers—and pictures of a smiling gray-haired woman and a smiling girl and two little boys. In front of him, on a desk, piles of neatly arranged papers, as though he had just looked up from his daily affairs. It was I who was hesitant and embarrassed: for I could not quickly adjust reality and preconception. It was he who made everything easy and hospitable.

While I sat talking with him a nurse brought in a telegram, which he slit open in the quick, nervous, incidental manner of the business man. He glanced at it and tossed it on the desk, proceeding with his conversation.

It came over me with a kind of shock. What futile urgency—if the man was going to die. Then I remembered, with a wave of pity, that he did not know!

It was not long before I could place him. He was quite a typical American business man—self-confident, positive, vital. He did not tell me in so many words that he was rich: he radiated it. He told me of a "deal" he had just "cleared up" in which he had made a "killing." I found that his secretary came in every morning to take care of "a lot of little matters."

I kept forgetting—but it would come over me suddenly and with a sinking sense of futility, "Why all these deals? What good making any more money? The man is going to die."

The next day when I stopped to see him I found the nurse reading a newspaper aloud, and when he began to talk of the depression in business and the outlook for certain stocks, I kept saying to myself, "Now, what is the use of all that?"

He talked again quite volubly about himself and his affairs: but presently he broke off, and I saw him looking at me with a slow, inscrutable gaze.

"Are you here for long?" he asked.

As I paused I thought his look intensified, and there was something deep down and far back in his narrowing eyes—or did I imagine it?—that was pitiful to see.

"The doctors," said I, "are promising me that I can go home for Christmas."

I shall never forget the pause that followed—my glance drifted away to the picture of the smiling gray-haired woman on his table—nor the peculiar tone of his voice—deep, still—one word: "Christmas!"

They had all said he did not know, but I knew as well as though he had told me in so many words. He knew! No doubt he had known all along! My whole heart went out to him so that I could scarcely keep the tears from my eyes. I looked at him again. Yes, there was a kind of mediocrity about the man, he had few intellectual resources, but what a fighter! What a fighter! He was playing the game straight through to the end. It seemed to me at the moment as though, of all things in the world, such courage, such steadiness, was most to be admired. He had not thought out a philosophy: he *had it*. He could walk up to death with it.

Telegrams, yes, why not? Deals, yes, why not? A secretary every morning to take his letters, why not? They were not futilities, they were of the essence of the matter. He was refusing to be beaten by the past or crushed by the future. He was living, as a man ought to live, every fibre of him, in the only moment he ever really possesses—this moment! It came to me with intolerable clarity: "Why, we're all going to die and don't know it; and this is what we should do about it."

I cannot tell what the man's religious beliefs were—if he had any. Once or twice during the few days I knew him he seemed on the point of saying something to me—I knew!—but the moment passed. How I should have liked to know! But of this I am certain: he had faith—faith of some kind. Men differ in that: I have mine and you yours. In its essence it is a deep, deep sense of confidence—of calmness—that whatever happens, whatever the process, it is natural, it is universal, it is according to law.

I saw, borne down the long corridor, a still, white-covered figure quite cured of the fever of living.

"To die is different from what anyone supposed—and luckier."

XI

LIFE AND THE DOCTOR

I will make a man more precious than fine gold.

M Y HOSPITAL grew on me as I came to know it better. Everything in it and about it began to interest me profoundly. I learned through books and in bits of conversation the story of the man who gave the money to found it. His portrait hangs there in the anteroom, a bluff business man, one of those Americans who insisted upon his practicality, and wrote his poetry in brick and mortar. At the main entrance to the vast building there stands, without warning or explanation, a colossal statue of the Christ, his hands outspread in welcome. Strange in that busy place: a personality as disturbing as ever to the spirit of man. On the pedestal these words are engraved:

Come unto me all ye that labour and are heavy laden and I
will give you rest.

I liked to watch the busy crowds swirling by in the passageways, pale new patients coming in, smiling patients going out, visitors to see the sick, hurrying doctors and nurses—few looking up as they went by. I thought of another line that might well be placed upon the pedestal: "Is it nothing to you, all ye that pass by?"

There were also the great doctors—the great *men*—who created the living hospital within its shell of brick and mortar, and by their genius made it famous. I had their books, one by one, and read deeply into their hopes and their aspirations, felt their passion for truth, was convinced by their practical sense. I was full of admiration. One of the greatest of them knew as much of the human spirit as of the human body.

It seemed to me, indeed, the more I saw, and learned, and felt, that of all institutions in this world, the hospital, at this moment of time, is supreme. It represents modern man at his best. It is the most objective and dispassionate in confronting the problems of life, the least controlled by prejudices or traditions or taboos. As I thought of it, it seemed to me far more vitally in contact with reality, more definite in its purpose, and therefore more effective as an institution, than the church, the school, the senate.

Here, I thought, a man's a man for a' that. He is accepted without regard to class, or race, or creed, or sex. In the ward where I lay, during many weeks of my sojourn, I had for neighbours a justice of the United States Supreme Court, a United States Senator, the president-elect of a Latin American republic, and a miscellaneous assortment of the rich and notable of the earth—all looking much alike in their hospital slips. Down the corridor a little way there opened the vast wards where lay the utterly poor and neglected of that city—the poorest white people, the poorest foreigners, the poorest Negroes. So far as the essentials of medical attention were concerned, they enjoyed exactly the same treatment as the Senators and the millionaires. A little less room, perhaps, in the public wards, and simpler food, but the same exactitude of scientific care by doctors and nurses. A black-hearted criminal, if he comes to the hospital shot through, is cared for and cured; he has the same attention as a saint might have—and no questions asked about either.

After I was able to make little venturesome excursions through the mazes of that endless institution, I walked one evening into the Negro ward. Every bed was filled; everywhere I looked there were cleanliness and order, and busy nurses and doctors. Some of these poor of the earth, even though ill, were probably warmer, cleaner, better fed, more comfortably housed than ever before in their lives. It was just at their supper time, and the orderlies were trundling in the steaming service tables. One old coloured man with kinky gray hair, propped up in his bed, eating his supper, looked so happy that I spoke to him.

"Dese folks," he responded, "am sholy de messengers ob de Lawd."

A little later, coming back slowly along the corridor, I heard sounds strange in that place. I stopped at the entrance of the passageway that led down into the Negro ward. They had finished their supper and had broken irresistibly into song. This was the refrain:

> "Oh, I know, I know
> The Lawd has laid his hands on me."

Standing there, listening, I could not keep the mist out of my eyes.

Yes, the colour of men still divides them, and their religions divide them, and their languages and their nations and their parties, but this great ship of souls accepts them all, carries them all onward together to their destination, steerage, third class, and first! Only one question is asked of any man: "Do you suffer?" We are all one in pain!

If it was the conviction of the preciousness of the soul of man that built the cathedral at Chartres, it is the conviction of the preciousness of his life that has built the matchless hospitals of America. As I thought of it, those long days, it seemed to me that the hospital cherishes a spirit, or an attitude, that the Church sadly lacks. I felt in it a respect for the human body and for human life beyond that in the Church, as it stands to-day, for the spirit of man. The hospital diagnoses before it prescribes; the Church prescribes before it diagnoses. The physician stands humble before the human body, studies it, doubts about it, wonders at it; labours to fit his remedies to the exact disease. Is there in any church an equivalent humility in the presence of the spirit of man? Is the priest willing to inquire and doubt and wonder? Does he *know* before he tries to cure? Must the Church cultivate certainty lest knowledge turn and rend it?

Once the physician let blood indiscriminately for almost every ill. Has the Church in its treatment of souls passed that stage in its development? And where, in any religious institution, is there such singleness of purpose, such objectivity of aim, as in the hospital?

And yet, having said all these things about the hospital, and truly said, for they are based upon what I myself saw and heard and thought, I have yet to speak of a limitation I felt deeply during the weeks I spent there. One of the vivid lesser characters that Shakespeare drew with such penetrating art was a doctor. I thought often, while in the hospital, of that nameless doctor in *Macbeth*. It is after the murder, and Lady Macbeth walks in her restless sleep. The doctor comes in, comes bustling in, all doctor, inquiring of the nurse:

"When was it she last walked?"

He is eager for all the facts before he makes his diagnosis. And then, you will remember, Lady Macbeth enters—in that scene that freezes the blood. She is washing her hands.

"Out, damned spot! out, I say . . . all the perfumes of Arabia will not sweeten this little hand. Oh, oh, oh!"

Faced with this appalling spectacle, the boundless agony of the soul, the doctor rises suddenly out of his profession, realizes that here are matters too great for him.

"This disease," he says, "is beyond my practice."

He watches the rising terror of the distraught Queen: "There's knocking at the gate": and out of his deep understanding as a man, he says:

"More needs she the divine than the physician."

It seemed to me—I may be wrong—that it is too rarely that the modern doctor, equipped with his myriad instruments, is willing to say, "This disease is beyond my practice," and more rarely still, "More needs she the divine than the physician."

When I thought, after eight doctors had weighed and tested and X-rayed every part of me, how little, after all, they knew of *me*, it came to me with extraordinary force, the vast ranges of human suffering, suffering that reacts upon the body, that is beyond the practice of the doctor. They try, humbly enough, to get inside the mind of the patient, but something fails in their art; something else is needed; some deeper, humbler understanding of the human spirit. There are such depths of human life

that the photograph never catches! Nearly all that is important
or uniquely interesting about man begins, as Matthew Arnold
once said, where nature ends. It is relatively easy to observe and
explain and treat the physical reactions of humankind, for they
are the common reactions of all animals and make up indeed
a large part of life: but it is the plane that lies above all this,
however profoundly affected by it, that so intensely matters. We
are all alike as animals: we are all different as human beings.
In the slight margin by which man lifts his head above the universal slime and *thinks,* lies all the interest and beauty of life,
likewise all the tragedy and sorrow—and joy.

What it seemed to me I wanted, passionately, in that hospital,
was not merely a cure for my defective body, but a way to live
with tranquillity in a troubled world of which my body was the
apt symbol. And where is that to be had in all its vast array of
medical lore, or among its most skilful physicians?

All my meditations brought me back inevitably to the conclusion of the early weeks in the gabled room. A man after all
cures himself! It is only as he comes to his own aid, takes possession of his own spirit, that he "recovers."

"To-day I have got out of all trouble or rather I have cast
out all trouble, for it was not outside, but within."

As I look back upon it, I can say honestly that my experience
in the hospital, miserable as it seemed at the time, was among
the most interesting of my life.

XII

CONVALESCENCE: "PLEASE YOU, DRAW NEAR"

. . . that serene and blessed mood
In which . . . we are laid asleep
In body, and become a living soul.

I SHALL never forget the still routine of the days of my slow
convalescence, especially the unhurried ease and silence of
the long evenings after the day nurse had gone home and I lay
propped up in my bed with a light over my shoulder and a price-
less book on the corner of the near-by table. What peace, what
ease, what comfort, now that the ordeal was over. While I was
sometimes in pain and often restless and uncomfortable—and
weak, weak!—yet there was an indescribable sense of renewed
security, a wayward freedom of the mind, I had not known
before in years I dare not count.

All my life, it seemed to me, I had been hard driven, often
forced to tasks that were not easily native to my gifts, that which
was most myself interrupted and retarded by a thousand dusty,
inconsequential affairs. Temptations to go here or hurry there,
see this or hear that, by some stupid outward urge. All the compulsions of loyalty and duty! Even in my own little place there
had seemed literally a conspiracy against quietude and thought,
against the deep examination of life, against such small effort
as a man may make to understand the world which surrounds
and so ruthlessly compels him.

But here, what unspeakable luxury! No sense of being driven
either by outward or inward taskmasters, no duties, no engage-
ments, no interruptions. None of the absurd compulsions of
property or the urgings of ambition or the weariness of routine.
All day long one can lie or sit still, save for the fortunate moments when the nurse comes in smiling with the tray, or in the

evening after a tap on one's door, with the prescribed "nourishment," which proves to be a glass of iced orange juice beaten foamy with the white of an egg—wholly delicious. The world has slipped away from us, and we do not care! So much that had seemed wayward becomes wisdom and joy. I wonder if there is anything in this world comparable to the sense of being fully alive within—warm and strong there, eager there! I shall never forget the recurring sense I had that whatever I may have lost in time or strength or money I had regained in self-possession. I was at liberty to think anything I liked, go anywhere I pleased, past, present, or future—I was free to see or hear or feel whatsoever I would or could. Here no one kept a clock on me! Not even that most arbitrary of clock keepers, myself. I could take up any book I liked—for I was as long-armed as the resources of that great hospital—and if I did not like it, I could put it down. I could write one sentence in my familiar book, or ten or twenty, or none at all, as I pleased, or I could turn to the wall (the nurse thinking I slept) and listen to the December rain drumming on the window, and let my mind go free among what William James calls "the deepest things of our nature . . . the dumb regions of the heart in which we dwell alone with our willingnesses and unwillingnesses, our faiths and our fears."

Many times in my life I have repeated Rodin's saying, a true maxim for every craftsman, that "slowness is beauty"—but until those days in the hospital I never knew fully what it meant. To read slowly, to think slowly, to feel slowly and deeply: what enrichment! In the past I have been so often greedy. I have gobbled down innumerable facts, ideas, stories, poetical illusions—I have gobbled down work—I have even gobbled down my friends!— and indeed had a kind of enjoyment of all of them—but rarely have I tasted the last flavour of anything, the final exquisite sense of personality or spirit that secretes itself in every work that merits serious attention, in every human being at all worth knowing. But in those heavenly evenings of silence and solitude I read only a little at a time and only the greatest books, especially those great-small books in which some master spirit has completely delivered himself. I read until I came upon something that stirred me deep down, something strong and hard, something a little difficult, at first, to understand, and there I stopped and slowly, slowly, turned it over in my mind until I knew exactly what it was the prophet or the poet or the philosopher was trying to say to me. And always, I found, the subtlest beauties, the deepest truths, came last.

In one of Dr. Osler's provocative addresses, for example, I found a reference to a passage in Sir Thomas Browne which he himself had loved. So I got me the *Urn-Burial* and the *Religio Medici* to find it, and read all around and about it, and wore it afterwards for many a day like a jewel in my mind—and love it yet!

". . . the iniquity of oblivion blindly scattereth her poppy and deals with the memory of man without regard to merit of perpetuity."

Writers have taken whole pages to say less!

Often I found passages, especially in the old books, that seemed, as the Quakers say, to speak to my condition, and these I sometimes committed to memory that I might have them ready, loaded weapons, when skulking pain attacked me or mutinous dullness threatened to wear me down.

"I affirm that tranquillity is nothing else than the good ordering of the mind. Constantly then give to thyself this retreat and renew thyself; and let thy principles be brief and fundamental, which, as soon as thou shalt recur to them, will be sufficient to cleanse the soul completely and to send thee back free from all discontent with the things to which thou returnest."

A page of Marcus Aurelius, indeed, is worth, any time, a day's slowness. What fortification of the spirit! What incentives to courage! Open anywhere, at random, and feel the keen, bracing, sometimes scarifying, truth.

"I have often wondered how it is that every man loves himself more than all the rest of men, but yet sets less value on his own opinion of himself than on the opinion of others."

Or of death:

"Thou hast embarked, thou hast made the voyage, thou art come to shore; get out."

Many and rich treasures were thus available in the days of my convalescence that I should have felt it impossible in my busy, ordinary life to enjoy. I thought often what a perfect thing it was to have all about me for days at a time such a variety of fine thoughts, plucked in passing out of old books like scented flowers from half-forgotten roadsides. I thought also that if I were again in my customary life I should not only lack the time, but possibly also the courage, to be going about wearing such ornaments—at least in a conspicuous buttonhole. What cowards we are, anyway! What Peters warming ourselves at the fire, denying that we know anything that is great or true or beautiful! How rarely we dare let anyone see our best possessions—the things we really live by—lest they fling names at us. I resolved, those days, never any more to hurry, never to appear what I was not, never to be constrained by the crowd. Ah, well. . . .

It was in this time of returning zest that I had the good fortune to read, or gloriously reread, a book that exactly fitted and interpreted my mood. It is not often—not once a year—not once in a lifetime, possibly—that one stumbles upon a book that perfectly and completely satisfies what he has at the moment burning in his mind. I shall never forget the long, still evening in the hospital when I read *The Tempest*—or how I turned from it late in the night with that sense of happiness and courage which only the greatest art can give to the spirit of man, saying over and over to myself those last words of Prospero, the ripe essence of his long experience:

"Please you, draw near."

It came to me then, as a kind of inspiration, that better than any other words I know, they express the final wisdom of men—men who live in a world, not perfect, but *human*.

"Please you, draw near."

What else is it that we desire after being buffeted by rude events, after being cast away on our own particular desert isle, after at last subduing our Caliban and setting free our Ariel, save to turn with a new and deep kind of passion to "beauteous

mankind," the "goodly creatures" all about us, and there, having become quiet within ourselves, saying with deep sincerity:
"Please you, draw near."

I have put down these incidents and thoughts of my convalescence just as they came to me. A certain exuberance of joyful relief is perhaps permissible after months of anxiety and discomfort. I make no excuse for it: I have rarely enjoyed anything more.

XIII

LETTERS DURING ILLNESS

A man's life of any worth is a continual Allegory, and very
few eyes can see the Mystery of his life. . . .

From a letter by JOHN KEATS.

I NEVER before prized letters as I did during those long weeks
in bed: nor read them oftener, for I learned that there is
much more to be had out of even brief and simple letters, if one
reads *into* them as well as *out* of them, than I had ever before
imagined. They are like any other expression of friendship: we
get in proportion as we give.

Harriet's letters were best, Harriet's letters, with their flowing
details, the unhurried, precious reassurances of the continuity
and usualness of life. I had a curious sense, in reading them, of
life flowing in tranquillity: all the small ordinary daily hap-
penings, the seasons going round, autumn deepening into winter. I felt somehow drawn into the placid regularity of nature.
And they nearly always set me smiling—as though I were at
home—and well again! When they came I liked to hold them
in my hand for some time and then to read them slowly.

"Mrs. Sargent's daughter—you remember little Inez Sargent—
has twins."

So, said I to myself, little Inez Sargent has twins. I could
remember only vaguely that there was such a person as Inez
Sargent, and twins are not a seventh-day marvel in the world,
but somehow it was pleasing and interesting to know that little
Inez Sargent had twins. Why shouldn't she have twins?

"John Heathcote has sold his Alderney cow."

How that little item brought back the veritable picture of
John, his jolly old wife in the doorway, and the ancient wagon
standing there by the barn, and the chickens scratching in the

sunny yard. John became so fond of his horses, his cow, his pigs, that it was news indeed to hear that he had sold any of them. There is a story we delight to tell one another regarding John's sale of another cow. The purchaser was shrewd and cold-eyed and insisted on knowing how well bred the cow was and how much milk she gave. Old John looked at her with affection and responded earnestly:

"She's a good cow and gives all the milk she possibly can."

Then there were always the beguiling references to garden or orchard or meadow.

"I had Frank over to put your bees in the winter boxes."

My bees! As I lay there in bed I could follow out in my imagination every step in the process I had so often performed myself: bringing the cases out of the storehouse, setting them up on blocks of wood, lifting the hives one after another and fitting them in place, afterwards packing them carefully around with shavings. What a beautiful process!

In the future, when friends of mine are ill, I shall know well the kind of letters that will rest them most: letters full of the healthy continuity of life—letters without commiseration.

Before I was well enough to write letters myself, save a few scrawling sentences, I could at least *think* letters. I could lie perfectly still and work out the most beautiful long letters, not only to friends who were near to me, but to old friends whom I had not seen for years. Presently, having written a letter I especially enjoyed to L—— I began to consider what he might reply to me, and I soon found myself answering my own letters. Oh, I was greedy for letters! It proved delightful and cheering to put myself in the place of various friends and to write as I thought they would write. It was surprising to me how vividly it brought them back to me: let me into their lives—as I, at least, imagined them to be.

I filled many hard half hours with these pleasant excursions. When they began, a little, to pall upon me, for it was, after all, only a game, it occurred to me suddenly, and with the delight which comes with an inventive idea, that I was by no means confined, in my imaginary correspondence, to friends I knew. I had all the world to pick from! So I wrote immediately to President Hoover and received in reply—that very day!—the most amazingly confidential letter regarding his life in the White House and his real opinion of various public men—including Senator Borah! I had no end of amusement out of this for a day or so, since his letter contained the most astonishing and unbelievable revelations. If I were to disclose it to the public, it would undoubtedly cause an explosion. So I shall preserve the amenities and keep the letter to myself.

I wrote to Mussolini, dictator of Italy. Our letters were couched in severely formal language, beginning, "Sir," and ending "I am, Sir, Your obedient servant." Never before in my life have I delighted in such beautifully elaborate ironies or invented icier rejoinders—for I don't like Mussolini. I give it as my unprejudiced judgment, since I was the author of all of them, that my letters to him were far superior to his letters to me.

But the most amusing of all was the letter I received from John D. Rockefeller, enclosing a new dime. I responded at once, in the most courteous manner, telling him in detail of all the ways in which I had considered expending his munificent gift. The more I wrote the more amusing the idea became, so that I must have laughed out loud. What a reckless spendthrift I was becoming! My nurse, who had thought me peacefully asleep in accordance with the doctor's orders, was at once aroused.

"What are you laughing at?" she asked.

"I was considering," said I, "how I would spend a new dime—if John D. Rockefeller should send me one."

I could see her face grow round with astonishment, which delighted me.

"Well, I never!" said my nurse.

I wonder if anyone has ever written such a letter to John D. Rockefeller. I think it might amuse him. Maybe I will post mine and see if he won't send me another dime.

These may seem ridiculous diversions, but they filled parts of many restless nights.

XIV

THE RETURN

Henceforth I ask not good-fortune—I myself am good-fortune,
Henceforth I whimper no more, postpone no more, need
   nothing.

AFTER a long illness, one's recovery comes like the spring
in our Northern valleys. It was in late April I came home
again. Days there were, the foredawn of the year, days of such
magical sweetness and warmth that it seemed of a certainty
spring had come. New soft foliage on the poplars, the golden
mists of the elm trees, hyacinths under the sumacs! One's mind
runs away toward recovery far faster than his body.

Then come days of sad withdrawal, days of cloudy hesitation
when the budding year retires within a gray cowl of penitence.
We have cold rains slanting down, flurries of reminiscent snow,
piercing winds out of the northwest, and all the world again
turns chill and drab.

One does not, fortunately, know it at the time, but there are
two periods of convalescence. I think I have not spoken too
ardently of the first, with its joyous sense of renewed security.
I found the second, after my return, more difficult to bear, in
certain ways, than the early days of my illness when pain and
discomfort were expected and studied occupations. I, too, had
my cold rains slanting down, I had my cowl of penitence. Heavy
weeks of slow recovery there were, when every instinct of my
nature cried out for rest. Stop! Wait! Any road I walked grew
intolerably long; any hill I climbed, too high; all the work I did,
too hard. Such an appetite for recovery, so little food to satisfy it!

In the hospital, during my convalescence, I had no need of
any outward action or responsibility; I could devote my entire

attention to delightful excursions in the quiet and happy country of the mind. I had now to take myself over, a going concern, and try to catch step with a swift-moving and clamorous world. Those who have themselves been ill will know well the feeling of that time, and the discouragements of it.

What a blessing, those days, I found in my garden and orchard, and especially among my bees. I shall not easily forget the spacious quietude of those May mornings, with the sun looking in over the hills of Pelham, and the dew still on the grass, the meadows green again, and the apple trees beginning to bloom.

I know of nothing that will more completely absorb the mind than the slow, careful, minute tasks of the bee master. Other familiar labour of the garden or farm or orchard, for want of variety, sometimes loses its charm, but one may find an inexhaustible delight in the strange ways of the bee people. After many years' experience I am as much interested as ever I was. I am still a besotted amateur!

In the hard days of my convalescence I found nothing that fitted so exactly the limitations of my physical strength and at the same time satisfied the appetite aroused during my illness for that which was slow and deep and still. One cannot force nature; a bee keeper who hurries soon repents!

How pleasant it was, then, sitting there in the scented orchard with my back to the sun, slowly going through the hives. Slowly! never making a false motion, lifting the bee-covered frames, examining the state of the brood and stores, watching for her majesty the queen, learning at a glance whether the colony has begun rearing drones, and finding and cutting out the new queen cells. A fascinating process, never more easily practised than at this season of the year when the bees are busy and comfortable with new stores of nectar and pollen coming in. One need scarcely wear a bee veil or gloves if he knows how to go about the delicate business with that courtesy and gentleness due to the manners and customs of an ancient society. When I began bee keeping, now long ago, I was often stung, but in the last half dozen years I have had scarcely a half dozen stings, and these were usually due to my own haste or stupidity. I think sometimes that almost all the mistakes I have made in my life have been the result of haste.

When I grew weary, and this at first was often enough, I stopped where I sat and watched the urgent, unself-conscious, strangely beguiling life of the world of the bee people with its unfathomable social laws and its intricate customs. I watched the workers darting out of the hive with a kind of fierce energy, lifting in the sunny air, circling once or more about, and then with swift certainty heading for the blossom fields where their harvest was making. I watched them coming in again heavily laden with pollen and nectar, often so weary with their load that they could not quite make the landing board, waddling into the hive like tipsy sailors with their dunnage bags full of yellow or brown or red pollen. I watched the young bees coming out when the sun grew warm and the air dry to play in front of the hive, using their new wings with inimitable grace, preparing themselves for the stern labour soon to come.

It is a beautiful process and grows upon one as he becomes intimately familiar with the significance of all the sights, sounds, odours of the hive, and the varied habits of its long-settled social life. A hard-and-fast communism if ever there was one, with the life of the individual wholly devoted to the welfare of the swarm! To look down into it one feels like some god watching for his own delight the flowing life of a world as distant from his own, as self-contained as it is unconscious of his existence. He may destroy it—destruction is easy for a god!—or he may, by acting upon laws wholly beyond the range of the bee world, work strange miracles with it—like putting into a colony frames of brood or honey the bees have not themselves made, or cutting out the queen cells, or clipping the wings of the queen herself so that the colony cannot swarm. He may in some degree direct the activities of the bees so that they serve his purposes as well as their own—purposes of which they know nothing—but he cannot, for all his power and his knowledge, change in the slightest particular the ages-old Law of the Hive. He himself, however omniscient, can work with the colony only as he himself also learns and obeys the laws of it.

222

I have sometimes speculated upon what might be the thinking of a philosopher of the swarm, if such could possibly be imagined. He would be no worker—workers are too busy making and banking their honey—nor yet a queen, since the queen is absorbed in the domestic affairs of the hive. Probably an old, idling drone with little to do in the world but loaf and invite his soul: *he* would be the Philosopher! He could perhaps predicate, from the evidences of what he might call Providence or Fate or Miracle—or Law!—the existence of a Power Beyond the Hive. He might speculate as to its attributes and its purposes, marvel at its paradoxes, consider its will, but what, after all, could he know of *Me?*

Often, if I tired of working with or watching the bees, I would recall, as I sat there in the sun, some of the things that had come to my mind while I was in the hospital, especially if they seemed applicable to the moment. One passage occurred to me that I did not even know I had kept in my memory. It was from Dr. Johnson, and I have since looked it up to see that I quoted it correctly.

"No man," said he, "is obliged to do as much as he can do. A man is to have part of his life to himself."

I liked especially the last half of this quotation and said it over a number of times as I sat there, idling, by the hives: "A man is to have part of his life to himself."

Another passage I repeated upon occasions when I began to feel, in my weakness, that the world was too much for me:

". . . a man of understanding hath lost nothing, if he yet have himselfe."

But I loved most of all, in those days, to lose myself completely in the unhurried enjoyment, the concentration of the entire mind, upon the simple tasks in hand. I liked even the somewhat monotonous work of preparing new hives, stringing the brood frames with wire, and setting in the foundation comb. I liked to fit together the comb-honey sections—how good the odour of the clean new white-wood!—and wax in the starters. There is salvation alike to worn bodies and tired souls in these quiet and simple processes of the hands. The knotted strands of life are thus by slow magic untangled, and one comes to be like a child, absorbed in play, with the world grown newly happy. And it is no mere anodyne of escape, for there is in it the ancient logic of labour, wherein the result is honey in the honeycomb!

All of these experiences and meditations helped greatly during the days of what I have called my second convalescence, before I dared test my strength with any real labour. Idle days they were, lazy, still, rich days, full of a kind of delight I had never quite felt before. For I found myself willing to be slow and quiet, to look long at one thing! In the old life I was scarcely ever able to wait until the full meaning, or beauty, of anything—whether the aspects of nature or the written word—came in upon me. I was too swift: what I planted yesterday in the fertile soil of my spirit I wanted to pull up to-day to see if the roots had sprouted. I was not willing to be quiet and await the sure processes of the sun and the rain. All Americans are something like that. In our bemused faith in speed we think some instrument can be had that will obliterate time and shorten growth; but the law of the spirit is not unlike that of the body: the period of silent gestation that must follow the conception of thought is immutable.

"Those too are triflers," says the philosopher, "who have wearied themselves in life by their activity."

As I grew stronger I began to have, day by day, a keener sense of life—the *intensity* of life. Even the small and disagreeable chores of the orchard and the land became immeasurably precious to me; I even had days when I felt that I could write again. I was humbly thankful that I could do anything at all! One morning in particular I remember vividly—so vividly that I wrote down an account of the incident in my notebook under the date of May 14th—I was standing at the top of a ladder, flinging out clouds of vile-smelling sulphur and arsenate of lead. We were spraying the apple trees. Down below, Frank, my helper, was pumping the ancient contraption which we had tinkered into another year's service.

"Pump, Frank, pump for your life."

And Frank pumped, and I sent a mist of poison into the topmost branches. We had studied the light morning airs and moved slowly around each tree until every calyx had had its minute attention.

"A good job," said Frank. "I guess that'll give 'em the stomach ache."

It may seem ridiculous, for this is quite the most disagreeable task of the garden, but it suddenly came over me, as I stood perched high on the ladder, in the full glory of the morning, that there was something incalculably and indescribably beautiful about it all. I was newly and intensely aware of the robins singing, and the bees humming in the near-by hives, and the sun looking down the hill with the promise of a fair and perfect morning. I caught myself saying under my breath: "Thank God, thank God." It seemed as though, doubter as I am, that God was somewhere not distant, and easily to be thanked. I felt like pinning this date in May, as Pascal pinned the date of his conversion, to an inner garment over my heart.

As I came up the hill a little later I saw pale yellow tulips blooming among the low-growing phlox, and the wisteria on the porch, grown eager in the summery days of May, hanging full of half-opened blossoms, delicate, lacy, more like a mist of beauty than a realized blooming—I saw all these things as I never had seen or felt them before.

"Thank God," I said, "I am well again! I can work again."

XV

THE PUMPKIN PIE

That which is not natural is not perfect.

IT WAS not really until autumn, a full year after I was taken ill, that I had final and convincing evidences of my recovery. To a man accustomed all his life to robust health—the health that glows with outdoor life—the loss of appetite which accompanies a long illness, though the doctors may consider it of minor importance, is nevertheless one of the major woes. For it is a fact that two of the senses which give us the most powerful grasp upon the good, homely realities of life—I mean the sense of smell and the sense of taste—lose their delight when one cannot enjoy his daily food. They told me I was convalescent long before I believed what they said. I did not go to dinner like an army with banners!

When the leaves began to turn, and the apples were ripe, and there was a frosty zest in the morning air, I began, after a long forenoon in the garden or orchard, or tramping in country roads, to be conscious that there was something in life quite worth living for. By twelve o'clock I was listening eagerly for a call from the house. And finally, one day, really for the first time, I knew I had come fully alive.

At dinner on that unforgettable occasion there appeared in all its glory the most perfect pumpkin pie that ever I saw in my life. It was like a full moon, crimped about with little flaky clouds of piecrust, and being just from the oven—I *hate* clammy pies! —it gave off the ambrosia of the gods. Nowhere else on earth, save in New England, has pumpkin pie reached the final stage of perfection: for in New England, by one of those daring incongruities or disharmonies that mark the highest art, it is often not made of pumpkin at all, but of squash.

There it was, then, reposing in all its refulgence of golden glory upon our largest dinner plate. Little brown and yellow bubbles had worked upon its surface a kind of autumnal pattern, and the crinkled rim of crust about it was exactly of the right colour to tempt the eye, for it promised to melt in the mouth.

"A wonderful pie," said I to Harriet.

"Wait until you taste it," said she.

So she drew the knife across it and cut out and lifted a generous slice—I give my word it was all of two inches thick!—and having placed it carefully upon a little plate, passed it along to me. There it was, a deep, luscious yellow, shading to orange, all warm and moist and rich and full of ravishing odours.

"This surely," said I, "is one of the great moments of life."

"Ridiculous," said Harriet, "eat it, eat it!"

"Slowly, slowly," said I, "one thing at a time. This is no occasion for usurpation by any one of the senses. This is not merely for tasting but for smelling and seeing, and, I think, for touching also——"

"Don't touch it! Eat it!"

"I expect also," said I, "if one's hearing were sufficiently acute—say as good as a honeybee's—he could also find keen enjoyment in listening to what is going on inside of this delectable pie——"

"I never saw your like," interrupted Harriet.

"All the faint little bubblings and boilings and dissolvings and settlings left over from the oven. He could see, too, if his eyes were perfect, the delicate aroma, the veritable spirit—one might call it the animate mist—rising from this pie——"

"Stop, stop!"

"As I said, the animate mist of the pie, charged with the spices of Araby, rising out of its delicious hidden recesses——"

"When *are* you going to eat that pie?"

"When I have enjoyed it sufficiently beforehand," said I to Harriet. "When I have reached the appropriate place in the ritual. Let me ask you this: is there any point is taking less enjoyment out of nature than one is capable of doing? Why walk on one leg when you have two? Or use one sense when you have five? In this degenerate and greedy age, are we grown to be savages, willing to bolt our beauty?"

"And," interposed Harriet with spirit, "philosophize until our pie is cold."

"And," continued I, "merely eat our pie?"

I found myself waving my fork in the air. The last remark of Harriet much impressed me; it was extremely sensible. So I fell to—as the unctuous older writers used to say—and without further excursions into philosophy or poetry ate every crumb of my triangle of pie.

I have thought since how I could express the sensations of that blissful moment, and have decided that language is a beggarly medium, wholly incapable, whether with adjectives, verbs, or nouns, of giving even a hazy conception of what I was experiencing. My only recourse is to ask any possible reader of these lines to think back, carefully, along the whole course of his life and recall the moment of his greatest gustatory adventure, the most poignant thrill that the art of cookery ever gave him, and let me assure him that my experience at dinner with that perfect pumpkin pie was equal to, or possibly greater than, his noblest moment.

"Well," said I, lifting at length my napkin, "this has been one of the notable incidents of my career."

"Ridiculous!" commented Harriet.

"I shall never forget it," said I. "Heaven has no greater bliss for the souls of the saved!"

With such evidences as these, how can I doubt the completeness of my recovery?

GREAT
POSSESSIONS

"Blessed of the Lord be His land, for the precious things of heaven, for the dew, and for the deep that coucheth beneath,

"And for the precious fruits brought forth by the sun, and for the precious things put forth by the moon,

"And for the chief things of the ancient mountains, and for the precious things of the lasting hills,

"And for the precious things of the earth and fullness thereof, and for the good will of Him that dwelt in the bush."

INTRODUCTION

I OFFER here a new book called "Great Possessions," dealing with the well-flavoured earth and with well-flavoured people.

It is now ten years since the first of these books, "Adventures in Contentment," was published. It was begun, as I have said elsewhere, with no thought of publication but for my own enjoyment, and the writings since that time, for the most part, have grown out of notes set down in little books wherever I chanced to be at the moment—on the roadside, in the woods, or at home.

I have tried to relate in a form somewhat veiled the experiences of that elusive, invisible life which in every man is so far more real, so far more important, than his visible activities—the real expression of a life much occupied in other employment. To paraphrase Ruskin, these are the pieces of time, knowledge, or sight which my share of sunshine and earth has permitted me to seize. "For the rest I ate and drank, loved and hated; my life was as the vapour and is not."

The response has been beyond my expectations, and continues a surprising thing to me. I did not know the world could be so full of friendly people. If I have not been able to answer, as they deserved, the many letters of these friends whom I have not yet seen, but whom I have felt, it is not for lack of willingness, nor for want of thorough appreciation, but because the task has been quite beyond me.

Nor can I allow this opportunity to pass, after ten years, to acknowledge how much I owe to the constant encouragement

231

of many friends. What could I have done—to mention only one —without the advice of John S. Phillips, the most sympathetic of readers, the most stimulating of critics. And I wonder sometimes how it happened that Tom Fogarty, of all the artists in America, should have been chosen to illustrate these writings, for Tom Fogarty is a true lover of the earth, and *thinks* what I write as fast as ever I can write it!

THE AUTHOR

I

THE WELL-FLAVOURED EARTH

"Sweet as Eden is the air
And Eden-sweet the ray.
No Paradise is lost for them
Who foot by branching root and stem,
And lightly with the woodland share
The change of night and day."

FOR these many years, since I have lived here in the country, I have had it in my mind to write something about the odour and taste of this well-flavoured earth. The fact is, both the sense of smell and the sense of taste have been shabbily treated in the amiable rivalry of the senses. Sight and hearing have been the swift and nimble brothers, and sight especially, the tricky Jacob of the family, is keen upon the business of seizing the entire inheritance, while smell, like hairy Esau, comes late to the blessing, hungry from the hills, and willing to trade its inheritance for a mess of pottage.

I have always had a kind of errant love for the improvident and adventurous Esaus of the Earth—I think they smell a wilder fragrance than I do, and taste sweeter things—and I have thought, therefore, of beginning a kind of fragrant autobiography, a chronicle of all the good odours and flavours that ever I have had in my life.

As I grow older, a curious feeling comes often to me in the spring, as it comes this spring more poignantly than ever before, a sense of the temporariness of all things, the swiftness of life, the sadness of a beauty that vanishes so soon, and I long to lay hold upon it as it passes by all the handles that I can. I would not only see it and hear it, but I would smell it and taste it and touch it, and all with a new kind of intensity and eagerness.

Harriet says I get more pleasure out of the smell of my supper than I get out of the supper itself.

"I never need to ring for you," says she, "but only open the kitchen door. In a few minutes I'll see you straighten up, lift your head, sniff a little, and come straight for the house."

"The odour of your suppers, Harriet," I said, "after a day in the fields, would lure a man out of purgatory."

My father before me had a singularly keen nose. I remember well when I was a boy and drove with him in the wild North Country, often through miles of unbroken forest, how he would sometimes break a long silence, lift his head with sudden awareness, and say to me:

"David, I smell open fields."

In a few minutes we were sure to come to a settler's cabin, a log barn, or a clearing. Among the free odours of the forest he had caught, afar off, the common odours of the work of man.

When we were tramping or surveying in that country, I have seen him stop suddenly, draw in a long breath, and remark:

"Marshes," or, "A stream yonder."

Part of this strange keenness of sense, often noted by those who knew that sturdy old cavalryman, may have been based, as so many of our talents are, upon a defect. My father gave all the sweet sounds of the world, the voices of his sons, the songs of his daughters, to help free the Southern slaves. He was deaf.

It is well known that when one sense is defective the others fly to the rescue, and my father's singular development of the sense of smell may have been due in part to this defect, though I believe it to have been, to a far larger degree, a native gift. He had a downright good nose. All his life long he enjoyed with more than ordinary keenness the odour of flowers, and would often pick a sprig of wild rose and carry it along with him in his hand, sniffing at it from time to time, and he loved the lilac, as I do after him. To ill odours he was not less sensitive, and was impatient of rats in the barn, and could smell them, among other odours, the moment the door was opened. He always had a peculiar sensitiveness to the presence of animals, as of dogs, cats, muskrats, cattle, horses, and the like, and would speak of them long before he had seen them or could know that they were about.

I recall once on a wild Northern lake, when we were working

along the shore in a boat, how he stopped suddenly and exclaimed:

"David, do you hear anything?"—for I, a boy, was ears for
him in those wilderness places.

"No, Father. What is it?"

"Indians."

And, sure enough, in a short time I heard the barking of their
dogs and we came soon upon their camp, where, I remember,
they were drying deer meat upon a frame of poplar poles over
an open fire. He told me that the smoky smell of the Indians,
tanned buckskin, parched wild rice, and the like, were odours
that carried far and could not be mistaken.

My father had a big, hooked nose with long, narrow nostrils.
I suppose that this has really nothing to do with the matter,
although I have come, after these many years, to look with a
curious interest upon people's noses, since I know what a vehicle
of delight they often are. My own nose is nothing to speak of,
good enough as noses go—but I think I inherited from my father
something of the power of enjoyment he had from that sense,
though I can never hope to become the accomplished smeller
he was.

I am moved to begin this chronicle because of my joy this
morning early—a May morning!—just after sunrise, when the
shadows lay long and blue to the west and the dew was still on
the grass, and I walked in the pleasant spaces of my garden. It
was so still . . . so still . . . that birds afar off could be heard
singing, and once through the crystal air came the voice of a
neighbour calling his cows. But the sounds and the silences, the
fair sights of meadow and hill I soon put aside, for the lilacs
were in bloom and the bush-honeysuckles and the strawberries.
Though no movement of the air was perceptible, the lilacs well
knew the way of the wind, for if I stood to the north of them
the odour was less rich and free than to the south, and I thought
I might pose as a prophet of wind and weather upon the basis
of this easy magic, and predict that the breezes of the day would
be from the north—as, indeed, they later appeared to be.

I went from clump to clump of the lilacs testing and com-

paring them with great joy and satisfaction. They vary notice-
ably in odour; the white varieties being the most delicate, while
those tending to deep purple are the richest. Some of the newer
double varieties seem less fragrant—and I have tested them
now many times—than the old-fashioned single varieties which
are nearer the native stock. Here I fancy our smooth Jacob has
been at work, and in the lucrative process of selection for the
eye alone the cunning horticulturist has cheated us of our right-
ful heritage of fragrance. I have a mind some time to practise
the art of burbankry or other kind of wizardry upon the old
lilac stock and select for odour alone, securing ravishing original
varieties—indeed, whole new gamuts of fragrance.

I should devise the most animating names for my creations,
such as the Double Delicious, the Air of Arcady, the Sweet
Zephyr, and others even more inviting, which I should enjoy
inventing. Though I think surely I could make my fortune out of
this interesting idea, I present it freely to a scent-hungry world—
here it is, gratis!—for I have my time so fully occupied during
all of this and my next two or three lives that I cannot attend to it.

I have felt the same defect in the cultivated roses. While the
odours are rich, often of cloying sweetness, or even, as in certain
white roses, having a languor as of death, they never for me
equal the fragrance of the wild sweet rose that grows all about
these hills, in old tangled fence rows, in the lee of meadow
boulders, or by some unfrequented roadside. No other odour
I know awakens quite such a feeling—light like a cloud, sug-
gesting free hills, open country, sunny air; and none surely has,
for me, such an after-call. A whiff of the wild rose will bring
back in all the poignancy of sad happiness a train of ancient
memories—old faces, old scenes, old loves—and the wild
thoughts I had when a boy. The first week of the wild-rose
blooming, beginning here about the twenty-fifth of June, is always
to me a memorable time.

I was a long time learning how to take hold of nature, and
think now with some sadness of all the life I lost in former years.
The impression the earth gave me was confused: I was as one
only half awake. A fine morning made me dumbly glad, a cool

evening, after the heat of the day, and the work of it, touched my spirit restfully; but I could have explained neither the one nor the other. Gradually as I looked about me I began to ask myself, "Why is it that the sight of these common hills and fields gives me such exquisite delight? And if it is beauty, why is it beautiful? And if I am so richly rewarded by mere glimpses, can I not increase my pleasure with longer looks?"

I tried longer looks both at nature and at the friendly human creatures all about me. I stopped often in the garden where I was working, or loitered a moment in the fields, or sat down by the roadside, and thought intently what it was that so perfectly and wonderfully surrounded me; and thus I came to have some knowledge of the Great Secret. It was, after all, a simple matter, as such matters usually are when we penetrate them, and consisted merely in shutting out all other impressions, feelings, thoughts, and concentrating the full energy of the attention upon what it was that I saw or heard at that instant.

At one moment I would let in all the sounds of the earth, at another all the sights. So we practise the hand at one time, the foot at another, or learn how to sit or to walk, and so acquire new grace for the whole body. Should we do less in acquiring grace for the spirit? It will astonish one who has not tried it how full the world is of sounds commonly unheard, and of sights commonly unseen, but in their nature, like the smallest blossoms, of a curious perfection and beauty.

Out of this practice grew presently, and as it seems to me instinctively, for I cannot now remember the exact time of its beginning, a habit of repeating under my breath, or even aloud, and in a kind of singsong voice, fragmentary words and sentences describing what it was that I saw or felt at the moment, as, for example:

"The pink blossoms of the wild crab-apple trees I see from the hill. . . . The reedy song of the wood thrush among the thickets of the wild cherry. . . . The scent of peach leaves, the odour of new-turned soil in the black fields. . . . The red of the maples in the marsh, the white of apple trees in bloom. . . . I cannot find Him out—nor know why I am here. . . ."

Some form of expression, however crude, seemed to reënforce and intensify the gatherings of the senses; and these words, afterward remembered, or even written down in the little book I sometimes carried in my pocket, seemed to awaken echoes, however faint, of the exaltation of that moment in the woods or fields, and enabled me to live twice where formerly I had been able to live but once.

It was by this simple process of concentrating upon what I saw or heard that I increased immeasurably my own joy of my garden and fields and the hills and marshes all about. A little later, for I was a slow learner, I began to practise the same method with the sense of smell, and still later with the sense of taste. I said to myself, "I will no longer permit the avid and eager eye to steal away my whole attention. I will learn to enjoy more completely all the varied wonders of the earth."

So I tried deliberately shutting the doorways of both sight and hearing, and centring the industry of my spirit upon the flavours of the earth. I tested each odour narrowly, compared it well with remembered odours, and often turned the impression I had into such poor words as I could command.

What a new and wonderful world opened to me then! My takings of nature increased tenfold, a hundredfold, and I came to a new acquaintance with my own garden, my own hills, and all the roads and fields around about—and even the town took on strange new meanings for me. I cannot explain it rightly, but it was as though I had found a new earth here within the old one, but more spacious and beautiful than any I had known before. I have thought, often and often, that this world we live in so dumbly, so carelessly, would be more glorious than the tinsel heaven of the poets if only we knew how to lay hold upon it, if only we could win that complete command of our own lives which is the end of our being.

At first, as I said, I stopped my work, or loitered as I walked, in order to see, or hear, or smell—and do so still, for I have entered only the antechamber of the treasure-house; but as I learned better the modest technic of these arts I found that the practice of them went well with the common tasks of the garden or farm, especially with those that were more or less monotonous, like cultivating corn, hoeing potatoes, and the like.

The air is just as full of good sights and good odours for the worker as for the idler, and it depends only upon the awareness, the aliveness, of our own spirits whether we toil like dumb animals or bless our labouring hours with the beauty of life. Such enjoyment and a growing command of our surroundings are possible, after a little practice, without taking much of that time we call so valuable and waste so sinfully. "I haven't time," says the farmer, the banker, the professor, with a kind of disdain for the spirit of life, when, as a matter of fact, he has all the time there is, all that anybody has—to wit, *this* moment, this great and golden moment!—but knows not how to employ it. He creeps when he might walk, walks when he might run, runs when he might fly—and lives like a woodchuck in the dark body of himself.

Why, there are men in this valley who scout the idea that farming, carpentry, merchantry, are anything but drudgery, defend all the evils known to humankind with the argument that "a man must live," and laugh at any one who sees beauty or charm in being here, in working with the hands, or, indeed, in just living! While they think of themselves cannily as "practical" men, I think them the most impractical men I know, for in a world full of boundless riches they remain obstinately poor. They are unwilling to invest even a few of their dollars unearned in the real wealth of the earth. For it is only the sense of the spirit of life, whether in nature or in other human beings, that lifts men above the beasts and curiously leads them to God, who is the spirit both of beauty and of friendliness. I say truly, having now reached the point in my life where it seems to me I care only for writing that which is most deeply true for me, that I rarely walk in my garden or upon the hills of an evening without thinking of God. It is in my garden that all things become clearer to me, even that miracle whereby one who has offended may still see God; and this I think a wonderful thing. In my garden I understand dimly why evil is in the world, and in my garden learn how transitory it is.

Just now I have come in from work, and will note freshly one of the best odours I have had to-day. As I was working in the corn, a lazy breeze blew across the meadows from the west, and after loitering a moment among the blackberry bushes sought me out where I was busiest. Do you know the scent of the blackberry? Almost all the year round it is a treasure-house of odours, even when the leaves first come out; but it reaches crescendo in blossom time when, indeed, I like it least, for being too strong. It has a curious fragrance, once well called by a poet "the hot scent of the brier," and aromatically hot it is and sharp like the briers themselves. At times I do not like it at all, for it gives me a kind of faintness, while at other times, as to-day, it fills me with a strange sense of pleasure as though it were the very breath of the spicy earth. It is also a rare friend of the sun, for the hotter and brighter the day, the hotter and sharper the scent of the brier.

Many of the commonest and least noticed of plants, flowers, trees, possess a truly fragrant personality if once we begin to know them. I had an adventure in my own orchard, only this spring, and made a fine new acquaintance in a quarter least of all expected. I had started down the lane through the garden one morning in the most ordinary way, with no thought of any special experience, when I suddenly caught a whiff of pure delight that stopped me short.

"What now can *that* be?" and I thought to myself that nature had played some new prank on me.

I turned into the orchard, following my nose. It was not the peach buds, nor the plums, nor the cherries, nor yet the beautiful new coloured leaves of the grape, nor anything I could see along the grassy margin of the pasture. There were other odours all about, old friends of mine, but this was some shy and pleasing stranger come venturing upon my land.

A moment later I discovered a patch of low green verdure upon the ground, and dismissed it scornfully as one of my ancient enemies. But it is this way with enemies, once we come to know them, they often turn out to have a fragrance that is kindly.

Well, this particular fierce enemy was a patch of chickweed.

Chickweed! Invader of the garden, cossack of the orchard! I discovered, however, that it was in full bloom and covered with small, star-like white blossoms.

"Well, now," said I, "are you the guilty rascal?"

So I knelt there and took my delight of it—and a rare, delicate good odour it was. For several days afterward I would not dig out the patch, for I said to myself, "What a cheerful claim it makes these early days, when most of the earth is still cold and dead, for a bit of immortality."

The bees knew the secret already, and the hens and the blackbirds! And I thought it no loss, but really a new and valuable pleasure, to divert my path down the lane for several days that I might enjoy more fully this new odour, and make a clear acquaintance with something fine upon the earth I had not known before.

II

OF GOOD AND EVIL ODOURS

O F ALL times of the day for good odours I think the early morning the very best, although the evening just after sunset, if the air falls still and cool, is often as good. Certain qualities or states of the atmosphere seem to favour the distillation of good odours and I have known times even at midday when the earth was very wonderful to smell. There is a curious, fainting fragrance that comes only with sunshine and still heat. Not long ago I was cutting away a thicket of wild spiræa which was crowding in upon the cultivated land. It was a hot day and the leaves wilted quickly, giving off such a penetrating, fainting fragrance that I let the branches lie where they fell the afternoon through and came often back to smell of them, for it was a fine thing thus to discover an odour wholly new to me.

I like also the first wild, sweet smell of new-cut meadow grass, not the familiar odour of new-mown hay, which comes a little later, and is worthy of its good report, but the brief, despairing odour of grass just cut down, its juices freshly exposed to the sun. One has it richly in the fields at the mowing. I like also the midday smell of peach leaves and peach-tree bark at the summer pruning: and have never let any one else cut out the old canes from the blackberry rows in my garden for the goodness of the scents which wait upon that work.

Another odour I have found animating is the odour of burning wastage in new clearings or in old fields, especially in the evening when the smoke drifts low along the land and takes to itself by some strange chemical process the tang of earthy things. It is a true saying that nothing will so bring back the emotion of a past time as a remembered odour. I have had from a whiff of fragrance caught in a city street such a vivid return of an old time and an old, sad scene that I have stopped, trembling there, with an emotion long spent and I thought forgotten.

Once in a foreign city, passing a latticed gateway that closed in a narrow court, I caught the odour of wild sweet balsam. I do not know now where it came from, or what could have caused it—but it stopped me short where I stood, and the solid brick walls of that city rolled aside like painted curtains, and the iron streets dissolved before my eyes, and with the curious dizziness of nostalgia, I was myself upon the hill of my youth—with the gleaming river in the valley, and a hawk sailing majestically in the high blue of the sky, and all about and everywhere the balsams—and the balsams—full of the sweet, wild odours of the north, and of dreaming boyhood.

And there while my body, the shell of me, loitered in that strange city, I was myself four thousand miles and a quarter of a century away, reliving, with a conscious passion that boyhood never knew, a moment caught up, like a torch, out of the smouldering wreckage of the past.

Do not tell me that such things die! They all remain with us—all the sights, and sounds, and thoughts of by-gone times—awaiting only the whiff from some latticed gateway, some closed-in court—to spring again into exuberant life. If only we are ready for the great moment!

As for the odour of the burning wastage of the fields at evening—I scarcely know if I dare say it—I find it produces in the blood of me a kind of primitive emotion, as though it stirred memories older than my present life. Some drowsy cells of the brain awaken to a familiar stimulus—the odour of the lodge-fire of the savage, the wigwam of the Indian. Racial memories!

But it is not the time of the day, nor the turn of the season, nor yet the way of the wind that matters most—but the ardour and glow we ourselves bring to the fragrant earth. It is a sad thing to reflect that in a world so overflowing with goodness of smell, of fine sights and sweet sounds, we pass by hastily and take so little of them. Days pass when we see no beautiful sight, hear no sweet sound, smell no memorable odour: when we exchange no single word of deeper understanding with a friend. We have lived a day and added nothing to our lives! A blind, grubbing, senseless life—that!

It is a strange thing, also, that instead of sharpening the tools by which we take hold of life we make studied efforts to dull them. We seem to fear life and early begin to stop our ears and close our eyes lest we hear and see too much: we clog our senses and cloud our minds. We seek dull security and ease and cease longer to desire adventure and struggle. And then—the tragedy of it—the poet we all have in us in youth begins to die, the philosopher in us dies, the martyr in us dies, so that the long, long time beyond youth with so many of us becomes a busy death. And this I think truer of men than of women: beyond forty many women just begin to awaken to power and beauty, but most men beyond that age go on dying. The task of the artist, whether poet, or musician, or painter, is to keep alive the perishing spirit of free adventure in men: to nourish the poet, the prophet, the martyr, we all have in us.

One's sense of smell, like the sense of taste, is sharpest when he is hungry, and I am convinced also that one sees and hears best when unclogged with food, undulled with drink, undrugged with smoke. For me, also, weariness, though not exhaustion, seems to sharpen all the senses. Keenness goes with leanness. When I have been working hard or tramping the country roads in the open air and come in weary and hungry at night and catch the fragrance of the evening along the road or upon the hill, or at barn-doors smell the unmilked cows, or at the doorway, the comfortable odours of cooking supper—how good that all is! At such times I know Esau to the core: the forthright, nature-loving, simple man he was, coming in dabbled with the blood of hunted animals and hungry for the steaming pottage.

It follows that if we take excessive joys of one sense, as of taste, nature, ever seeking just balances, deprives us of the full enjoyment of the others. "I am stuffed, cousin," cries Beatrice in the play, " I cannot smell." "I have drunk," remarks the Clown in Arcady, "what are roses to me?" We forget that there are five chords in the great scale of life—sight, hearing, smell, taste, touch—and few of us ever master the chords well enough to get the full symphony of life, but are something like little pig-tailed girls playing Peter Piper with one finger while all the music of the universe is in the Great Instrument, and all to be had for the taking.

Of most evil odours, it can be said that they are temporary or unnecessary: and any unpleasant odour, such as that of fruit sprays in spring, or fertilizer newly spread on the land, can be borne and even welcomed if it is appropriate to the time and place. Some smells, evil at first, become through usage not unpleasant. I once stopped with a wolf-trapper in the north country, who set his bottle of bait outside when I came in. He said it was "good and strong" and sniffed it with appreciation. I agreed with him that it was strong. To him it was not unpleasant, though made of the rancid fat of the muscallonge. All nature seems to strive against evil odours, for when she warns us of decay she is speeding decay: and a manured field produces later the best of all odours. Almost all shut-in places sooner or later acquire an evil odour: and it seems a requisite for good smells that there be plenty of sunshine and air; and so it is with the hearts and souls of men. If they are long shut in upon themselves they grow rancid.

III

FOLLOW YOUR NOSE!

"Listen to the Exhortation of the Dawn—
Look to this day! For it is Life,
The very Life of Life!"

ON A spring morning one has only to step out into the open
country, lift his head to the sky—and follow his nose. . . .

It was a big and golden morning, and Sunday to boot, and
I walked down the lane to the lower edge of the field, where
the wood and the marsh begin. The sun was just coming up
over the hills and all the air was fresh and clear and cool. High
in the heavens a few fleecy clouds were drifting, and the air
was just enough astir to waken the hemlocks into faint and
sleepy exchanges of confidence.

It seemed to me that morning that the world was never before
so high, so airy, so golden. All filled to the brim with the essence
of sunshine and spring morning—so that one's spirit dissolved
in it, became a part of it. Such a morning! Such a morning!

From that place and just as I was I set off across the open land.

It was the time of all times for good odours—soon after sunrise—before the heat of the day had drawn off the rich distilla-
tions of the night.

In that keen moment I caught, drifting, a faint but wild fragrance upon the air, and veered northward full into the way
of the wind. I could not at first tell what this particular odour
was, nor separate it from the general good odour of the earth;
but I followed it intently across the moor-like open land. Once
I thought I had lost it entirely, or that the faint northern airs
had shifted, but I soon caught it clearly again, and just as I was
saying to myself, "I've got it, I've got it!"—for it is a great pleas-

246

ure to identify a friendly odour in the fields—I saw, near the bank of the brook, among ferns and raspberry bushes, a thornapple tree in full bloom.

"So there you are!" I said.

I hastened toward it, now in the full current and glory of its fragrance. The sun, looking over the taller trees to the east, had crowned the top of it with gold, so that it was beautiful to see; and it was full of honey bees as excited as I.

A score of feet onward toward the wind, beyond the thornapple tree, I passed wholly out of the range of its fragrance into another world, and began trying for some new odour. After one or two false scents, for this pursuit has all the hazards known to the hunter, I caught an odour long known to me, not strong, nor yet very wonderful, but distinctive. It led me still a little distance northward to a sunny slope just beyond a bit of marsh, and, sure enough, I found an old friend, the wild sweet geranium, a world of it, in full bloom, and I sat down there for some time to enjoy it fully.

Beyond that, and across a field wild with tangles of huckleberry bushes and sheep laurel where the bluets and buttercups were blooming, and in shady spots the shy white violet, I searched for the odour of a certain clump of pine trees I discovered long ago. I knew that I must come upon it soon, but could not tell just when or where. I held up a moistened finger to make sure of the exact direction of the wind, and bearing, then, a little eastward, soon came full upon it—as a hunter might surprise a deer in the forest. I crossed the brook a second time and through a little marsh, making it the rule of the game never to lose for an instant the scent I was following—even though I stopped in a low spot to admire a mass of thrifty blue flags, now beginning to bloom—and came thus to the pines I was seeking. They are not great trees, nor noble, but gnarled and angular and stunted, for the soil in that place is poor and thin, and the winds in winter keen; but the brown blanket of needles they spread and the shade they offer the traveller are not less hospitable; nor the fragrance they give off less enchanting. The odour of the pine is one I love.

I sat down there in a place I chose long ago—a place already as familiar with pleasing memories as a favourite room—so that I wonder that some of the notes I have written there do not of themselves exhale the very odour of the pines.

And all about was hung a fair tapestry of green, and the earthy floor was cleanly carpeted with brown, and the roof above was in arched mosaic, the deep, deep blue of the sky seen through the gnarled and knotted branches of the pines. Through a little opening among the trees, as through a window, I could see the cattle feeding in the wide meadows, all headed alike, and yellow butterflies drifted across the open spaces, and there were bumblebees and dragonflies. And presently I heard some one tapping, tapping, at the door of the wood and glancing up quickly I saw my early visitor. There he was, as neighbourly as you please, and not in the least awed by my intrusion; there he was, far out on the limb of a dead tree, stepping energetically up and down, like a sailor reefing a sail, and rapping and tapping as he worked —a downy woodpecker.

"Good morning, sir," I said.

He stopped for scarcely a second, cocked one eye at me, and went back to his work again. Who was I that I should interrupt his breakfast?

And I was glad I was there, and I began enumerating, as though I were the accredited reporter for the *Woodland Gazette,* all the good news of the day.

"The beech trees," I said aloud, "have come at last to full leafage. The wild blackberries are ready to bloom, the swamp roses are budded. Brown planted fields I see, and drooping elms, and the young crows cry from their nests on the knoll. . . . I know now that, whoever I am, whatever I do, I am welcome here; the meadows are as green this spring for Tom the drunkard, and for Jim the thief, as for Jonathan the parson, or for Walt the poet: the wild cherry blooms as richly, and the odour of the pine is as sweet——"

At that moment, like a flame for clearness, I understood some of the deep and simple things of life, as that we are to be like the friendly pines, and the elm trees, and the open fields, and reject no man and judge no man. Once, a long time ago, I read a sober treatise by one who tried to prove with elaborate knowledge that, upon the whole, good was triumphant in this world, and that probably there was a God, and I remember going out dully afterward upon the hill, for I was weighed down with a strange depression, and the world seemed to me a hard, cold, narrow place where good must be heavily demonstrated in books. And as I sat there the evening fell, a star or two came out in the clear blue of the sky, and suddenly it became all simple to me, so that I laughed aloud at that laborious big-wig for spending so many futile years in seeking doubtful proof of what he might have learned in one rare hour upon my hill. And far more than he could prove—far more. . . .

As I came away from that place I knew I should never again be quite the same person I was before. . . .

Well, we cannot remain steadily upon the heights. At least I cannot, and would not if I could. After I have been out about so long on such an adventure as this, something lets go inside of me, and I come down out of the mountain—and yet know deeply that I have been where the bush was burning; and have heard the Voice in the Fire.

So it was yesterday morning. I realized suddenly that I was hungry—commonly, coarsely hungry. My whole attention, I was going to say my whole soul, shifted to the thought of ham and eggs! This may seem a tremendous anti-climax, but it is, nevertheless, a sober report of what happened. At the first onset of this new mood, the ham-and-eggs mood, let us call it, I was a little ashamed or abashed at the remembrance of my wild flights, and had a laugh at the thought of myself floundering around in the marshes and fields a mile from home, when Harriet, no doubt, had breakfast waiting for me! What absurd, contradictory, inconsistent, cowardly creatures we are, anyway!

The house seemed an inconceivable distance away, and the only real thing in the world the gnawing emptiness under my belt. And I was wet to my knees, and the tangled huckleberry bushes and sheep laurel and hardhack I had passed through so joyously a short time before now clung heavily about my legs

249

as I struggled through them. And the sun was hot and high—and there were innumerable small, black buzzing flies. . . .

To cap the climax, whom should I meet as I was crossing the fence into the lower land but my friend Horace. He had been out early looking for a cow that had dropped her calf in the woods, and was now driving them slowly up the lane, the cow a true pattern of solicitous motherhood, the calf a true pattern of youth, dashing about upon uncertain legs.

"Takin' the air, David?"

I amuse Horace. Horace is an important man in this community. He has big, solid barns, and money in the bank, and a reputation for hardheadedness. He is also known as a "driver"; and has had sore trouble with a favourite son. He believes in "goin' it slow" and "playin' safe," and he is convinced that "ye can't change human nature."

His question came to me with a kind of shock. I imagined with a vividness impossible to describe what Horace would think if I answered him squarely and honestly, if I were to say:

"I've been down in the marshes following my nose—enjoying the thorn apples and the wild geraniums, talking with a woodpecker and reporting the morning news of the woods for an imaginary newspaper."

I was hungry, and in a mood to smile at myself anyway (good-humouredly and forgivingly as we always smile at ourselves!) before I met Horace, and the flashing vision I had of Horace's dry, superior smile finished me. Was there really anything in this world but cows and calves, and great solid barns, and oatcrops, and cash in the bank?

"Been in the brook?" asked Horace, observing my wet legs.

Talk about the courage to face cannon and Cossacks! It is nothing to the courage required to speak aloud in broad daylight of the finest things we have in us! I was not equal to it.

"Oh, I've been down for a tramp in the marsh," I said, trying to put him off.

But Horace is a Yankee of the Yankees and loves nothing better than to chase his friends into corners with questions, and leave them ultimately with the impression that they are somehow less sound, sensible, practical, than he is—and he usually proves it, not because he is right, but because he is sure, and in a world of shadowy half-beliefs and half-believers he is without doubts.

"What ye find down there?" asked Horace.

"Oh, I was just looking around to see how the spring was coming on."

"Hm-m," said Horace, eloquently, and when I did not reply, he continued, "Often git out in the morning as early as this?"

"Yes," I said, "often."

"And do you find things any different now from what they would be later in the day?"

At this the humour of the whole situation dawned on me and I began to revive. When things grow hopelessly complicated, and we can't laugh, we do either one of two things: we lie or we die. But if we can laugh, we can fight! And be honest!

"Horace," I said, "I know what you are thinking about."

Horace's face remained perfectly impassive, but there was a glint of curiosity in his eye.

"You've been thinking I've been wasting my time beating around down there in the swamp just to look at things and smell of things—which you wouldn't do. You think I'm a kind of impractical dreamer, now, don't you, Horace? I'll warrant you've told your wife just that more than once. Come, now!"

I think I made a rather shrewd hit, for Horace looked uncomfortable and a little foolish.

"Come now, honest!" I laughed and looked him in the eye.

"Waal, now, ye see——"

"Of course you do, and I don't mind it in the least."

A little dry gleam of humour came in his eye.

"Ain't ye?"

It's a fine thing to have it straight out with a friend.

"No," I said, "I'm the practical man and you're the dreamer. I've rarely known in all my life, Horace, such a confirmed dreamer as you are, nor a more impractical one."

Horace laughed.

"How do ye make that out?"

251

With this my spirit returned to me and I countered with a question as good as his. It is as valuable in argument as in war to secure the offensive.

"Horace, what are you working for, anyhow?"

This is always a devastating shot. Ninety-nine out of every hundred human beings are desperately at work grubbing, sweating, worrying, thinking, sorrowing, enjoying, without in the least knowing why.

"Why, to make a living—same as you," said Horace.

"Oh, come now, if I were to spread the report in town that a poor neighbour of mine—that's you, Horace—was just making his living, that he himself had told me so, what would you say? Horace, what are you working for? It's something more than a mere living."

"Waal, now, I'll tell ye, if ye want it straight, I'm layin' aside a little something for a rainy day."

"A little something!" this in the exact inflection of irony by which here in the country we express our opinion that a friend has really a good deal more laid aside than anybody knows about. Horace smiled also in the exact manner of one so complimented.

"Horace, what are you going to do with that thirty thousand dollars?"

"Thirty thousand!" Horace looks at me and smiles, and I look at Horace and smile.

"Honest now!"

"Waal, I'll tell ye—a little peace and comfort for me and Josie in our old age, and a little something to make the children remember us when we're gone. Isn't that worth working for?"

He said this with downright seriousness. I did not press him further, but if I had tried I could probably have got the even deeper admission of that faith that lies, like bed rock, in the thought of most men—that honesty and decency here will not be without its reward there, however they may define the "there." Some "prophet's paradise to come!"

"I knew it!" I said. "Horace, you're a dreamer, too. You are dreaming of peace and comfort in your old age, a little quiet house in town where you won't have to labour as hard as you do now, where you won't be worried by crops and weather, and where Mrs. Horace will be able to rest after so many years of care and work and sorrow—a kind of earthly heaven! And you are dreaming of leaving a bit to your children and grandchildren, and dreaming of the gratitude they will express. All dreams, Horace!"

"Oh, waal——"

"The fact is, you are working for a dream, and living on dreams—isn't that true?"

"Waal, now, if you mean it that way——"

"I see I haven't got you beaten yet, Horace!"

He smiled broadly.

"We are all amiable enough with our own dreams. You think that what you are working for—your dream—is somehow sounder and more practical than what I am working for."

Horace started to reply, but had scarcely debouched from his trenches when I opened on him with one of my twenty-fours.

"How do you know that you are ever going to be old?"

It hit.

"And if you do grow old, how do you know that thirty thousand dollars—oh, we'll call it that—is really enough, provided you don't lose it before, to buy peace and comfort for you, or that what you leave your children will make either you or them any happier? Peace and comfort and happiness are terribly expensive, Horace—and prices have been going up fast since this war began!"

Horace looked at me uncomfortably, as men do in the world when you shake the foundations of the tabernacle. I have thought since that I probably pressed him too far; but these things go deep with me.

"No, Horace," I said, "you are the dreamer—and the impractical dreamer at that!"

For a moment Horace answered nothing; and we both stood still there in the soft morning sunshine with the peaceful fields and woods all about us, two human atoms struggling hotly with questions too large for us. The cow and the new calf were long out of sight. Horace made a motion as if to follow them up the lane, but I held him with my glittering eye—as I think of it since, not without a kind of amusement at my own seriousness.

"I'm the practical man, Horace, for I want my peace now, and my happiness now, and my God now. I can't wait. My barns may burn or my cattle die, or the solid bank where I keep my deferred joy may fail, or I myself by tomorrow be no longer here."

So powerfully and vividly did this thought take possession of me that I cannot now remember to have said a decent good-bye to Horace (never mind, he knows me!). At least when I was halfway up the hill I found myself gesticulating with one clenched fist and saying to myself with a kind of passion: "Why wait to be peaceful? Why not be peaceful now? Why not be happy now? Why not be rich now?"

For I think it truth that a life uncommanded now is uncommanded; a life unenjoyed now is unenjoyed; a life not lived wisely now is not lived wisely: for the past is gone and no one knows the future.

As for Horace, is he convinced that he is an impractical dreamer? Not a bit of it! He was merely flurried for a moment in his mind, and probably thinks me now, more than ever before, just what I think him. Absurd place, isn't it, this world?

So I reached home at last. You have no idea, unless you have tried it yourself, how good breakfast tastes after a three-mile tramp in the sharp morning air. The odour of ham and eggs, and new muffins, and coffee, as you come up the hill—there is an odour for you! And it was good to see Harriet.

"Harriet," I said, "you are a sight for tired eyes."

IV

THE GREEN PEOPLE

I HAVE always had a fondness, when upon my travels about
the world of the near-by woods and fields, for nipping a bit
of a twig here and there and tasting the tart or bitter quality of
it. I suppose the instinct descends to me from the herbivorous
side of my distant ancestry. I love a spray of white cedar, especially the spicy, sweet inside bark, or a pine needle, or the tender, sweet, juicy end of a spike of timothy grass drawn slowly
from its close-fitting sheath, or a twig of the birch that tastes like
wintergreen.

I think this no strange or unusual instinct, for I have seen
many other people doing it, especially farmers around here, who
go through the fields nipping the new oats, testing the red-top,
or chewing a bit of sassafras bark. I have in mind a clump of
shrubbery in the town road, where an old house once stood, of
the kind called here by some the "sweet-scented shrub," and the
branches of it nearest the road are quite clipped and stunted for
being nipped at by old ladies who pass that way and take to
it like cats to catnip.

For a long time this was a wholly unorganized, indeed all
but unconscious, pleasure, a true pattern of the childish way we
take hold of the earth; but when I began to come newly alive to
all things—as I have already related—I chanced upon this curious, undeveloped instinct.

"What is it I have here?" I asked myself, for I thought this
might be a new handle for getting hold of nature.

Along one edge of my field is a natural hedge of wild cherry,
young elms and ashes, dogwood, black raspberry bushes and the

like, which has long been a pleasure to the eye, especially in the early morning when the shadows of it lie long and cool upon the meadow. Many times I have walked that way to admire it, or to listen for the catbirds that nest there, or to steal upon a certain gray squirrel who comes out from his home in the chestnut tree on a fine morning to inspect his premises.

It occurred to me one day that I would make the acquaintance of this hedge in a new way; so I passed slowly along it where the branches of the trees brushed my shoulder and picked a twig here and there and bit it through. "This is cherry," I said; "this is elm, this is dogwood." And it was a fine adventure to know old friends in new ways, for I had never thought before to test the trees and shrubs by their taste and smell. After that, whenever I passed that way, I closed my eyes and tried for further identifications by taste, and was soon able to tell quickly half a dozen other varieties of trees, shrubs, and smaller plants along that bit of meadow.

Presently, as one who learns to navigate still water near shore longs for more thrilling voyages, I tried the grassy old roads in the woods, where young trees and other growths were to be found in great variety: and had a joy of it I cannot describe, for old and familiar places were thus made new and wonderful to me. And when I think of those places, now, say in winter, I grasp them more vividly and strongly than ever I did before, for I think not only how they look, but how they taste and smell, and I even know many of the growing things by the touch of them. It is certain that our grasp of life is in direct proportion to the variety and warmth of the ways in which we lay hold of it. No thought —no beauty and no joy.

On these excursions I have often reflected that if I were blind, I should still find here unexplored joys of life, and should make it a point to know all the friendly trees and shrubs around about by the taste or smell or touch of them. I think seriously that this method of widening the world of the blind, and increasing their narrower joys, might well be developed, though it would be wise for such as do take it to borrow first the eyes of a friend to see that no poison ivy, which certain rascally birds plant along our fences and hedges, is lurking about.

Save for this precaution I know of nothing that will injure the taster, though he must be prepared, here and there, for shocks and thrills of bitterness. A lilac leaf, for example, and to a scarcely lesser degree the willow and the poplar are, when bitten through, of a penetrating and intense bitterness; but do no harm, and will daunt no one who is really adventurous. There is yet to be written a botany, or, better yet, a book of nature, for the blind.

It is by knowing human beings that we come to understand them, and by understanding them come to love them, and so it is with the green people. When I was a boy in the wild north country trees were enemies to be ruthlessly fought—to be cut down, sawed, split, burned—anything to be rid of them. The ideal in making a home place was to push the forest as far away from it as possible. But now, when I go to the woods, it is like going among old and treasured friends, and with riper acquaintance the trees come to take on, curiously, a kind of personality, so that I am much fonder of some trees than of others, and instinctively seek out the companionship of certain trees in certain moods, as one will his friends.

I love the unfolding beeches in spring, and the pines in winter; the elms I care for afar off, like great aloof men, whom I can admire; but for friendly confidences give me an apple tree in an old green meadow.

In this more complete understanding I have been much aided by getting hold of my friends of the hedges and hills in the new ways I have described. At times I even feel that I have become a fully accepted member of the Fraternity of the Living Earth, for I have already received many of the benefits which go with that association; and I know now for a certainty that it makes no objection to its members because they are old, or sad, or have sinned, but welcomes them all alike.

The essential taste of the cherry and peach and all their numerous relatives is, in variation, that of the peach pit, so that the whole tribe may be easily recognized, though it was some time before I could tell with certainty the peach from the cherry. The oak shoot, when chewed a little, tastes exactly like the smell of new oak lumber; the maple has a peculiar taste and smell of its own that I can find no comparison for, and the poplar is one of the bitterest trees that ever I have tasted. The evergreen trees —pines, spruces, hemlocks, balsams, cedars—are to me about the pleasantest of all, both in taste and odour, and though the spruces and pines taste and smell much alike at first, one soon learns to distinguish them. The elm has a rather agreeable, nondescript, bitterish taste, but the linden is gummy and of a mediocre quality, like the tree itself, which I dislike. Some of the sweetest flowering shrubs, such as the lilac, have the bitterest of leaves and twigs or, like certain kinds of clematis, have a seed that when green is sharper than cayenne pepper, while others, like the rose, are pleasanter in flavour. The ash tree is not too bitter and a little sour.

I give here only a few of the commoner examples, for I wish to make this no tedious catalogue of the flavours of the green people. I am not a scientist, nor would wish to be taken for one. Only last winter I had my pretensions sadly shocked when I tasted twigs cut from various trees and shrubs and tried to identify them by taste or by smell, and while it was a pleasing experiment I found I could not certainly place above half of them; partly, no doubt, because many growing things keep their flavours well wrapped up in winter. No, I have not gone far upon this pleasant road, but neither am I in any great hurry; for there yet remains much time in this and my future lives to conquer the secrets of the earth. I plan to devote at least one entire life to science, and may find I need several!

One great reason why the sense of taste and the sense of smell have not the same honour as the sense of sight or of hearing is that no way has yet been found to make a true art of either. For sight, we have painting, sculpturing, photography, architecture, and the like; and for hearing, music; and for both, poetry and the drama. But the other senses are more purely personal, and have not only been little studied or thought about, but are the ones least developed, and most dimmed and clogged by the customs of our lives.

For the sense of smell we have, indeed, the perfumer's art,

but a poor rudimentary art it is, giving little freedom for the artist who would draw his inspirations freshly from nature. I can, indeed, describe poorly in words the odours of this June morning—the mingled lilacs, late wild cherries, new-broken soil, and the fragrance of the sun on green verdure, for there are here both lyrical and symphonic odours—but how inadequate it is! I can tell you what I feel and smell and taste, and give you, perhaps, a desire another spring to spend the months of May and June in the country, but I can scarcely make you live again the very moment of life I have lived, which is the magic quality of the best art. The art of the perfumer which, like all crude art, thrives upon blatancy, does not make us go to gardens, or love the rose, but often instils in us a kind of artificiality, so that perfumes, so far from being an inspiration to us, increasing our lives, become often the badge of the abnormal, used by those unsatisfied with simple, clean, natural things.

And as a people deficient in musical art delights in ragtime tunes, so a people deficient in the true art of tasting and smelling delights in ragtime odours and ragtime tastes.

I do not know that the three so-called lesser senses will ever be organized to the point where they are served by well-established arts, but this I do know—that there are three great ways of entering upon a better understanding of this magic earth which are now neglected.

I think we have come upon hasty and heated days, and are too much mastered by the god of hurry and the swift and greedy eye. We accept flashing pictures of life for life itself; we rush here and rush there and, having arrived, rush away again—to what sensible purpose? Be still a little! Be still!

I do not mean by stillness, stagnation nor yet lazy contentment, but life more deeply thought about, more intensely realized, an activity so concentrated that it is quiet. Be still then!

So it is that, though I am no worshipper of the old, I think the older gardeners had in some ways a better practice of the art than we have, for they planted not for the eye alone but for the nose and the sense of taste and even, in growing such plants as the lamb's tongue, to gratify, curiously, the sense of touch.. They loved the scented herbs, and appropriately called them simples. Some of these old simples I am greatly fond of, and like to snip a leaf as I go by to smell or taste; but many of them, I here confess, have for me a rank and culinary odour—as sage and thyme and the bold scarlet monarda, sometimes called bergamot.

But if their actual fragrance is not always pleasing, and their uses are now grown obscure, I love well the names of many of them—whether from ancient association or because the words themselves fall pleasantly upon the ear, as, for example, sweet marjoram and dill, anise and summer savoury, lavender and sweet basil. Coriander! Caraway! Cumin! And "there's rosemary, that's for remembrance; pray you, love, remember . . . there's fennel for you, and columbines: there's rue for you: and here's some for me——" All sweet names that one loves to roll under his tongue.

I have not any great number of these herbs in my own garden, but, when I go among those I do have, I like to call them by their familiar names as I would a dignified doctor or professor, if ever I knew him well enough.

It is in this want of balance and quietude that the age fails most. We are all for action, not at all for reflection; we think there are easy ways to knowledge and short cuts to perfection; we are for laws rather than for life.

And this reminds me inevitably of a mellow-spirited old friend who lives not a thousand miles from here—I must not tell his name—whose greatest word is "proportion." At this moment, as I write, I can hear the roll of his resonant old voice on the syllable p-o-r—prop-o-rtion. He is the kind of man good to know and to trust.

If ever I bring him a hard problem, as, indeed, I delight to do, it is a fine thing to see him square himself to meet it. A light comes in his eye, he draws back his chin a little and exclaims occasionally: "Well—well!"

He will have all the facts and circumstances fully mobilized, standing up side by side before him like an awkward squad, and there's nothing more awkward than some facts that have to stand out squarely in daylight! And he inquires into their ancestry, makes them run out their tongues, and pokes them once or twice in the ribs, to make sure that they are lively and robust facts capable of making a good fight for their lives. He never likes to see any one thing too large, as a church, a party, a reform, a new book, or a new fashion, lest he see something else too small; but will have everything, as he says, in true proportion. If he occasionally favours a little that which is old, solid, well-placed, it is scarcely to be measured to him as a fault in an age so overwhelmed with the shiny new.

He is a fine, up-standing, hearty old gentleman with white hair and rosy cheeks, and the bright eyes of one who has lived all his life with temperance. One incident I cannot resist telling, though it has nothing directly to do with this story, but it will let you know what kind of a man my old friend is, and when all is said, it would be a fine thing to know about any man. Not long ago he was afflicted with a serious loss, a loss that would have crushed some men, but when I met him not long afterward, though the lines around his eyes were grown deeper, he greeted me in his old serene, courtly manner. When I would have comforted him with my sympathy, for I felt myself near enough to speak of his loss, he replied calmly:

"How can we know whether a thing is evil until we reach the end of it? It may be good!"

One of the events I esteem among the finest of the whole year is my old friend's birthday party. Every winter, on the twenty-sixth of February, a party of his friends drop in to see him. Some of us go out of habit, drawn by our affection for the old gentleman; others, I think, he invites, for he knows to perfection the delicate shadings of companionship which divide those who come unbidden from those, not less loved but shyer, who must be summoned.

Now this birthday gathering has one historic ceremony which none of us would miss, because it expresses so completely the essence of our friend's generous and tolerant, but just, nature. He is, as I have said, a temperate man, and dislikes as much as any one I know the whole alcohol business; but living in a community where the struggle for temperance has often been waged intemperately, and where there is a lurking belief that cudgelling laws can make men virtuous, he publishes abroad once a year his declaration of independence.

After we have been with our friend for an hour or so, and are well warmed and happy with the occasion, he rises solemnly and goes to the toby-closet at the end of his generous fireplace, where the apple-log specially cut for the occasion is burning merrily, and as we all fall silent, knowing well what is coming, he unlocks the door and takes from the shelf a bottle of old peach brandy which, having uncorked, he gravely smells of and possibly lets his nearest neighbour smell of too. Then he brings from the sideboard a server set with diminutive glasses that have been polished until they shine for the great occasion, and, having filled them all with the ripe liquor, he passes them around to each of us. We have all risen and are becomingly solemn as he now proposes the toast of the year—and it is always the same toast:

"Here's to moderation—in all things!"

He takes a sip or two, and continues:

"Here's to temperance—the queen of the virtues."

So we all drink off our glasses. Our mellow old friend smacks his lips, corks the tall bottle, and returns it to his toby-closet, where it reposes undisturbed for another year.

"And now, gentlemen," he says, heartily, "let us go in to dinner." . . .

As I think of it, now that it is written, this story bears no very close relationship to my original subject, and yet it seemed to follow naturally enough as I set it down, and to belong with the simple and well-flavoured things of the garden and fields; and recalling the advice of Cobbett to his nephew on the art of writing, "never to alter a thought, for that which has come of itself into your mind is likely to pass into that of another more readily and with more effect than anything which you can by reflection invent," I leave it here just as I wrote it, hoping that the kinship of my genial old friend with simple and natural and temperate things may plainly appear.

V

PLACES OF RETIREMENT

"Good God! how sweet are all things here!
How beautiful the fields appear!
    How cleanly do we feed and lie!
Lord! what good hours do we keep!
How quietly we sleep!"
                    CHARLES COTTON (a friend of
                            Izaak Walton)

April 29th.

I HAVE been spending a Sunday of retirement in the woods. I came out with a strange, deep sense of depression, and though I knew it was myself and not the world that was sad, yet I could not put it away from me. . . . As I write, the wood seems full of voices, the little rustling of leaves, the minute sounds of twigs chafing together, the cry of frogs from the swamp so steady and monotonous that it scarcely arrests attention. Of odours, a-plenty! Just behind me, so that by turning my head I can see into their cool green depths, are a number of hemlock trees, the breath of which is incalculably sweet. All the earth—the very earth itself—has a good rich growing odour, pleasant to smell.

These things have been here a thousand years—a million years—and yet they are not stale, but are ever fresh, ever serene, ever here to loosen one's crabbed spirit and make one quietly happy. It seems to me I could not live if it were not possible often to come thus alone to the woods.

. . . On later walking I discover that here and there on warm southern slopes the dog-tooth violet is really in bloom, and worlds of hepatica, both lavender and white, among the brown leaves. One of the notable sights of the hillsides at this time of the year is the striped maple, the long wands rising straight and chaste among thickets of less-striking young birches and chestnuts, and having a bud of a delicate pink—a marvel of minute beauty. A little trailing arbutus I found and renewed my joy with one of the most exquisite odours of all the spring; Solomon's seal thrusting up vivid green cornucopias from the lifeless earth, and often near a root or stone the red partridge berries among their bright leaves. The laurel on the hills is sharply visible, especially when among deciduous trees, and along the old brown roads are patches of fresh wintergreen. In a cleft of the hills near the top of Norwottuck, though the day is warm, I found a huge snowbank—the last held trench of old winter, the last guerilla of the cold, driven to the fastnesses of the hills. . . . I have enjoyed this day without trying. After the first hour or so of it all the worries dropped away, all the ambitions, all the twisted thoughts——

It is strange how much thrilling joy there is in the discovery of the ages-old miracle of returning life in the woods: each green adventurer, each fragrant joy, each bird-call—and the feel of the soft, warm sunshine upon one's back after months of winter. On any terms life is good. The only woe, the only Great Woe, is the woe of never having been born. Sorrow, yes; failure, yes; weakness, yes; the sad loss of dear friends—yes! But oh, the good God: I still live!

Being alone without feeling alone is one of the great experiences of life, and he who practises it has acquired an infinitely valuable possession. People fly to crowds for happiness, not knowing that all the happiness they find there they must take with them. Thus they divert and distract that within them which creates power and joy, until by flying always away from themselves, seeking satisfaction from without rather than from within, they become infinitely boresome to themselves, so that they can scarcely bear a moment of their own society.

But if once a man have a taste of true and happy retirement, though it be but a short hour, or day, now and then, he has found, or is beginning to find, a sure place of refuge, of blessed renewal, toward which in the busiest hours he will find his thoughts wistfully stealing. How stoutly will he meet the buffets of the world if he knows he has such a place of retirement where all is well-ordered and full of beauty, and right counsels prevail, and true things are noted.

As a man grows older, if he cultivate the art of retirement, not indeed as an end in itself, but as a means of developing a richer and freer life, he will find his reward growing surer and greater until in time none of the storms or shocks of life any longer disturbs him. He might in time even reach the height attained by Diogenes, of whom Epictetus said, "It was not possible for any man to approach him, nor had any man the means of laying hold upon him to enslave him. He had everything easily loosed, everything only hanging to him. If you laid hold of his property, he would rather have let it go and be yours than he would have followed you for it; if you laid hold of his leg he would have let go his leg: if all of his body, all his poor body; his intimates, friends, country, just the same. For he knew from whence he had them, and from whom and on what conditions."

The best partners of solitude are books. I like to take a book with me in my pocket, although I find the world so full of interesting things—sights, sounds, odours—that often I never read a word in it. It is like having a valued friend with you, though you walk for miles without saying a word to him or he to you: but if you really know your friend, it is a curious thing how, subconsciously, you are aware of what he is thinking and feeling about this hillside or that distant view. And so it is with books. It is enough to have this writer in your pocket, for the very thought of him and what he would say to these old fields and pleasant trees is ever freshly delightful. And he never interrupts at inconvenient moments, nor intrudes his thoughts upon yours unless you desire it.

I do not want long books and least of all story books in the woods—these are for the library—but rather scraps and extracts and condensations from which thoughts can be plucked like flowers and carried for a while in the buttonhole. So it is that I am fond of all kinds of anthologies. I have one entitled "Traveller's Joy," another, "Songs of Nature," and I have lately found the best one I know called "The Spirit of Man" by Robert Bridges, the English laureate. Other little books that fit well in the pocket on a tramp, because they are truly companionable, are Ben Jonson's "Timber," one of the very best, and William Penn's "Fruits of Solitude." An anthology of Elizabethan verse, given me by a friend, is also a good companion.

It is not a discourse or a narrative we want as we walk abroad, but conversation. Neither do we want people or facts or stories, but a person. So I open one of these little books and read therein the thoughtful remark of a wise companion. This I may reply to, or merely enjoy, as I please. I am in no hurry, as I might be with a living companion, for my book friend, being long dead, is not impatient and gives me time to reply, and is not resentful if I make no reply at all. Submitted to such a test as this few writers, old or new, give continued profit or delight. To be considered in the presence of the great and simple things of nature, or worn long in the warm places of the spirit, a writer must have supreme qualities of sense or humour, a great sensitiveness to beauty, or a genuine love of goodness—but above all he must somehow give us the flavour of personality. He must be a true companion of the spirit.

There is an exercise given to young soldiers which consists in raising the hands slowly above the head, taking in a full breath at the same time, and then letting them down in such a way as to square the shoulders. This leaves the body erect, the head high, the eyes straight ahead, the lungs full of good air. It is the attitude that every man at arms should wish to take. After a day in the woods I feel some such erectness of spirit, a lift of the head, and a clearer and calmer vision, for I have raised up my hands to the heavens, and drawn in the odours and sights and sounds of the good earth.

One of the great joys of such times of retirement—perhaps the greatest of the joys—is the return, freshened and sweetened, to the common life. How good then appear the things of the garden and farm, the house and shop, that weariness had staled; how good the faces of friends.

VI

NO TRESPASS

I LIVE in a country of beautiful hills, and in the last few years, since I have been here with Harriet, I have made familiar and pleasant acquaintance with several of them. . . .

One hill I know is precious to me for a peculiar reason. Upon the side of it, along the town road, are two or three old farms with lilacs like trees about their doorways, and ancient apple orchards with great gnarly branches, and one has an old garden of hollyhocks, larkspurs, zinnias, mignonette, and I know not how many other old-fashioned flowers. Wild grapes there are along the neglected walls, and in a corner of one of them, by a brook, a mass of sweet currant which in blossom time makes all that bit of valley a bower of fragrance. I have gone that way often in spring for the sheer joy of the friendly odours I had across the ancient stone fences.

The largest and stoniest of the farms is owned by an old man named Howieson. A strange, brown-clad, crooked, crabbed old man, I have seen him often creeping across his fields with his horses. An ineffective worker all his life long, he has scarcely made a living from his stony acres. His farm is tipped up behind upon the hill and runs below to the brook, and the buildings are old and worn, and a rocky road goes by to the town. Once, in more prosperous days, before the factories took over the winter work of these hill farms, the busy families finished shoes, and wove cloth, and plaited straw hats—and one I know was famous for wooden bowls craftily hollowed out of maple knots—and the hill people relied upon their stony fields for little more than their food. But in these later days, the farm industries are gone, the houses are no longer overflowing with children, for there is nothing for children to do, and those who remain are old or discouraged. Some homes have entirely disappeared, so that all that remains is a clump of lilacs or a wild tangle of rose bushes about a grass-covered or bush-grown cellar wall. The last thing to disappear is not that which the old farmers most set their hearts upon, their fine houses and barns or their cultivated fields, but the one touch of beauty they left—lilac clump or rose-tangle.

Old Howieson, with that passion for the sense of possession which thrives best when the realities of possession are slipping away, has posted all his fields with warnings against intrusion. You may not enter this old field, nor walk by this brook, nor climb this hill, for all this belongs, in fee simple, to James Howieson!

NO TRESPASS

JAMES HOWIESON

For a long time I did not meet James Howieson face to face, though I had often seen his signs, and always with a curious sense of the futility of them. I did not need to enter his fields, nor climb his hill, nor walk by his brook; but as the springs passed and the autumns whitened into winter, I came into more and more complete possession of all those fields that he so jealously posted. I looked with strange joy upon his hill, saw April blossom in his orchard, and May colour the wild grape leaves along his walls. June I smelled in the sweet vernal of his hay fields, and from the October of his maples and beeches I gathered rich crops—and put up no hostile signs of ownership, paid no taxes, worried over no mortgage, and often marvelled that he should be so poor within his posted domain and I so rich without.

One who loves a hill, or a bit of valley, will experiment long until he finds the best spot to take his joy of it; and this is no more than the farmer himself does when he experiments year after year to find the best acres for his potatoes, his corn, his oats, his hay. Intensive cultivation is as important in these wider fields of the spirit as in any other. If I consider the things that I hear and see and smell, and the thoughts that go with them or grow out of them, as really valuable possessions, contributing to the wealth of life, I cannot see why I should not willingly give to them a tenth or a hundredth part of the energy and thought I give to my potatoes or my blackberries or to the writing I do.

I chose a place in a field just below Old Howieson's farm, where there is a thorn-apple tree to sit or lie under. From the thorn-apple tree, by turning my head in one direction, I can look up at the crown of the hill with its green hood of oaks and maples and chestnuts, and high above it I can see the clouds floating in the deep sky, or, if I turn my head the other way, for I am a kind of monarch there on the hill and command the world to delight me, I can look off across the pleasant valley with its spreading fields and farmsteads set about with trees, and the town slumbering by the riverside. I come often with a little book in one pocket to read from, and a little book in the other to write in, but I rarely use either the one or the other, for there is far too much to see and think about.

From this spot I make excursions round about, and have had many strange and interesting adventures: and now find thoughts of mine, like lichens, upon all the boulders and old walls and oak trees of that hillside. Sometimes I climb to the top of the hill. If I am in a leisurely mood I walk lawfully around Old Howieson's farm by a kind of wood lane that leads to the summit, but often I cross his walls, all regardless of his trespass signs, and go that way to the top.

It was on one of these lawless excursions in Old Howieson's field that I first saw that strange old fellow who is known hereabouts as the Herbman. I came upon him so suddenly that I stopped short, curiously startled, as one is startled at finding anything human that seems less than human. He was kneeling there among the low verdure of a shallow valley, and looked like an old gray rock or some prehistoric animal. I stopped to look at him, but he paid no heed, and seemed only to shrink into himself as though, if he kept silent, he might be taken for stock or stone. I addressed him, but he made no answer. I went nearer, with a sensation of uncanny wonder; but he did not so much as glance up at me, though he knew I was there. His old brown basket was near him and the cane beside it. He was gathering pennyroyal.

"Another man who is taking an unexpected crop from Old Howieson's acres," I thought to myself.

I watched him for some moments, quite still, as one might watch a turtle or a woodchuck—and left him there.

Since then I have heard something about him, and seen him once or twice. A strange old man, a wanderer upon the face of the fragrant earth. Spring and summer he wears always an old overcoat, and carries a basket with double covers, very much worn and brown with usage. His cane is of hickory with a crooked root for a handle, this also shiny with age. He gathers bitter-bark, tansy, ginseng, calamus, smartweed, and slippery elm, and from along old fences and barnyards, catnip and bone-set. I suppose he lives somewhere, a hole in a log, or the limb of a tree, but no one knows where it is, or how he dries or cures his findings. No one knows his name: perhaps he has forgotten it himself. A name is no great matter anyway. He is called simply the Herbman. He drifts into our valley in the spring, is seen here and there on the hills or in the fields, like the crows or the blackbirds, and disappears in the fall with the robins and the maple leaves. Perhaps he is one of those favoured souls to whom life is all spring and summer.

The age has passed him by, and except for certain furtive old women, few care now for his sovereign remedies.

I met him once in the town road, and he stopped humbly without lifting his eyes, and opening his basket let out into the air such a fragrance of ancient simples as I never smelled before. He said nothing at all; but took out dry bundles of catnip, sassafras, slippery elm, to show me. He had also pennyroyal for healing teas, and calamus and bitter-bark for miseries. I selected a choice assortment of his wares to take home to Harriet, but could get him to name no price. He took what I gave without objection and without thanks, and went his way. A true man of the hills.

As I said, I came often to the field below Old Howieson's farm. I think the old man saw me coming and going, for the road winds along the side of the hill within sight of his house, skirts a bit of wood, and with an unexpected turn comes out triumphantly to the top of the ridge beyond.

At the turn of the road I always disappeared, for I crossed the wall into the field below Old Howieson's farm, and mysteriously failed to appear to the watchful eye upon the ridge beyond. What could be more provoking or suspicious! To go in at one end of a well-travelled road and not to come out in the regular and expected way at the other! Or to be suspected of not being deferential toward trespass signs, or observant of closed ways! How disturbing to all those who dwell tremulously within posted enclosures of whatever sort, or those who base their sense of possession upon stamped paper, or take their God from a book. Men have been crucified for less.

Sooner or later those who cross boundaries clash with those who defend boundaries: and those who adventure offend those who seek security; but it was a long time before I came face to face with Old Man Howieson.

This was the way of it: Well back of Howieson's buildings and reaching upward upon the face of the hill stretches a long and narrow field, a kind of barren back pasture with boulders in it, and gnarly hawthorn trees, and a stunted wild apple or so. A stone fence runs down one side of the cleared land and above it rises the hill. It is like a great trough or ravine which upon still spring evenings gathers in all the varied odours of Old Howieson's farm and orchard and brings them down to me as I sit in the field below. I need no book then, nor sight of the distant town, nor song of birds, for I have a singular and incomparable album of the good odours of the hill. This is one reason why I chose this particular spot in the fields for my own, and it has given me a secret name for the place which I will not here disclose. If ever you should come this way in May, my friend, I might take you there of an evening, but could warrant you no joy of it that you yourself could not take. But you need not come here, or go there, but stop where you are at this moment, and I here assure you that if you look up, and look in, you, also, will see something of the glory of the world.

One evening I had been upon the hill to seek again the pattern and dimensions of my tabernacle, and to receive anew the tables of the law. I had crossed Old Howieson's field so often that I had almost forgotten it was not my own. It was indeed mine by the same inalienable right that it belonged to the crows that flew across it, or to the partridges that nested in its coverts, or the woodchucks that lived in its walls, or the squirrels in its chestnut trees. It was mine by the final test of all possession—that I could use it.

He came out of a thicket of hemlocks like a wraith of the past, a gray and crabbed figure, and confronted me there in the wide field. I suppose he thought he had caught me at last. I was not at all startled or even surprised, for as I look back upon it now I know that I had always been expecting him. Indeed, I felt a lift of the spirit, the kind of jauntiness with which one meets a crucial adventure.

He stood there for a moment quite silent, a grim figure of denial, and I facing him.

"You are on my land, sir," he said.

I answered him instantly and in a way wholly unexpected to myself:

"You are breathing my air, sir."

He looked at me dully, but with a curious glint of fear in his eye, fear and anger, too.

"Did you see the sign down there? This land is posted."

"Yes," I said, "I have seen your signs. But let me ask you: If I were not here would you own this land any more than you do now? Would it yield you any better crops?"

It is never the way of those who live in posted enclosures, of whatever sort, to reason. They assert.

"This land is posted," said the old man doggedly.

"Are you sure you own it?" I asked. "Is it really yours?"

"My father owned this farm before me," he said, "and my

grandfather cleared this field and built these walls. I was born in that house and have lived there all my life."

"Well, then, I must be going—and I will not come here again," I said. "I am sorry I walked on your land——"

I started to go down the hill, but stopped, and said, as though it were an afterthought:

"I have made some wonderful discoveries upon your land, and that hill there. You don't seem to know how valuable this field is. . . . Good-bye."

With that I took two or three steps down the hill—but felt the old man's hand on my arm.

"Say, mister," he asked, "are you one of the electric company men? Is that high-tension line comin' across here?"

"No," I said, "it is something more valuable than that!"

I walked onward a few steps, as though I was quite determined to get out of his field, but he followed close behind me.

"It ain't the new trolley line, is it?"

"No," I said, "it isn't the trolley line."

"What is it, then?"

In that question, eager and shrill, spoke the dry soul of the old man, the lifelong hope that his clinging ownership of those barren acres would bring him from the outside some miraculous profit.

His whole bearing had changed. He had ceased to be truculent or even fearful, but was now shrilly beseeching. A great wave of compassion came over me. I was sorry for him, imprisoned there within the walls of his own making, and expecting wealth from the outside when there was wealth in plenty within and everywhere about him.

But how could I help him? You can give no valuable thing to any man who has not the vision to take it. If I had told him what I found upon his hill or in his fields he would have thought me—well, crazy; or he would have suspected that under cover of such a quest I hid some evil design. As well talk adventure to an old party man, or growth to a set churchman.

So I left him there within his walls. So often when we think we are barring other people out, we are only barring ourselves in. The last I saw of him as I turned into the road was a gray and crabbed figure standing alone, looking after me, and not far off his own sign:

> NO TRESPASS
>
> JAMES HOWIESON

Sometime, I thought, this old farm will be owned by a man who is also capable of possessing it. More than one such place I know already has been taken by those who value the beauty of the hills and the old walls, and the boulder-strewn fields. One I know is really possessed by a man who long ago had a vision of sheep feeding on fields too infertile to produce profitable crops, and many others have been taken by men who saw forests growing where forests ought to grow. For real possession is not a thing of inheritance or of documents, but of the spirit; and passes by vision and imagination. Sometimes, indeed, the trespass signs stand long—so long that we grow impatient—but nature is in no hurry. Nature waits, and presently the trespass signs rot away, one arm falls off, and lo! where the adventurer found only denial before he is now invited to—"pass." The old walls are conquered by the wild cherries and purple ivy and blackberry bushes, and the old Howiesons sleep in calm forgetfulness of their rights upon the hills they thought they possessed, and all that is left is a touch of beauty—lilac clump and wild-rose tangle.

VII

LOOK AT THE WORLD!

"Give me to struggle with weather and wind;
Give me to stride through the snow;
Give me the feel of the chill on my cheeks,
And the glow and the glory within!"

March 17th.

THE joy of winter: the downright joy of winter! I tramped to-day through miles of open, snow-clad country. I slipped in the ruts of the roads or ploughed through the drifts in the fields with such a sense of adventure as I cannot describe.

Day before yesterday we had a heavy north wind with stinging gusts of snow. Yesterday fell bright and cold with snow lying fine and crumbly like sugar. To the east of the house where I shovelled a path the heaps are nearly as high as my shoulder . . .

This perfect morning a faint purplish haze is upon all the hills, with bright sunshine and still, cold air through which the chimney smoke rises straight upward. Hungry crows flap across the fields, or with unaccustomed daring settle close in upon the manure heaps around the barns. All the hillsides glisten and sparkle like cloth of gold, each glass knob on the telephone poles is like a resplendent jewel, and the long morning shadows of the trees lie blue upon the snow. Horses' feet crunch upon the road as the early farmers go by with milk for the creamery— the frosty breath of each driver fluttering aside like a white scarf. Through the still air ordinary voices cut sharply and clearly, and a laugh bounds out across the open country with a kind of superabundance of joy. I see two men beating their arms as they follow their wood sled. They are bantering one another noisily. I see a man shovelling snow from his barn doors; as each shovelful rises and scatters, the sun catches it for an instant and it falls, a silvery shower. . . . I tramped to-day through miles of it: and whether in broken roads or spotless fields, had great joy of it. It was good to stride through opposing drifts and to catch the tingling air upon one's face. The spring is beautiful indeed, and one is happy at autumn, but of all the year no other mornings set the blood to racing like these; none gives a greater sense of youth, strength, or of the general goodness of the earth.

Give me the winter: give me the winter! Not all winter, but just winter enough, just what nature sends.

. . . Dry air in the throat so cold at first as to make one cough; and dry, sharp, tingling air in the nostrils; frost on beard and eyebrows; cheeks red and crusty, so that to wrinkle them hurts: but all the body within aglow with warmth and health. Twice the ordinary ozone in the air, so that one wishes to whistle or sing, and if the fingers grow chill, what are shoulders for but to beat them around!

It is a strange and yet familiar experience how all things present their opposites. Do you enjoy the winter? Your neighbour loathes or fears it. Do you enjoy life? To your friend it is a sorrow and a heaviness. Even to you it is not always alike. Though the world itself is the same to-day as it was yesterday and will be to-morrow—the same snowy fields and polar hills, the same wintry stars, the same infinitely alluring variety of people—yet to-day you, that were a god, have become a grieving child.

Even at moments when we are well pleased with the earth we often have a wistful feeling that we should conceal it lest it hurt those borne down by circumstances too great or too sad for them. What is there to offer one who cannot respond gladly to the beauty of the fields, or opens his heart widely to the beckoning of friends? And we ask ourselves: Have I been tried as this man has? Would I be happy then? Have I been wrung with sorrow, worn down by ill-health, buffeted with injustice as this man has? Would I be happy then?

I saw on my walk to-day an old woman with a crossed shawl upon her breast creeping out painfully to feed her hens. She lives on a small, ill-kept farm I have known for years. She is old and poor and asthmatic, and the cold bites through her with the sharpness of knives. The path to the hen-house is a kind of via dolorosa, a terror of slipperiness and cold. She might avoid it: her son, worthless as he is, might do it for her, but she clings to it as she clings to her life. It is the last reason for staying here! But the white fields and drifted roads are never joyfully met, never desired. She spends half the summer dreading the return of winter from the severities of which she cannot escape.

Nor is it all mere poverty, though she is poor, for there are those who would help to send her away, but she will not go. She is wrapped about with Old Terrors, Ancient Tyrannies— that Terror of the Unknown which is more painful even than the Terror of the Known: those Tyrannies of Habit and of Place which so often and so ruthlessly rule the lives of the old. She clings desperately to the few people she knows (" 'tis hard to die among strangers!") and the customs she has followed all her life. Against the stark power of her tragic helplessness neither the good nor the great of the earth may prevail. This reality too . . .

I had a curious experience not long ago: one of those experiences which light up as in a flash some of the fundamental things of life. I met a man in the town road whom I have come to know rather more than slightly. He is a man of education and has been "well-off" in the country sense—is still, so far as I know—but he has a sardonic outlook upon life. He is discouraged about human nature. Thinks that politics are rotten, and that the prices of potatoes and bread are disgraceful. The state of the nation—and of the world—is quite beyond temperate expression. Few rays of joy seem to illuminate his pathway.

As we approached in the town road I called out to him:
"Good morning."
He paused and, to my surprise, responded:
"Are you happy?"
It had not occurred to me for some time whether I was happy or not, so I replied:
"I don't know; why do you ask?"

He looked at me in a questioning, and I thought rather indignant, way.

"Why shouldn't a man be happy?" I pressed him.

"Why *should* he be? Answer me that!" he responded. "Why should he be? Look at the world!"

With that he passed onward with a kind of crushing dignity.

I have laughed since when I have recalled the tone of his voice as he said, "Look at the world!" Gloomy and black it was. It evidently made him indignant to be here.

But at the moment his bitter query, the essential attitude of spirit which lay behind it, struck into me with a poignancy that stopped me where I stood. Was I, then, all wrong about the world? I actually had a kind of fear lest when I should look up again I should find the earth grown wan and bleak and unfriendly, so that I should no longer desire it.

"Look at the world!" I said aloud.

And with that I suddenly looked all around me and it is a strange, deep thing, as I have thought of it since, how the world came back upon me with a kind of infinite, calm assurance, as beautiful as ever it was. There were the hills and the fields and the great still trees—and the open sky above. And even as I looked down the road and saw my sardonic old friend plodding through the snow—his very back frowning—I had a sense that he belonged in the picture, too—and couldn't help himself. That he even had a kind of grace, and gave a human touch to that wintry scene! He had probably said a great deal more than he meant!

Look at the world!

Well, look at it.

VIII

A GOOD APPLE

"I am made immortal by apprehending my possession of incorruptible goods."

I HAVE just had one of the pleasant experiences of life. From time to time, these brisk winter days, I like to walk across the fields to Horace's farm. I take a new way each time and make nothing of the snow in the fields or the drifts along the fences. . . .

"Why," asks Harriet, "do you insist on struggling through the snow when there's a good beaten road around?"

"Harriet," I said, "why should any one take a beaten road when there are new and adventurous ways to travel?"

When I cross the fields I never know at what moment I may come upon some strange or surprising experience, what new sights I may see, what new sounds I may hear, and I have the further great advantage of appearing unexpectedly at Horace's farm. Sometimes I enter by the cow lane, sometimes by way of the old road through the wood-lot, or I appear casually, like a gust of wind, around the corner of the barn, or I let Horace discover me leaning with folded arms upon his cattle fence. I have come to love doing this, for unexpectedness in visitors, as in religion and politics, is disturbing to Horace and, as sand-grits in oysters produce pearls, my unexpected appearances have more than once astonished new thoughts in Horace, or yielded pearly bits of native humour.

Ever since I have known him, Horace has been rather high-and-mighty with me; but I know he enjoys my visits, for I give him always, I think, a pleasantly renewed sense of his own superiority. When he sees me his eye lights up with the comfortable knowledge that he can plough so much better than I can, that his corn grows taller than mine, and his hens lay more eggs. He is a wonderfully practical man, is Horace; hard-headed, they call it here. And he never feels so superior, I think, as when he finds me sometimes of a Sunday or an evening walking across the fields where my land joins his, or sitting on a stone fence, or lying on my back in the pasture under a certain friendly thorn-apple tree. This he finds it difficult to understand, and thinks it highly undisciplined, impractical, no doubt reprehensible.

One incident of the sort I shall never forget. It was on a June day only a year or so after I came here, and before Horace knew me as well as he does now. I had climbed the hill to look off across his own high-field pasture, where the white daisies, the purple fleabane, and the buttercups made a wild tangle of beauty among the tall herd's grass. Light airs moved billowing across the field, bobolinks and meadow larks were singing, and all about were the old fences, each with its wild hedgerow of choke cherry, young elms, and black raspberry bushes, and beyond, across miles and miles of sunny green countryside, the mysterious blue of the ever-changing hills. It was a spot I loved then, and have loved more deeply every year since.

Horace found me sitting on the stone fence which there divides our possessions; I think he had been observing me with amusement for some time before I saw him, for when I looked around his face wore a comfortably superior, half-disdainful smile.

"David," said he, "what ye doin' here?"

"Harvesting my crops," I said.

He looked at me sharply to see if I was joking, but I was perfectly sober.

"Harvestin' yer crops?"

"Yes," I said, the fancy growing suddenly upon me, "and just now I've been taking a crop from the field you think you own."

I waved my hand to indicate his high-field pasture.

"Don't I own it?"

"No, Horace, I'm sorry to say, not all of it. To be frank with

280

you, since I came here, I've quietly acquired an undivided interest in that land. I may as well tell you first as last. I'm like you, Horace, I'm reaching out in all directions."

I spoke in as serious a voice as I could command: the tone I use when I sell potatoes. Horace's smile wholly disappeared. A city feller like me was capable of anything!

"How's that?" he exclaimed sharply. "What do you mean? That field came down to me from my grandfather Jamieson."

I continued to look at Horace with great calmness and gravity.

"Judging from what I now know of your title, Horace," said I, "neither your grandfather Jamieson nor your father ever owned all of that field. And I've now acquired that part of it, in fee simple, that neither they nor you ever really had."

At this Horace began to look seriously worried. The idea that any one could get away from him anything that he possessed, especially without his knowledge, was terrible to him.

"What do you mean, Mr. Grayson?"

He had been calling me "David," but he now returned sharply to "Mister." In our country when we "Mister" a friend something serious is about to happen. It's the signal for general mobilization.

I continued to look Horace rather coldly and severely in the eye.

"Yes," said I, "I've acquired a share in that field which I shall not soon surrender."

An unmistakable dogged look came into Horace's face, the look inherited from generations of land-owning, home-defending, fighting ancestors. Horace is New England of New England.

"Yes," I said, "I have already had two or three crops from that field."

"Huh!" said Horace. "I've cut the grass and I've cut the rowen every year since you bin here. What's more, I've got the money fer it in the bank."

He tapped his fingers on the top of the wall.

"Nevertheless, Horace," said I, "I've got my crops, also, from that field, and a steady income, too."

"What crops?"

"Well, I've just now been gathering in one of them. What do

you think of the value of the fleabane, and the daisies, and the yellow five-finger in that field?"

"Huh!" said Horace.

"Well, I've just been cropping them. And have you observed the wind in the grass—and those shadows along the southern wall? Aren't they valuable?"

"Huh!" said Horace.

"I've rarely seen anything more beautiful," I said, "than this field and the view across it—I'm taking that crop now, and later I shall gather in the rowen of goldenrod and aster, and the red and yellow of the maple trees—and store it all away in *my* bank —to live on next winter."

It was some time before either of us spoke again, but I could see from the corner of my eye that mighty things were going on inside of Horace; and suddenly he broke out into a big laugh and clapped his knee with his hand in a way he has.

"Is that all!" said Horace.

I think it only confirmed him in the light esteem in which he held me. Though I showed him unmeasured wealth in his own fields, ungathered crops of new enjoyment, he was unwilling to take them, but was content with hay. It is a strange thing to me, and a sad one, how many of our farmers (and be it said in a whisper, other people, too) own their lands without ever really possessing them: and let the most precious crops of the good earth go to waste.

After that, for a long time, Horace loved to joke me about my crops and his. A joke with Horace is a durable possession.

"S'pose you think that's your field," he'd say.

"The best part of it," I'd return, "but you can have all I've taken, and there'll still be enough for both of us."

"You're a queer one!" he'd say, and then add sometimes, dryly, "but there's one crop ye don't git, David," and he'd tap his pocket where he carries his fat, worn, leather pocketbook. "And as fer feelin's, it can't be beat."

So many people have the curious idea that the only thing the world desires enough to pay its hard money for is that which can be seen or eaten or worn. But there never was a greater mistake. While men will haggle to the penny over the price of hay, or fight for a cent more to the bushel of oats, they will turn out their very pockets for strange, intangible joys, hopes, thoughts, or for a moment of peace in a feverish world—the unknown great possessions.

So it was that one day, some months afterward, when we had been thus bantering each other with great good humour, I said to him:

"Horace, how much did you get for your hay this year?"

"Off that one little piece," he replied, "I figger fifty-two dollars."

"Well, Horace," said I, "I have beaten you. I got more out of it this year than you did."

"Oh, I know what you mean——"

"No, Horace, you don't. This time I mean just what you do: money, cash, dollars."

"How's that, now?"

"Well, I wrote a little piece about your field, and the wind in the grass, and the hedges along the fences, and the weeds among the timothy, and the fragrance of it all in June and sold it last week——" I leaned over toward Horace and whispered behind my hand—in just the way he tells me the price he gets for his pigs.

"What!" he exclaimed.

Horace had long known that I was "a kind of literary feller," but his face was now a study in astonishment.

"*What?*"

Horace scratched his head, as he is accustomed to do when puzzled, with one finger just under the rim of his hat.

"Well, I vum!" said he.

Here I have been wandering all around Horace's barn—in the snow—getting at the story I really started to tell, which probably supports Horace's conviction that I am an impractical and unsubstantial person. If I had the true business spirit I should have gone by the beaten road from my house to Horace's, borrowed the singletree I went for, and hurried straight home. Life is so short when one is after dollars! I should not have wallowed through the snow, nor stopped at the top of the hill to look for a moment across the beautiful wintry earth—gray sky and bare wild trees and frosted farmsteads with homely smoke rising from the chimneys—I should merely have brought home a single-tree—and missed the glory of life! As I reflect upon it now, I believe it took me no longer to go by the fields than by the road; and I've got the singletree as securely with me as though I had not looked upon the beauty of the eternal hills, nor reflected, as I tramped, upon the strange ways of man.

Oh, my friend, is it the settled rule of life that we are to accept nothing not expensive? It is not so settled for me; that which is freest, cheapest, seems somehow more valuable than anything I pay for; that which is given better than that which is bought; that which passes between you and me in the glance of an eye, a touch of the hand, is better than minted money!

I found Horace upon the March day I speak of just coming out of his new fruit cellar. Horace is a progressive and energetic man, a leader in this community, and the first to have a modern fruit cellar. By this means he ministers profitably to that appetite of men which craves most sharply that which is hardest to obtain: he supplies the world with apples in March.

It being a mild and sunny day, the door of the fruit cellar was open, and as I came around the corner I had such a whiff of fragrance as I cannot describe. It seemed as though the vials of the earth's most precious odours had been broken there in Horace's yard! The smell of ripe apples!

In the dusky depths of the cellar, down three steps, I could see Horace's ruddy face.

"How are ye, David," said he. "Will ye have a Good Apple?"

So he gave me a good apple. It was a yellow Bellflower without a blemish, and very large and smooth. The body of it was waxy yellow, but on the side where the sun had touched it, it blushed a delicious deep red. Since October it had been in the dark, cool storage-room, and Horace, like some old monkish connoisseur of wines who knows just when to bring up the bottles of a certain vintage, had chosen the exact moment in all the year when the vintage of the Bellflower was at its best. As he passed it to me I caught a scent as of old crushed apple blossoms, or fancied I did—or it may have been the still finer aroma of friendship which passed at the touching of our fingers.

It was a hand-filling apple and likewise good for tired eyes, an antidote for winter, a remedy for sick souls.

"A wonderful apple!" I said to Horace, holding it off at arm's length.

"No better grown anywhere," said he, with scarcely restrained pride.

I took my delight of it more nearly; and the odour was like new-cut clover in an old orchard, or strawberry leaves freshly trod upon, or the smell of peach wood at the summer pruning—how shall one describe it?—at least a compound or essence of all the good odours of summer.

"Shall I eat it?" I asked myself, for I thought such a perfection of nature should be preserved for the blessing of mankind. As I hesitated, Horace remarked:

"It was grown to be eaten."

So I bit into it, a big liberal mouthful, which came away with a rending sound such as one hears sometimes in a winter's ice-pond. The flesh within, all dewy with moisture, was like new cream, except a rim near the surface where the skin had been broken; here it was of a clear, deep yellow.

New odours came forth and I knew for the first time how perfect in deliciousness such an apple could be. A mild, serene, ripe, rich bouquet, compounded essence of the sunshine from these old Massachusetts hills, of moisture drawn from our grudging soil, of all the peculiar virtues of a land where the summers make up in the passion of growth for the long violence of winter; the compensatory aroma of a life triumphant, though hedged about by severity, was in the bouquet of this perfect Bellflower.

Like some of the finest of wines and the warmest of friends it was of two flavours, and was not to be eaten for mere nourishment, but was to be tasted and enjoyed. The first of the flavours came readily in a sweetness, richness, a slight acidity, that it might not cloy; but the deeper, more delicate flavour came later

—if one were not crudely impatient—and was, indeed, the very soul of the fruit. One does not quickly arrive at souls either in apples or in friends. And I said to Horace with solemnity, for this was an occasion not to be lightly treated:

"I have never in my life tasted a finer apple."

"There is no finer apple," said Horace with conviction.

With that we fell to discussing the kinds and qualities of all the apples grown this side China, and gave our more or less slighting opinions of Ben Davises and Greenings and Russets, and especially of trivial summer apples of all sorts, and came to the conclusion at last that it must have been just after God created this particular "tree yielding fruit" that he desisted from his day's work and remarked that what he saw was good. The record is silent upon the point, and Moses is not given to adjectives, but I have often wondered what He would have said if He had not only seen the product of His creation, but *tasted* it.

I forgot to say that when I would have slurred the excellence of the Baldwin in comparison with the Bellflower, Horace began at once to interpose objections, and defended the excellence and perfection of that variety. . . . He has fifty barrels of Baldwins in his cellar.

While we talked with much enjoyment of the lore of apples and apple-growing, I finished the Bellflower to the very core, and said to Horace as I reluctantly tossed aside the stem and three seeds:

"Surely this has been one of the rare moments of life."

IX
I GO TO THE CITY

"Surely, man is a wonderfull, vaine, divers, and wavering subject: it is very hard to ground any directly constant and
uniforme judgement upon him."

THOUGH I live most of the time in the country, as I love
best to do, sometimes I go to the city and find there much
that is strange and amusing. I like to watch the inward flow of
the human tide in the morning, and the ebb at evening, and
sometimes in the slack tide of noon I drift in one of the eddies
where the restless life of the city pauses a moment to refresh
itself. One of the eddies I like best of all is near the corner of
Madison Square, where the flood of Twenty-third Street swirls
around the bulkhead of the Metropolitan tower to meet the
transverse currents of Madison Avenue. Here, of a bright morning when Down-at-Heels is generously warming himself on the
park benches, and Old Defeat watches Young Hurry striding
by, one has a royal choice of refreshment: a "red-hot" enfolded
in a bun from the dingy sausage wagon at the curb, or a plum
for a penny from the Italian with the trundle cart, or news of the
world in lurid gulps from the noon edition of the paper—or else
a curious idea or so flung out stridently over the heads of the
crowd by a man on a soap box.

I love this corner of the great city; I love the sense of the
warm human tide flowing all about me. I love to look into the
strange, dark, eager, sensitive, blunt faces.

The other noon, drifting there in that human eddy, I stopped
to listen to a small, shabby man who stood in transitory eminence
upon his soap box, half his body reaching above the knobby
black soil of human heads around him—black, knobby soil that
he was seeking, there in the spring sunshine, to plough with

strange ideas. He had ruddy cheeks and a tuft of curly hair set like an upholstery button on each side of his bald head. The front teeth in his upper jaw were missing, and as he opened his mouth one could see the ample lining of red flannel.

He raised his voice penetratingly to overcome the noise of the world, straining until the dark-corded veins of his throat stood out sharply and perspiration gleamed on his bald forehead. As though his life depended upon the delivery of his great message he was explaining to that close-packed crowd that there was no God.

From time to time he offered for sale pamphlets by R. G. Ingersoll and Frederic Harrison, with grimy back numbers of a journal called the "Truth-Seeker."

By the slant and timbre of his speech he was an Englishman; he had a gift of vigorous statement, and met questioners like an intellectual pugilist with skilful blows between the eyes: and his grammar was bad.

I stood for some time listening to him while he proved with excellent logic, basing his reasoning on many learned authorities, that there was no God. His audience cheered with glee his clever hits, and held up their hands for the books he had for sale.

"Who is this speaker?" I asked the elbowing helper who came through the crowd to deliver the speaker's wares and collect the silver for them. "Who is this speaker who says there is no God?"

"Henry Moore," he responded.

"And who," I asked, "is Henry Moore?"

"He is an Englishman and was brought up a Presbyterian— but he seen the light."

"And no longer thinks there is any God?"

"Nope."

"And these books prove the same thing?"

"Yep."

So I bought one of them, thinking it wonderful that proof of so momentous a conclusion could be had for so small a sum.

This Henry Moore could fling arguments like thunderbolts; he could marshal his authorities like an army; he could talk against the roar of the city and keep his restless audience about him; and if he did not believe in God he had complete faith in Haeckel and Jacques Loeb, and took at face value the lightest utterances of John Stuart Mill.

I enjoyed listening to Henry Moore. I enjoyed looking into the faces all around me—mostly keen foreign or half-foreign faces, and young faces, and idle faces, and curious faces, and faces that drank in, and faces that disdainfully rejected.

After a time, however, I grew unaccountably weary of the vehemence of Henry Moore and of the adroit helper who hawked his books. And suddenly I looked up into the clear noon blue of the ancient sky. A pigeon was flying across the wide open spaces of the square, the sunlight glinting on its wings. I saw the quiet green tops of the trees in the park, and the statue of Roscoe Conkling, turning a nonchalant shoulder toward the heated speaker who said there was no God. How many strange ideas, contradictory arguments, curious logic, have fallen, this last quarter century, upon the stony ears of Roscoe Conkling! Far above me the Metropolitan tower—that wonder work of men—lifted itself grandly to the heavens, and all about I suddenly heard and felt the roar and surge of the mighty city, the mighty, careless, busy city, thousands of people stirring about me, souls full of hot hopes and mad desires, unsatisfied longings, unrealized ideals. And I stepped out of the group who were gathered around the man who said there was no God. . . .

But I still drifted in the eddy, thinking how wonderful and strange all these things were, and came thus to another group, close gathered at the curb. It was much smaller than the other, and at the centre stood a patriarchal man with a white beard, and with him two women. He was leaning against the iron railing of the park, and several of the freethinker's audience, freshly stuffed with arguments, had engaged him hotly. Just as I approached he drew from his pocket a worn, leather-covered Bible, and said, tapping it with one finger:

"For forty years I have carried this book with me. It contains more wisdom than any other book in the world. Your friend there can talk until he is hoarse—it will do no harm—but the world will continue to follow the wisdom of this book."

A kind of exaltation gleamed in his eye, and he spoke with

an earnestness equal to that of Henry Moore. He, too, was a street speaker, waiting with his box at his side to begin. He would soon be standing up there to prove, also with logic and authority, that there was a God. He, also, would plough that knobby black soil of human heads with the share of his vehement faith. The two women were with him to sing their belief, and one had a basket to take up a collection, and the other, singling me out as I listened with eagerness, gave me a printed tract, a kind of advertisement of God.

I looked at the title of it. It was called: "God in His World." "Does this prove that God is really in the world?" I asked. "Yes," she said. "Will you read it?"

"Yes," I said, "I am glad to get it. It is wonderful that so great a truth can be established in so small a pamphlet—and all for nothing."

She looked at me curiously, I thought, and I put the tract by the side of the pamphlet I had bought from the freethinker, and drifted again in the eddy.

The largest crowd of all was close packed about a swarthy young chap whose bushy hair waved in response to the violence of his oratory. He, too, was perspiring with his ideas. He had a marvellous staccato method of question and answer. He would shoot a question like a rifle bullet at the heads of his audience, and then stiffen back like a wary boxer, both clenched hands poised in a tremulous gesticulation, and before any one could answer his bulletlike question, he was answering it himself. As I edged my way nearer to him I discovered that he, also, had a little pile of books at his feet which a keen-eyed assistant was busily selling. How well-established the technic of this art of the city eddies! How well-studied the psychology!

I thought this example the most perfect of them all, and watched with eagerness the play of the argument as it was mirrored in the intent faces all about me. And gradually I grew interested in what the man was saying, and thought of many good answers I could give to his questionings if he were not so cunning with answers of his own. Finally, in the midst of one of his loftiest flights, he demanded, hotly:

"Are you not, every one of you, a slave of the capitalist class?"

It was perfectly still for a second after he spoke, and before I knew what I was doing, I responded:

"Why, no, I'm not."

It seemed to astonish the group around me: white faces turned my way.

But it would have been difficult to dash that swarthy young man. He was as full of questions as a porcupine is full of quills.

"Well, sir," said he, "if I can prove to you that you are a slave, will you believe it?"

"No," I said, "unless you make me feel like a slave, too! No man is a slave who does not feel slavish."

But I was no match for that astonishing young orator; and he had the advantage over me of a soap box! Moreover, at that moment, the keen-eyed assistant, never missing an opportunity, offered me one of his little red books.

"If you can read this without feeling a slave," he remarked, "you're John D. himself in disguise."

I bought his little red book and put it with the pamphlet of the freethinker, and the tract of the God-fearing man, and stepped out of that group, feeling no more servile than when I went in. And I said to myself:

"This, surely, is a curious place to be in."

For I was now strangely interested in these men of the eddy.

"There are more gods preached here," I said, "than ever were known on the Acropolis."

Up the square a few paces I saw a covered wagon with a dense crowd around it. And in front of it upon a little platform which raised the speaker high above the heads of the audience stood a woman, speaking with shrill ardour. Most of the hearers were men; and she was telling them with logic and authority that the progress of civilization waited upon the votes of women. The army of the world stood still until the rear rank of its women could be brought into line! Morals languished, religion faded, industries were brutalized, home life destroyed! If only women had their rights the world would at once become a beautiful and charming place! Oh, she was a powerful and earnest speaker; she made me desire above everything, at the first opportunity, to use my share of the power in this Government to provide each woman with a vote. And just as I had reached this compliant stage there came a girl smiling and passing her little basket. The sheer art of it! So I dropped in my coin and took the little leaflet she gave me and put it side by side with the other literature of my accumulating library.

And so I came away from those hot little groups with their perspiring orators, and felt again the charm of the tall buildings and the wide sunny square, and the park with Down-at-Heels warming his ragged shanks—and the great city clanging heedlessly by. How serious they all were there in their eddies! Is there no God? Will woman suffrage or socialism cure all the evils of this mad world—which, ill as it is, we would not be without? Is a belief for forty years in the complete wisdom of the Book the final solution? Why do not all of the seeking and suffering thousands flowing by in Twenty-third Street stop here in the eddies to seek the solution of their woes, the response to their hot desires?

So I came home to the country, thinking of what I had seen and heard, asking myself, "What is the truth, after all? What *is* real?"

And I was unaccountably glad to be at home again. As I came down the hill through the town road the valley had a quiet welcome for me, and the trees I know best, and the pleasant fields of corn and tobacco, and the meadows ripe with hay. I know of nothing more comforting to the questioning spirit than the sight of distant hills. . . .

I found that Bill had begun the hay cutting. I saw him in the lower field as I came by in the road. There he was, stationed high on the load, and John, the Pole, was pitching on. When he saw me he lifted one arm high in the air and waved his hand—and I in return gave him the sign of the Free Fields.

"Harriet," I said, "it seems to me I was never so glad before to get home."

"It's what you always say," she remarked placidly.

"This time it's true!" And I put the pamphlets I had accumulated in the city eddies upon the pile of documents which I fully intend to read but rarely get to.

The heavenly comfort of an old shirt! The joy of an old hat!

As I walked down quickly into the field with my pitchfork on my shoulder to help Bill with the hay, I was startled to see, hanging upon a peach tree at the corner of the orchard, a complete suit of black clothes. Near it, with the arms waving gently in the breeze, was a white shirt and a black tie, and at the foot of the tree a respectable black hat. It was as though the peach tree had suddenly, on that bright day, gone into mourning.

I laughed to myself.

"Bill," I said, "what does this mean?"

Bill is a stout jolly chap with cheeks that look, after half a day's haying, like raw beefsteaks. He paused on his load, smiling broadly, his straw hat set like a halo on the back of his head.

"Expected a funeral," he said cheerfully.

Bill is the undertaker's assistant, and is always on call in cases of emergency.

"What happened, Bill?"

"They thought they'd bury 'im this afternoon, but they took an' kep' 'm over till to-morrow."

"But you came prepared."

"Yas, no time to go home in hayin'. The pump fer me, and the black togs."

Bill calls the first rakings of the hay "tumbles," and the scattered re-rakings, which he despises, he calls "scratchings." I took one side of the load and John, the Pole, the other, and we put on great forkfuls from the tumbles which Bill placed skilfully at the corners and sides of the load, using the scratchings for the centre.

John, the Pole, watched the load from below. "Tank he too big here," he would say, or, "Tank you put more there"; but Bill told mostly by the feel of the load under his feet or by the "squareness of his eye." John, the Pole, is a big, powerful fellow, and after smoothing down the load with his fork he does not bother to rake up the combings, but gathering a bunch of loose hay with his fork, he pushes it by main strength, and very quickly, around the load, and running his fork through the heap, throws it upon the mountain-high load in a twinkling—an admirable, deft performance.

Hay-making is a really beautiful process: the clicking mower cutting its clean, wide swath, a man stepping after, where the hay is very heavy, to throw the windrow back a little. Then, after lying to wilt and dry in the burning sun—all full of good odours—the horse-rake draws it neatly into wide billows, and after that, John, the Pole, and I roll the billows into tumbles. Or, if the hay is slow in drying, as it was not this year, the kicking tedder goes over it, spreading it widely. Then the team and rack on the smooth-cut meadow and Bill on the load, and John and I pitching on; and the talk and badinage that goes on, the excitement over disturbed field mice, the discussion of the best methods of killing woodchucks, tales of marvellous exploits of loaders and stackers, thrilling incidents of the wet year of '98 when two men and one team saved four acres of hay by working all night—"with lanterns, I jing"—much talk of how she goes on, "she" being the hay, and no end of observations upon the character, accomplishments, faults, and excesses of the sedate old horses waiting comfortably out in front, half hidden by the mountain of hay above them and nibbling at the tumbles as they go by.

Then the proud moment when Bill the driver, with legs apart, almost pushing on the reins, drives his horses up the hill.

"Go it, Dick. Let 'er out, Daisy. Stiddy, ol' boy. Whoa, there. Ease down now. Hey, there, John, block the wheel—block the wheel, I tell ye. Ah-h now, jes' breathe a bit. I jing, it's hot."

And then the barn, the cavernous dark doors, the hoofs of the horses thundering on the floor, the smell of cattle from below, the pigeons in the loft whirring startled from their perches. Then the hot, scented, dusty "pitching off" and "mowing in"—a fine process, an *honest* process: men sweating for what they get.

As I came in from the field that night the sun was low in the hills, and a faint breeze had begun to blow, sweetly cool after the burning heat of the day. And I felt again that curious deep sense I have so often here in the country, of the soundness and reality of the plain things of life.

294

X

THE OLD STONE MASON

OF WELL-FLAVOURED men, I know none better than those who live close to the soil or work in common things. Men are like roses and lilacs, which, too carefully cultivated to please the eye, lose something of their native fragrance. One of the best-flavoured men I know is my friend, the old stone mason.

To-day I rode over with the old stone mason to select some wide stones for steps in my new building. The old man loves stones. All his life long—he is now beyond seventy years old—he has lived among stones, lifted stones, fitted stones. He knows all the various kinds, shapes, sizes, and where they will go best in a wall. He can tell at a glance where to strike a stone to make it fit a particular place, and out of a great pile he can select with a shrewd eye the stone for the exact opening he has to fill. He will run his stubby rough hand over a stone and remark:

"Fine face that. Ye don't see many such stones these days," as though he were speaking of the countenance of a friend.

I veritably believe there are stones that smile at him, stones that frown at him, stones that appear good or ill-humoured to him as he bends his stocky strong body to lift or lay them. He is a slow man, a slow, steady, geologic man, as befits one who works with the elemental stuff of nature. His arms are short and his hands powerful. He has been a servant of stones in this neighbourhood alone for upward of fifty years.

He loves stones and can no more resist a good stone than I a good book. When going about the country, if he sees comely stones in a wayside pile, or in a fine-featured old fence he will have them, whether or no, and dickers for them with all the eagerness, sly pride, and half-concealed cunning with which a lover of old prints chaffers for a Seymour Haden in a second-hand book shop. And when he has bought them he takes the first idle day he has, and with his team of old horses goes into the hills, or wherever it may be, and brings them down. He has them piled about his barn and even in his yard, as another man might have flower beds. And he can tell you, as he told me to-day, just where a stone of such a size and such a face can be found, though it be at the bottom of a pile. No book lover with a feeling sense for the place in his cases where each of his books may be found has a sharper instinct than he. In his pocket he carries a lump of red chalk, and when we had made our selections he marked each stone with a broad red cross.

I think it good fortune that I secured the old stone mason to do my work, and take to myself some credit for skill in enticing him. He is past seventy years old, though of a ruddy fresh countenance and a clear bright eye, and takes no more contracts, and is even reluctantly persuaded to do the ordinary stone work of the neighbourhood. He is "well enough off," as the saying goes, to rest during the remainder of his years, for he has lived a temperate and frugal life, owns his own home with the little garden behind it, and has money in the bank. But he can be prevailed upon, like an old artist who has reached the time of life when it seems as important to enjoy as to create, he can sometimes be prevailed upon to lay a wall for the joy of doing it.

So I had the stone hauled onto the ground, the best old field stone I could find, and I had a clean, straight foundation dug, and when all was ready I brought the old man over to look at it. I said I wanted his advice. No sooner did his glance light upon the stone, no sooner did he see the open and ready earth than a new light came in his eye. His step quickened and as he went about he began to hum an old tune under his breath. I knew then that I had him! He had taken fire. I could see that his eye was already selecting the stones that should "go down," the fine square stones to make the corners or cap the wall, and measuring with a true eye the number of little stones for the fillers. In no time at all he had agreed to do my work; indeed, would have felt aggrieved if I had not employed him.

I enjoyed the building of the wall, I think, as much as he did, and helped him what I could by rolling the larger stones close down to the edge of the wall. As the old man works he talks, if any one cares to listen, or if one does not care to listen he is well content to remain silent among his stones. But I enjoyed listening, for nothing in this world is so fascinating to me as the story of how a man has come to be what he is. When we think of it there are no abstract adventures in this world, but only your adventure and my adventure, and it is only as we come to know a man that we can see how wonderful his life has been.

He told me all about the great walls and the little walls—miles and miles of them—he has built in the course of fifty years. He told of crude boyhood walls when he was a worker for wages only, he told of proud manhood walls when he took contracts for foundations, retaining walls, and even for whole buildings, such as churches, where the work was mostly of stone; he told me of thrilling gains and profits, and of depressing losses; and he told me of his calm later work, again on wages, for which he is chosen as a master of his craft. A whole long lifetime of it— and the last years the best of all!

As we drove up yesterday to select the steps from his piles of old field stone, riding behind his great, slow, hairy-hoofed horse, in the battered and ancient wagon, he pointed with his stubby whip to this or that foundation, the work of his hands.

"Fine job, that," said he, and I looked for the first time in my life at the beautiful stonework beneath the familiar home of a friend. I had seen the house a thousand times, and knew well the people in it, but my unobservant eye had never before rested consciously upon that bit of basement wall. How we go through life, losing most of the beauties of it from sheer inability to see! But the old man, as he drives about, rarely sees houses at all, especially wooden houses, and for all modern stucco and cement work he entertains a kind of lofty contempt. Sham work of a hasty and unskilled age! He never, I think, put in a shovelful of cement except in the place where it belongs, as a mortar for good walls, and never will do so as long as he lives. So long as he lives the standards of high art will never be debased!

He built that foundation, and this chimney; he worked on the tower of the Baptist church in the town, "and never yet has there been a crack in her, winter or summer"; and more than forty years ago he laid the cornerstone of the old schoolhouse, the foundation walls of which stand to-day as sound and strong as they were when they were put down.

In dry walls I think the old stone mason takes the greatest pride of all: for it is in the dry wall—I mean by that a wall laid without mortar—that the sheer art of the mason comes most into play. Any one can throw a wall together if he has mortar to make it stick, but a dry wall must stand out for what it is, built solid from the bottom up, each stone resting securely upon those below it, and braced and nested in by the sheer skill of the mason. The art of the dry wall is the ancient heritage of New England and speaks not only of the sincerity and the conscientiousness of the old Puritan spirit but strikes the higher note of beauty. Many of the older walls I know are worth going far to see, for they exhibit a rare sense of form and proportion, and are sometimes set in the landscape with a skill that only the Master-Artist himself could exceed. Those old, hard-wrought stone fences of the Burnham Hills and Crewsbury, the best of them, were honestly built, and built to last a thousand years. A beautiful art—and one that is passing away! It is the dry wall that stands of itself that the old stone mason loves best of all.

As we drove along the road the old man pointed out to me with his stubby whip so many examples of his work that it seemed finally as if he had borne a hand in nearly everything done in this neighbourhood in the last half-century. He has literally built himself into the country and into the town, and at seventy years of age he can look back upon it all with honest pride. It stands. No jerry work anywhere. No cracks. It stands.

I never realized before how completely the neighbourhood rests upon the work of this simple old man. He *founded* most of the homes here, and upon his secure walls rest many of the stores, the churches, and the schools of the countryside. I see again how important each man is to the complete fabric of civilization and know that we are to leave no one out, despise no one, look down upon no one.

He told me stories of this ancient settler and of that.

"He was a powerful queer man—he wanted the moss left on his stones when I put 'em in; never a hammer touched the facings of *his* wall. . . .

"That is properly a woman's wall. She was the boss, you might call it, and wanted stone, but *he* wanted brick. So you see the front, where people can see it, is of stone, but the sides is all brick."

Thus like the true artist that he is, he has not only built himself, his own honesty, truth, skill, into the town, but he has built in the inexhaustible peculiarities, the radiant charm, the hates and the loves, of the people of this place. He has mirrored his own little age in stone. He knows the town, indeed, better than most of us, having a kind of stone-age knowledge of it— the fundamental things men build in when they set about building permanently.

"And that is what you might call a spite wall," said he, showing me a long wall leading between two shady homes, making one of them a prison on the south, and the other a prison on the north. He told me the story of an ancient and bitter quarrel between two old friends, a story which sounded to-day among spring blossoms like the account of some ancient baronial feud.

But if the old stone mason has built walls to keep enemies apart how many more walls has he built to keep friends together! How many times has he been consulted by shy lovers seeking a foundation for a new home, a new family, how many times by Darby and Joan planning a resting place for the sunny closing years of their lives! He could point, indeed, to one wall that symbolized hatred: all the others meant homes, roof-trees, families, or they were the foundations for the working places of men, or else, like the tower of the church, they pointed heavenward and were built to the glory of God.

The old stone mason has not the slightest idea that he has done anything unusual or wonderful. He is as simple and honest a man as ever I knew; and if he has pride, simple and honest also in that. He was anxious not to charge me too much for the stone I bought—in an age like this! I have never talked with him about God, or about religion: I had no need to.

He has done his duty in other ways by his time and his place. He has brought up a large family of children; and has known sorrow and loss, as well as happiness and contentment. Two of his children were taken in one day with pneumonia. He told me about it with a quaver in his old voice.

"How long ago was it?" I asked.

"Twenty-seven years."

He has sons and daughters left, and two of the sons he has well trained as stone masons after him. They are good as young men go in a degenerate age. They insist on working in cement! He has grandchildren in school, and spoils them.

He is also a man of public interests and upon town-meeting day puts on his good clothes and sits modestly toward the back of the hall. Though he rarely says anything he always has a strong opinion, an opinion as sound and hard as stones and as simple, upon most of the questions that come up. And he votes as he thinks, though the only man in meeting who votes that way. For when a man works in the open, laying walls true to lines and measurements, being honest with natural things, he comes clear, sane, strong, upon many things. I would sooner trust his judgment upon matters that are really important as between man and man, and man and God, than I would trust the town lawyer. And if he has grown a little testy with some of the innovations of modern life, and thinks they did everything better forty years ago—and says so—he speaks, at least, his honest conviction.

If I can lay my walls as true as he does, if I can build myself a third part as firmly into any neighbourhood as he has into this, if at seventy years of age—if ever I live to lay walls with joy at that time of life—if I can look back upon *my* foundations, *my* heaven-pointing towers, and find no cracks or strains in them, I shall feel that I have made a great success of my life. . . .

I went out just now: the old man was stooping to lift a heavy stone. His hat was off and the full spring sunshine struck down warmly upon the ruddy bald spot on the top of his head, the white hair around about it looking silvery in that light. As he placed the stone in the wall, he straightened up and rubbed his stubby hand along it.

"A fine stone that!" said he.

XI

AN AUCTION OF ANTIQUES

"I would not paint a face
   Or rocks or streams or trees
Mere semblances of things—
   But something more than these.

"I would not play a tune
   Upon the sheng or lute
Which did not also sing
   Meanings that else were mute."

JOHN TEMPLETON died on the last day of August, but it was not until some weeks later that his daughter Julia, that hard-favoured woman, set a time for the auction. It fell happily upon a mellow autumn day, and as I drove out I saw the apples ripening in all the orchards along the road, and the corn was beginning to look brown, and the meadows by the brook were green with rowen. It was an ideal day for an auction, and farmers and townsmen came trooping from all parts of the country, for the Templeton antiques were to be sold.

John Templeton lived in one house for seventy-eight years; he was born there—and you will find the like of that in few places in America. It was a fine house for its time, for any time, and not new when John Templeton was born. A great, solid, square structure, such as they built when the Puritan spirit was virile in New England, with an almost Greek beauty of measured lines. It has a fanlight over the front door, windows exquisitely proportioned, and in the centre a vast brick chimney. Even now, though weathered and unpainted, it stands four-square upon the earth with a kind of natural dignity. A majestic chestnut tree grows near it, and a large old barn and generous sheds, now somewhat dilapidated, ramble away to the rear.

Enclosing the fields around about are stone fences representing the infinite labour of John Templeton's forebears. More toil has gone into the stone fences of New England, free labour of a free people, than ever went into the slave-driven building of the Pyramids of Egypt.

I knew John Templeton in his old age—a stiff, weather-beaten old man driving to town in a one-horse buggy.

"How are you, Mr. Templeton?"

"Comin' on, comin' on." This was his invariable reply.

He had the old New England pronunciation, now disappearing. He said "rud" for road, "daown" for down, and gave an indescribable twist to the word garden, best spelled "gardin." He had also the old New England ways. He was forehanded with his winter woodpile, immaculately neat with his dooryard, determined in his Sunday observance, and if he put the small apples in the middle of the barrel he refused to raise tobacco, lest it become a cause of stumbling to his neighbour. He paid his debts, disciplined his children, and in an age which has come to look chummily upon God, he dreaded His wrath.

He grew a peculiar, very fine variety of sweet apple which I have never seen anywhere else. He called it the Pumpkin Sweet, for it was of a rich yellow. I can see him yet, driving into town with a shallow wagon box half full of this gold of the orchard; can see him turn stiffly to get one of the apples for me; can hear him say in the squeaky voice of age:

"Ye won't find no sweeter apples hereabout, I can tell ye that."

He was a dyed-in-the-wool abolition Republican and took the Boston *Transcript* for forty-six years. He left two cords of them piled up in a back storeroom. He loved to talk about Napoleon Bonaparte and the Battle of Waterloo, and how, if there had not been that delay of half an hour, the history of the world might have been different. I can see him saying, with the words puffing out his loose cheeks:

"And then Blooker kem up——"

To the very last, even when his eyes were too dim to read and his voice was cracked, he would start up, like some old machine set awhirring when you touched the rusty lever, and talk about the Battle of Waterloo.

303

No one, so far as I know, ever heard him complain, or bemoan his age, or regret the change in the times; and when his day came, he lay down upon his bed and died.

"Positively nothing will be reserved," were the familiar words of the poster, and they have a larger meaning in an old country neighbourhood than the mere sale of the last pan and jug and pig and highboy. Though we live with our neighbours for fifty years we still secretly wonder about them. We still suspect that something remains covered, something kept in and hidden away, some bits of beauty unappreciated—as they are, indeed, with ourselves. But death snatches away the last friendly garment of concealment; and after the funeral the auction. We may enter now. The doors stand at last flung widely open; all the attics have been ransacked; all the chests have been turned out; a thousand privacies stand glaringly revealed in the sunny open spaces of the yard. Positively nothing will be reserved; everything will be knocked down to the highest bidder. What wonder that the neighbourhood gathers, what wonder that it nods its head, leaves sentences half uttered, smiles enigmatically.

Nearly all the contents of the house had been removed to the yard, under the great chestnut tree. A crowd of people, mostly women, were moving about among the old furniture, the old furniture that had been in John Templeton's family for no one knows how long—old highboys and lowboys, a beautifully simple old table or so, and beds with carved posts, and hand-wrought brasses, and an old tall clock that struck with sonorous dignity. These things, which had been temptingly advertised as "antiques," a word John Templeton never knew, were only the common serviceable things of uncounted years of family life.

Nothing about the place was of any great value except the antiques, and it was these that drew the well-dressed women in automobiles from as far away as Hempfield and Nortontown; and yet there were men in plenty to poke the pigs, look sarcastically at the teeth of the two old horses, and examine with calculating and rather jeering eyes John Templeton's ancient buggy, and the harness and the worn plough and cultivator and mowing machine. Everything seems so cheap, so poor, so un-protected, when the spirit has departed.

Under the chestnut tree the swarthy auctioneer with his amiable countenance and ironical smile acquired through years of dispassionate observation of the follies of human emotion, the mutability of human affairs, the brevity of human endeavour, that brought everything at last under his hammer—there by the chestnut tree the auctioneer had taken his stand in tempo-rary eminence upon an old chest, with an ancient kitchen cup-board near him which served at once as a pulpit for exhorta-tion, and a block for execution. Already the well-worn smile had come pat to his countenance, and the well-worn witticisms were ready to his tongue.

"Now, gentlemen, if you'll give me such attention as you can spare from the ladies, we have here to-day——"

But I could not, somehow, listen to him: the whole scene, the whole deep event, had taken hold upon me strangely. It was so full of human meaning, human emotion, human pathos. I drifted away from the crowd and stepped in at the open door of the old house, and walked through the empty, resounding rooms with their curious old wallpaper and low ceilings and dusty win-dows. And there were the old fireplaces where the heavy brick had been eaten away by the pokings and scrapings of a century; and the thresholds worn by the passage of many feet, the romping feet of children, the happy feet of youth—the bride passed here on her wedding night with her arm linked in the arm of the groom—the sturdy, determined feet of maturity; the stumbling feet of old age creeping in; the slow, pushing feet of the bearers with the last burden, crowding out——

The air of the house had a musty, shut-in odour, ironically cut through, as all old things are, by the stinging odour of the new: the boiling of the auction coffee in the half-dismantled kitchen, the epochal moment in the life of Julia Templeton. I could hear, occasionally, her high, strident, worried voice order-ing a helper about. Such a hard-favoured woman!

It is the studied and profitable psychology of the auction that the rubbish must be sold first—pots and bottles and jugs at five-cent bids, and hoes at ten—and after that, the friction of the contest having warmed in the bidders an amiable desire to purchase goods they do not want and cannot use, the auctioneer gradually puts forth the treasures of the day.

As I came out of the old house I could see that the mystic web had been spun, that the great moment of the sale was arriving. The auctioneer was leaning forward now upon the tall cupboard with an air of command, and surveying the assembled crowd with a lordly eye.

"Now, Jake, careful there—pass it along—steady. . . . We come now to the cheff dooves of the day, the creem delly creems of this sale. Gentlemen *and* ladies, it is a great moment in the life of an auctioneer when he can offer, for sale, free and without reservation, such treasures as these. . . ."

I could feel the warming interest of the crowd gathering in more closely about Mr. Harpworth, the furtive silences of shrewd bargainers, eagerness masked as indifference, and covetousness cloaking itself with smiling irony. It is in the auction that trade glorifies itself finally as an Art.

"Here, gentlemen *and* ladies, is a genuine antique, hand-wrought and solid all the way through. Just enough worn to give the flavour and distinction of age. Well built in the first place, plain, simple lines, but, ladies, *beautiful*——"

It was the tall four-post bed he was selling; and he now put his hand upon this object of hardy service with a cunningly simulated air of deference. It was to be profaned by no irreverent handling!

"What am I offered for this heirloom of the Templeton family? Ten? Ten! Fifteen over there—thank you, Mr. Cody. Why, gentlemen, that bed cannot be duplicated in America! A real product of Colonial art! Look at the colour of it! Where will you find such depth of colour in any modern piece? Age varnished it, gentlemen, age and use—the use of a hundred years. . . . Twenty over there, twenty I hear, twenty, twenty—make it thirty. . . . Speak up now, Ike, we know you've come here to-day to make your fortune—do I hear thirty?"

No sooner had the great bed been sold ("it's yours, Mrs. Craigie, a treasure and dirt cheap") there came an ancient pair of hand-wrought andirons, and a spider-legged table, and a brass warming-pan, and a banjo clock. . . .

I scarcely know how to explain it, but the sale of these inanimate antiques, so charged with the restrained grace, the reticent beauty, the serviceable strength, of a passing age, took hold upon me with strange intensity. In times of high emotion the veil between sight and insight slips aside and that which lies about us suddenly achieves a higher reality. We are conscious of

> "Something beside the form
> Something beyond the sound."

It came to me with a thrill that this was no mere sale of antique wood and brass and iron, but a veritable auction, here symbolized, of the decaying fragments of a sternly beautiful civilization.

I looked off across the stony fields, now softly green in the sunlight, from which three generations of the Templeton family had wrung an heroic living; I looked up at the majestic old house where they had lived and married and died. . . .

As my eye came back to the busy scene beneath the chestnut tree it seemed to me, how vividly I cannot describe—that beside or behind the energetic and perspiring Mr. Harpworth there stood Another Auctioneer. And I thought he had flowing locks and a patriarchal beard, and a scythe for a sign of the uncertainty of life, and a glass to mark the swiftness of its passage. He was that Great Auctioneer who brings all things at last under his inexorable hammer.

After that, though Mr. Harpworth did his best, he claimed my attention only intermittently from that Greater Sale which was going on at his side, from that Greater Auctioneer who was conducting it with such consummate skill—for *he* knew that nothing is for sale but life. The mahogany highboy, so much packed and garnered life cut into inanimate wood; the andirons, so much life; the bookshelves upon which John Templeton kept his "Life of Napoleon Bonaparte," so much life. Life for sale, gentlemen! What am I offered to-day for this bit of life—and this —and this——

Mr. Harpworth had paused, for even an auctioneer, in the high moment of his art, remains human; and in the silence following the cessation of the metallic click of his voice, "Thirty, thirty, thirt, thirt—make it thirty-five—thank you—forty," one could hear the hens gossiping in the distant yard.

"There were craftsmen in those days, gentlemen," he was resuming; "look at this example of their art—there is quality here and durability——"

At this point the Great Auctioneer broke in upon my attention and caught up Mr. Harpworth's words:

"Yes, quality and durability—quality and durability. I also have here to-day, and will offer you, gentlemen, a surpassing antique, not built of wood nor fashioned in brass or iron, but a thing long attached to these acres and his house. I present for your consideration the married life of John Templeton and Hannah his wife. They lived together forty years, and the record scarcely shows a dent. In all that time hardly a word of love passed between them; but never a word of hatred, either. They had a kind of hard and fast understanding, like the laws of Moses. He did the work of the fields and she did the work of the house, from sunrise to sunset. On Sunday they went to church together. He got out at five o'clock to milk and harness up; and it made double work for her, what with getting the children cleaned, and the milk taken care of, and the Sunday dinner made ready. But neither he nor she ever doubted or complained. It was the Lord's way. She bore him eight children. She told him before the last one came that she was not equal to it. . . . After that she was an invalid for seventeen years until she died. And there was loss of children to bear between them, and sickness, and creeping age—but this bit of furniture held firm to the last. Gentlemen, it was made solid, no veneer, a good job all the way through."

As he spoke I thought that his roving eye (perhaps it was only my own!) fell upon Johnny Holcomb, whose married life has been full of vicissitudes.

"John, take this home with you; *you* can use it."

"Nope, no such married life for me," I thought I could hear him responding, rather pleased than not to be the butt of the auctioneer.

"Do I hear any bids?" the Great Auctioneer was saying, almost in the words of Mr. Harpworth. *"What!* No one wants a married life like this? Well, put it aside, Jake. It isn't wanted. Too old-fashioned."

It was Julia Templeton herself who now appeared with certain of the intimate and precious "bedroom things"—a wonderful old linen bedspread, wrought upon with woollen figures, and exhaling an ancient and exquisite odour of lavender, and a rag rug or so, and a little old rocking chair with chintz coverings in which more than one Templeton mother had rocked her baby to sleep. Julia herself——

I saw Julia, that hard-favoured woman, for the first time at that moment, really saw her. How fiercely she threw down the spread and the rugs! How bold and unweeping her eyes! How hard and straight the lines of her mouth!

"Here they are, Mr. Harpworth!"

How shrill her voice; and how quickly she turned back to the noisy kitchen! I could see the angular form, the streakings of gray in her hair. . . .

"What am I offered now for this precious antique? This hand-made spread? Everything sold without reserve! Come, now, don't let this opportunity slip by." He leaned forward confidentially and persuasively: "Fellah citizens, styles change and fashions pass away, but things made like these, good lines, strong material, honest work, they never grow old. . . ."

Here the Shadowy Auctioneer broke in again and lifted me out of that limited moment.

"A true word!" he was saying. "Styles change and fashions pass away, and only those things that are well made, and made for service—the beautiful things—remain. I am offering to-day, without reservation, another precious antique. What will you give for such a religious faith as that of John Templeton? Worn for a lifetime and sound to the end. He read the Bible every

Sunday morning of his life, went to church, and did his religious duty by his children. Do you remember young Joe Templeton? Wouldn't learn his chapter one Sunday, and the old gentleman prayed about it and then beat him with a hitching strap. Joe ran away from home and made his fortune in Minnesota. Nearly broke the mother's heart, and old John's, too; but he thought it right, and never repented it. Gentlemen, an honest man who feared God and lived righteously all his days! What am I offered for this durable antique, this characteristic product of New England? Do I hear a bid?"

At this I felt coming over me that strange urge of the auction, to bid and to buy. A rare possession indeed, not without a high, stern kind of beauty! It would be wonderful to possess such a faith; but what had I to offer that Shadowy Auctioneer? What coin that would redeem past times and departed beliefs?

It was curious how the words of Mr. Harpworth fitted into the fabric of my imaginings. When he next attracted my attention he was throwing up his hands in a fine semblance of despair. We were such obtuse purchasers!

"I think," said Mr. Harpworth, "that this crowd came here to-day only to eat Julia Templeton's auction luncheon. What's the matter with this here generation? You don't want things that are well made and durable, but only things that are cheap and flashy. Put 'er aside, Jake. We'll sell 'er yet to some historical museum devoted to the habits and customs of the early Americans."

He was plainly disgusted with us, and we felt it keenly, and were glad and pleased when, a moment later, he gave evidence of being willing to go on with us, paltry as we were.

"Jake, pass up that next treasure."

His spirits were returning; his eyes gleamed approvingly upon the newly presented antique. He looked at us with fresh confidence; he was still hopeful that we would rise to his former good opinion of us.

"And now before I sell the hall clock—by Willard, date of 1822—I am going to offer what is probably the best single piece in this sale. . . ."

Here again the Old Auctioneer, having caught his cue, broke in. When he spoke, who could listen to Mr. Harpworth?

" . . . the best single piece in this sale, gentlemen! I offer you now the Templeton family pride! A choice product of old New England. A little battered, but still good and sound. The Templetons! They never did anything notable except to work, work early and late, summer and winter, for three generations. They were proud of any one who bore the Templeton name; they were proud even of Jim, simple Jim, who got a job driving the delivery wagon at the hill store, and drove it for twenty-two years and was drowned in Mill River. I'll tell you what family pride meant to old John Templeton. . . ."

I thought he leaned forward to take us into his confidence, motioning at the same time toward the house.

"You know Julia Templeton——"

Know her? Of course we knew her! Knew her as only the country knows its own.

"When Julia ran away with that sewing-machine agent—it was her only chance!—old John Templeton drove his best cow into town and sold her, he mortgaged his team of horses, and went after the girl and brought her home with him. They were firm and strong and as righteous as God with her; and they paid off, without whining, the mortgages on the horses, and never spoke of the loss of the cow—but never forgot it. They held up their heads to the end. Gentlemen, what am I offered for this interesting antique, this rare work of art?"

The auction was considered, upon the whole, a great success. Mr. Harpworth himself said so. Ike, the Jewish dealer, bought the family clock and the spring-tooth harrow, and even bid on the family crayon portraits (the frames could be sold for something or other); a Swede bought the pigs and the old buggy; an Irish teamster bid in John Templeton's horses, and a Pole, a good man, I know him well, bought the land, and will no doubt keep his geese in the summer kitchen, and get rich from the cultivation of the ancient fields. While old John Templeton bowed himself humbly before a wrathful God he would never go down on his knees, as the Poles do, to the fertile earth. And—I forgot—an Italian from Nortontown bought for a song the apple and chestnut crops, and busy third generation Americans loaded in the antiques and drove off with them to the city.

The last I saw of Julia Templeton, that hard-favoured woman, she was standing, an angular figure, in the midst of the wreck of the luncheon dishes, one arm wrapped in her apron, the other hand shading her eyes while she watched the company, in wagons and automobiles, trailing away to the westward, and the towns. . . .

The sale was over; but the most valuable antiques of all found no purchasers: they were left behind with Julia Templeton: only she could use them.

XII

A WOMAN OF FORTY-FIVE

W E HAVE an Astonishing Woman in this community. She acts in a way that no one expects, and while we are intensely interested in everything she does, and desire to know about it to the uttermost detail, we are inclined to speak of her in bated breath.

Some Woman to Talk About in a country neighbourhood is a kind of public necessity. She fills one of the stated functions like the town assessor, or the president of the Dorcas Society; and if ever the office falls vacant we have immediate resort to one of those silent elections at which we choose our town celebrities. There are usually several candidates, and the campaign is accompanied by much heated argument and exemplification. We have our staunch party men and our irresponsible independents on whom you can never put your finger; and if we are sometimes a little vague in our discussion of principles and issues we share with our national political leaders an intense interest in personalities. Prominent citizens "come out" for this candidate or that, we "spring surprises," and launch new booms, and often, at the last moment, we are taken off our feet by the circulation of rohrbacks. I take a pardonable pride, however, in saying, to the credit of our democratic institutions, that most of the candidates elected are chosen strictly upon merit.

I shall never forget the afternoon, now more than a year ago, that Harriet came up the road bearing the news which, beyond a doubt, placed the present incumbent in office; and has served to keep her there, despite the efforts in certain quarters, which shall be nameless, to use that pernicious instrument of radicalism, the recall.

I can always tell when Harriet brings important news. She has a slightly quicker step, carries her head a little more firmly, and when she speaks impresses her message upon me with a lowered voice. When Harriet looks at me severely and drops down an octave I prepare for the worst.

"David," she said, "Mary Starkweather has gone to live in the barn!"

"In the *barn!*"

"In the barn."

I don't know quite why it is, but I dislike being surprised, and do my best to cover it up, and, besides, I have always liked Mary Starkweather. So I remarked, as casually as I could:

"Why not? It's a perfectly good barn."

"David Grayson!"

"Well, it is. It's a better building to-day than many of the people of this town live in. Why shouldn't Mary Starkweather live in the barn if she wants to? It's her barn."

"But, *David*—there are her children—and her husband!"

"There always are, when anybody wants to live in a barn."

"I shall not talk with you any more," said Harriet, "until you can be serious."

I had my punishment, as I richly deserved to have, in the gnawing of unsatisfied curiosity, which is almost as distressing as a troubled conscience.

Within the next few days, I remember, I heard the great news buzzing everywhere I went. We had conjectured that the barn was being refitted for the family of a caretaker, and it was Mary Starkweather herself, our sole dependable representative of the Rich, who was moving in! Mary Starkweather, who had her house in town, and her home in the country, and her automobiles, and her servants, and her pictures, and her books, to say nothing of her husband and her children and her children's maid—going to live in her barn! I leave it to you if there was not a valid reason for our commotion.

It must have been two weeks later that I went to town by the upper hill road in order to pass the Starkweather place. It is a fine old estate, the buildings, except the barn, set well back from the road with a spacious garden near them, and pleasant fields stretching away on every hand. As I skirted the shoulder of the hill I looked eagerly for the first glimpse of the barn. I confess that I had woven a thousand stories to explain the mystery, and had reached the point where I could no longer resist seeing if I could solve it.

Well, the barn was transformed. Two or three new windows, a door with a little porch, a lattice or so for vines, a gable upon the roof lifting an inquiring eyebrow—and what was once a barn had become a charming cottage. It seemed curiously to have come alive, to have acquired a personality of its own. A corner of the great garden had been cut off and included in the miniature grounds of the cottage; and a simple arbour had been built against a background of wonderful beech trees. You felt at once a kind of fondness for it.

I saw Mary Starkweather in her garden, in a large straw hat, with a trowel in her hand.

"How are you, David Grayson?" she called out when I stopped.

"I have been planning for several days," I said, "to happen casually by your new house."

"Have you?"

"You don't know how you have stirred our curiosity. We haven't had a good night's rest since you moved in."

"I've no doubt of it," she laughed. "Won't you come in? I'd like to tell you all about it."

"I also prepared to make excuses for not stopping," I said, "and thought up various kinds of urgent business, such as buying a new snow shovel to use next winter, but after making these excuses I intended to stop—if I were sufficiently urged."

"You are more than urged: you are commanded."

As I followed her up the walk she said earnestly:

"Will you do me a favour? When you come in will you tell me the first impression my living-room gives you? No second thoughts. Tell me instantly."

315

"I'll do it," I said, my mind leaping eagerly to all manner of mysterious surmises.

At the centre of the room she turned toward me and with a sweeping backward motion of the arms, made me a bow—a strong figure instinct with confident grace: a touch of gray in the hair, a fleeting look of old sadness about the eyes.

"Now, David Grayson," she said, "quick!"

It was not that the room itself was so remarkable as that it struck me as being confusingly different from the heavily comfortable rooms of the old Starkweather house with their crowded furnishings, their overloaded mantels, their plethoric bookcases.

"I cannot think of you yet," I stumbled, "as being here."

"Isn't it *like* me?"

"It is a beautiful room——" I groped lamely.

"I was afraid you would say that."

"But it is. It really is."

"Then I've failed, after all."

She said it lightly enough, but there was an undertone of real disappointment in her voice.

"I'm in rather the predicament," I said, "of old Abner Coates. You probably don't know Abner. He sells nursery stock, and each spring when he comes around and I tell him that the peach trees or the raspberry bushes I bought of him the year before have not done well, he says, with the greatest astonishment, 'Wal, now, ye ain't said what I hoped ye would.' I see that I haven't said what you hoped I would."

It was too serious a matter, however, for Mary Starkweather to joke about.

"But, David Grayson," she said, "isn't it *simple?*"

I glanced around me with swift new comprehension.

"Why, yes, it *is* simple."

I saw that my friend was undergoing some deep inner change of which this room, this renovated barn, were mere symbols.

"Tell me," I said, "how you came to such a right-about-face."

"It's just that!" she returned earnestly. "It *is* a right-about-face. I think I am really in earnest for the first time in my life."

I had a moment of flashing wonder if her marriage had not

316

been in earnest, a flashing picture of Richard Starkweather with his rather tired, good-humoured face, and I wondered if her children were not earnest realities to her, if her busy social life had meant nothing. Then I reflected that we all have such moments, when the richest experiences of the past seem as nothing in comparison with the fervour of this glowing moment.

"Everything in my life in the past," she was saying, "seems to have happened to me. Life has done things *for* me; I have had so few chances of doing anything for myself."

"And now you are expressing yourself."

"Almost for the first time in my life!"

She paused. "All my life, it seems to me, I have been smothered with things. Just things! Too much of everything. All my time has been taken up in caring for things and none in enjoying them."

"I understand!" I said with a warm sense of corroboration and sympathy.

"I had so many pictures on my walls that I never saw, really saw, any of them. I saw the dust on them, I saw the cracks in the frames that needed repairing, I even saw better ways of arranging them, but I very rarely saw, with the inner eye, what the artists were trying to tell me. And how much time I have wasted on mere food and clothing—it is appalling! I had become nothing short of a slave to my house and my things."

"I see now," I said, "why you have just one rose on your table."

"Yes"—she returned eagerly—"isn't it a beauty! I spent half an hour this morning looking for the best and most perfect rose in the garden, and there it is!"

She was now all alight with her idea, and I saw her, as we sometimes see our oldest friends, as though I had not seen her before. She was that phenomenon of the modern world—the free woman of forty-five.

When a woman reaches the old age of youth, the years between forty and forty-five, she either surrenders or revolts. In the older days in America it was nearly always surrender. Those women of a past generation bore many children: how many graves there are in our hill cemeteries of women of forty to fifty who died leaving families of five or eight or ten children! How many second and third wives there were, often with second and third families. Or if they did not die, how terribly they toiled, keeping the house, clothing the children, cooking the food. Or if they bore no children, yet they were bound down by a thousand chains of convention and formality.

But in these days we have a woman of forty-five who has not surrendered. She is a vigorous, experienced, active-minded human being, just beginning to look restlessly around her and take a new interest in the world. Such a woman was Mary Stark-weather; and this was her first revolt.

"You cannot imagine," she was saying, "what a joy it has been to unaccumulate! To get rid of things! To select."

"To become an artist in life!"

"Yes! At last! What a lot of perfectly worthless trash accumulates around us. Not beautiful, not even useful! And it is not only the lives of the well-to-do that are choked and cluttered with things. I wish you could see the house of our Polish farmer. He's been saving money, and filling up his house with perfectly worthless ornaments—ornate clocks, gorgeous plush furniture, impossible rugs—and yet he is only doing what we are all doing on a more elaborate scale."

I laughed.

"That reminds me of a family of squirrels that lives in an oak tree on my hill," I said. "I am never tired of watching them. In the fall they work desperately, stealing all the hickory nuts and chestnuts on my neighbour Horace's back pastures, five times as many as they need, and then they forget, half the time, where they've hidden them. We're all more or less in the squirrel stage of civilization."

"Yes," she responded. "There are my books! I gathered up books for years, just squirrel fashion, until I forgot what I had or where I put them. You cannot know what joy I'm going to have in selecting just the essential books, the ones I want by me for daily companions. All the others, I see now, are temporary rubbish."

"And you've made your selections?"

"No, but I'm making them. You'll laugh when you come next time and I show them to you. Oh, I am going to be stern with myself. I'm not going to put a single book in that case for show, nor a single one to give the impression that I'm profoundly interested in Egypt or Maeterlinck or woman suffrage, when I'm positively not."

"It's terribly risky," I said.

"And I'm terribly reckless," she responded.

As I went onward toward the town I looked back from the hilltop beyond the big house for a last glimpse of the reconstructed barn, and with a curious warm sense of having been admitted to a new adventure. Here was life changing under my eyes! Here was a human being struggling with one of the deep common problems that come to all of us. The revolt from things! The struggle with superfluities!

And yet as I walked along the cool aisles of the woods with the quiet fields opening here and there to the low hill ridges, and saw the cattle feeding, and heard a thrush singing in a thicket, I found myself letting go—how can I explain it?—relaxing! I had been keyed up to a high pitch there in that extraordinary room. Yes, it *was* beautiful—and yet as I thought of the sharp little green gate, the new gable, the hard, clean mantel with the cloisonné vase, it wanted something. . . .

As I was gathering the rowen crop of after-enjoyment which rewards us when we reflect freshly upon our adventures, whom should I meet but Richard Starkweather himself in his battered machine. The two boys, one of whom was driving, and the little girl, were with him.

"How are you, David?" he called out. "Whoa, there! Draw up, Jamie."

We looked at each other for a moment with that quizzical, half-humorous look that so often conveys, better than any spoken words, the sympathetic greeting of friends. I like Richard Starkweather.

He had come up from the city looking rather worn, for the weather had been trying. He has blue, honest, direct-gazing eyes with small humour wrinkles at the corners. I never knew a man with fewer theories, or with a simpler devotion to the thing at hand, whatever it may be. At everything else he smiles, not cynically, for he is too modest in his regard for his own knowledge; he smiles at everything else because it doesn't seem quite real to him.

"Been up to see Mary's new house?" he asked.

"Yes." And for the life of me I couldn't help smiling in response.

"It's a wonder—isn't it?"

He thought his wife a very extraordinary woman. I remember his saying to me once, "David, she's got the soul of a poet and brain of a general."

"It *is* a wonder," I responded.

"I can't decide yet what chair to sit in, nor just what she wants the kids to do."

I still smiled.

"I expect she hasn't determined yet," he went drawling on, "in what chair I will look most decorative."

He ruminated.

"You know, she's got the idea that there's too much of everything—guess there is, too—and that she ought to select only those things that are essential. I've been wondering, if she had more than one husband whether or not she'd select me——"

The restless young Jamie was now starting the machine, and Richard Starkweather leaned out and said to me in parting:

"Isn't she a wonder! Did all the planning herself—wouldn't have an architect—wouldn't have a decorator—all I could do——"

As he turned around I saw him throw one arm carelessly about the shoulders of the sturdy younger boy who sat next him.

When I got home I told Harriet all about what I had seen and heard. I think I must feel when I am retailing such fascinating neighbourhood events to Harriet—how she *does* enjoy them!—I must feel very much as she does when she is urging me to have just a little more of the new gingerbread.

In the next few months I watched with indescribable interest the unfolding of the drama of Mary Starkweather. I saw her from time to time that summer and she seemed, and I think she

320

was, happier than ever she had been before in her whole life. Making over her garden, selecting the "essential books," choosing the best pictures for her rooms, even reforming the clothing of the boys, all with an emphasis upon perfect simplicity—her mind was completely absorbed. Occasionally Richard appeared upon the stage, a kind of absurd Greek chorus of one, who remarked what a wonderful woman this was and poked fun at himself and at the new house, and asserted that Mary could be as simple as ever she liked, he insisted on thick soup for dinner and would not sacrifice his beloved old smoking jacket upon the altar of any new idea.

"She's a wonder, David," he'd wind up; "but this simple life is getting more complicated every day."

It was in December, about the middle of the month, as I remember, that I had a note one day from Mary Starkweather.

"The next time you go to town," it ran, "stop in and see me. I've made a discovery."

With such a note as that in my hand it appeared imperative that I go to town at once. I discovered, to Harriet's astonishment, that we were running out of all sorts of necessaries.

"Now, David," she said, "you know perfectly well that you're just making up to call on Mary Starkweather."

"That," I said, "relieves my conscience of a great burden."

As I went out of the door I heard her saying: "Why Mary Starkweather should *care* to live in her barn. . . ."

It was a sparkling cold day, sun on the snow and the track crunching under one's feet, and I walked swiftly and with a warm sense of coming adventure.

To my surprise there was no smoke in the cottage chimney, and when I reached the door I found a card pinned upon it:

PLEASE CALL AT THE HOUSE

Mary Starkweather herself opened the door—she had seen me coming—and took me into the big comfortable old living-room, the big, cluttered, overfurnished living-room, with the two worn upholstered chairs at the fireplace, in which a bright log fire was now burning. There was a pleasant litter of books and

321

magazines, and a work basket on the table, and in the bay window an ugly but cheerful green rubber plant in a tub.

"Well!" I exclaimed.

"Don't smile—not yet."

As I looked at her I felt not at all like smiling.

"I know," she was saying, "it does have a humorous side. I can see that. Dick has seen it all along. Do you know, although Dick pretends to pooh-pooh everything intellectual, he has a really penetrating mind."

I had a sudden vision of Dick in his old smoking jacket, standing in the midst of the immaculate cottage that was once a barn, holding his pipe with one finger crooked around the stem just in front of his nose in the way he had, and smiling across at me.

"Have you deserted the cottage entirely?"

"Oh, we may possibly go back in the spring——" She paused and looked into the fire, her fine, strong face a little sad in composure, full of thought.

"I am trying to be honest with myself, David. Honest above everything else. That's fundamental. It seems to me I have wanted most of all to learn how to live my life more freely and finely. . . . I thought I was getting myself free of things when, as a matter of fact, I was devoting more time to them than ever before—and, besides that, making life more or less uncomfortable for Dick and the children. So I've taken my courage squarely in my hands and come back here into this blessed old home, this blessed, ugly, stuffy old home—I've learned *that* lesson."

At this, she glanced up at me with that rare smile which sometimes shines out of her very nature: the smile that is herself.

"I found," she said, "that when I had finished the work of becoming simple—there was nothing else left to do."

I laughed outright, for I couldn't help it, and she joined me. How we do like people who can laugh at themselves.

"But," I said, "there was sound sense in a great deal that you were trying to do."

"The fireplace smoked; and the kitchen sink froze up; and the cook left because we couldn't keep her room warm."

"But you were right," I interrupted, "and I am not going to be put off by smoking fireplaces or chilly cooks; you were right. We do have too much, we are smothered in things, we don't enjoy what we do have——"

I paused.

"And you were making a beautiful thing, a beautiful house."

"The trouble with making a beautiul thing," she replied, "is that when you have got it done you must straightway make another. Now I don't want to keep on building houses or furnishing rooms. I am not after beauty—I mean primarily—what I want is to *live,* live simply, live greatly."

She was desperately in earnest.

"Perhaps," I said, feeling as though I were treading on dangerous ground, "you were trying to be simple for the sake of being simple. I wonder if true simplicity is ever anything but a by-product. If we aim directly for it, it eludes us; but if we are on fire with some great interest that absorbs our lives to the uttermost, we forget ourselves into simplicity. Everything falls into simple lines around us, like a worn garment."

I had the rather uncomfortable feeling on the way home that I had been preachy; and the moment you become preachy you begin to build up barriers between yourself and your friends: but that's a defect of character I've never been able, quite, to overcome. I keep thinking I've got the better of it, but along will come a beautiful temptation and down I go—and come out as remorseful as I was that afternoon on the way home from Mary Starkweather's.

A week or two later I happened to meet Richard Starkweather on the street in Hempfield. He was on his way home.

"Yes," he said, "we're in the old house again until spring, anyway. I haven't been so comfortable in a year. And, say," here he looked at me quizzically, "Mary has joined the new cemetery association; you know they're trying to improve the resting places of the forefathers, and, by George, if they didn't elect her chairman at the first meeting. She's a wonder!"

XIII

HIS MAJESTY—BILL RICHARDS

WELL, I have just been having an amusing and delightful adventure—and have come to know a Great Common Person. His name is Bill Richards, and he is one of the hereditary monarchs of America. He belongs to our ruling dynasty.

I first saw Bill about two weeks ago, and while I was strongly interested in him I had no idea, at the time, that I should ever come to know him well. It was a fine June day, and I was riding on the new trolley line that crosses the hills to Hewlett—a charming trip through a charming country—and there in the open car just in front of me sat Bill himself. One huge bare forearm rested on the back of the seat, the rich red blood showing through the weathered brown of the skin. His clean brown neck rose strongly from the loose collar of his shirt, which covered but could not hide the powerful lines of his shoulders. He wore blue denim and khaki, and a small round felt hat tipped up jauntily at the back. He had crisp, coarse light hair, rather thin—not by age, but by nature—so that the ruddy scalp could be seen through it, and strong jaws and large firm features, and if the beard was two days old, his face was so brown, so full of youthful health, that it gave no ill impression.

He could not sit still for the very life that was in him. He seemed to have some grand secret with the conductor and frequently looked around at him, his eyes full of careless laughter, and once or twice he called out—some jocose remark. He helped the conductor, in pantomime, to pull the cord and stop or start the car, and he watched with the liveliest interest each passenger getting on or getting off. A rather mincing young girl with a flaring red ribbon at her throat was to him the finest comedy in the world, so that he had to wink a telegram to the conductor about her. An old woman with a basket of vegetables who delayed the car was exquisitely funny.

I set him down as being about twenty-two years old and some kind of outdoor workman, not a farmer.

When he got off, which was before the car stopped, so that he had to jump and run with it, he gave a wild flourish with both arms, grimaced at the conductor, and went off down the road whistling for all he was worth. How I enjoyed the sight of him! He was so charged with youthful energy, so overflowing with the joy of life, that he could scarcely contain himself. What a fine place the world was to him! And what comical and interesting people it contained! I was sorry when he got off.

Two or three days later I was on my way up the town road north of my farm when I was astonished and delighted to see Bill for the second time. He was coming down the road pulling a wire over the crosspiece of a tall telephone pole (the company is rebuilding and enlarging its system through our town). He was holding the wire close drawn over his right shoulder, his strong hands gripped and pressed upon his breast. The veins stood out in his brown neck where the burlap shoulder pad he wore was drawn aside by the wire. He leaned forward, stepping first on his toe, which he dug into the earth and then, heavily letting down his heel, he drew the other foot forward somewhat stiffly. The muscles stood out in his powerful shoulders and thighs. His legs were double-strapped with climbing spurs. He was a master lineman.

As I came alongside he turned a good-humoured sweaty face toward me.

"It's dang hot," said he.

"It is," said I.

There is something indescribably fascinating about the sight of a strong workman in the full swing of his work, something— yes, beautiful! A hard pull of a job, with a strong man doing it joyfully, what could be finer to see? And he gave such a jaunty sense of youth and easy strength!

325

I watched him for some time, curiously interested, and thought I should like well to know him, but could not see just how to go about it.

The man astride the cross-arm who was heaving the wire forward from the spool on the distant truck suddenly cried out:

"Ease up there, Bill, she's caught."

So Bill eased up and drew his arm across his dripping face.

"How many wires are you putting up?" I asked, fencing for some opening.

"Three," said Bill.

Before I could get in another stroke the man on the pole shouted:

"Let 'er go, Bill." And Bill let 'er go, and buckled down again to his job.

"Gee, but it's hot," said he.

In the country there are not so many people passing our way that we cannot be interested in all of them. That evening I could not help thinking about Bill, the lineman, wondering where he came from, how he happened to be what he was, who and what sort were the friends he made, and the nature of his ambitions, if he had any. Talk about going to the North Pole! It is not to be compared, for downright fascination, with the exploration of an undiscovered human being.

With that I began to think how I might get at Bill, the lineman, and not merely weather talk, or wages talk, or work talk, but at Bill himself. He was a character quite unusual in our daily lives here in the country. I wondered what his interests could be, surely not mine nor Horace's nor the Starkweathers'. As soon as I began trying to visualize what his life might be, I warmed up to a grand scheme of capturing him, if by chance he was to be found the next day upon the town road.

All this may seem rather absurd in the telling, but I found it a downright good adventure for a quiet evening, and fully believe I felt for the moment like General Joffre planning to meet the Germans on the Marne.

"I have it!" I said aloud.

"You have what?" asked Harriet, somewhat startled.

"The grandest piece of strategy ever devised in this town," said I.

With that I went delving in a volume of universal information I keep near me, one of those knowing books that tells you how tall the great Pyramid is and why a hen cackles after laying an egg, and having found what I wanted I asked Harriet if she could find a tape measure around the place. She is a wonderful person and knows where everything is. When she handed me the tape measure she asked me what in the world I was so mysterious about.

"Harriet," I said, "I'm going on a great adventure. I'll tell you all about it to-morrow."

"Nonsense," said Harriet.

It is this way with the fancies of the evening—they often look flat and flabby and gray the next morning. Quite impossible! But if I'd acted on half the good and grand schemes I've had o' nights I might now be quite a remarkable person.

I went about my work the next morning just as usual. I even avoided looking at the little roll of tape on the corner of the mantel as I went out. It seemed a kind of badge of my absurdity. But about the middle of the forenoon, while I was in my garden, I heard a tremendous racket up the road. Rattle—bang, zip, toot! As I looked up I saw the boss lineman and his crew careering up the road in their truck, and the bold driver was driving like Jehu, the son of Nimshi. And there were ladders and poles clattering out behind, and rolls of wire on upright spools rattling and flashing in the sunshine, and the men of the crew were sitting along the sides of the truck with hats off and hair flying as they came bumping and bounding up the road. It was a brave thing to see going by on a spring morning!

As they passed, whom should I see but Bill himself, at the top of the load, with a broad smile on his face. When his eye fell on me he threw up one arm, and gave me the railroad salute.

"Hey, there!" he shouted.

"Hey there, yourself," I shouted in return—and could not help it.

I had a curious warm feeling of being taken along with that jolly crowd of workmen, with Bill on the top of the load.

It was this that finished me. I hurried through an early dinner, and taking the tape measure off the mantel I put it in my pocket as though it were a revolver or a bomb, and went off up the road feeling as adventurous as ever I felt in my life. I never said a word to Harriet but disappeared quietly around the lilac bushes. I was going to waylay that crew, and especially Bill. I hoped to catch them at their nooning.

Well, I was lucky. About a quarter of a mile up the road, in a little valley near the far corner of Horace's farm, I found the truck, and Bill just getting out his dinner pail. It seems they had flipped pennies and Bill had been left behind with the truck and the tools while the others went down to the mill pond in the valley below.

"How are you?" said I.

"How are *you*?" said he.

I could see that he was rather cross over having been left behind.

"Fine day," said I.

"You bet," said he.

He got out his pail, which was a big one, and seated himself on the roadside, a grassy, comfortable spot near the brook which runs below into the pond. There were white birches and hemlocks on the hill, and somewhere in the thicket I heard a wood thrush singing.

"Did you ever see John L. Sullivan?" I asked.

He glanced up at me quickly, but with new interest.

"No, did you?"

"Or Bob Fitzsimmons?"

"Nope—but I was mighty near it once. I've seen 'em both in the movies."

"Well, sir," said I, "that's interesting. I should like to see them myself. Do you know what made me speak of them?"

He had spread down a newspaper and was taking the luncheon out of his "bucket," as he called it, including a large bottle of coffee; but he paused and looked at me with keen interest.

"Well," said I, "when I saw you dragging that wire yesterday I took you to be a pretty husky citizen yourself."

He grinned and took a big mouthful from one of his sandwiches. I could see that my shot had gone home.

"So when I got back last night," I said, "I looked up the arm measurements of Sullivan and Fitzsimmons in a book I have and got to wondering how they compared with mine and yours. They were considerably larger than mine——"

Bill thought this a fine joke and laughed out in great good humour.

"But I imagine you'd not be far behind either of them."

He looked at me a little suspiciously, as if doubtful what I was driving at or whether or not I was joking him. But I was as serious as the face of nature; and proceeded at once to get out my tape measure.

"I get very much interested in such things," I said, "and I had enough curiosity to want to see how big your arm really was."

He smiled broadly.

"You're a queer one," said he.

But he took another bite of sandwich, and clenching his great fist drew up his forearm until the biceps muscles looked like a roll of Vienna bread—except that they had the velvety gleam of life. So I measured first one arm, then the other.

"By George!" said I, "you're ahead of Fitzsimmons, but not quite up to Sullivan."

"Fitz wasn't a heavy man," said Bill, "but a dead game fighter."

I saw then that I had him! So I sat down on the grass near by and we had great talk about the comparative merits of Fitzsimmons and Sullivan and Corbett and Jack Johnson, a department of knowledge in which he outdistanced me. He even told me of an exploit or two of his own, which showed that he was able to take care of himself.

While we talked he ate his luncheon, and a downright gargantuan luncheon it was, backed by an appetite which if it were offered to the highest bidder on the New York Stock Exchange would, I am convinced, bring at least ten thousand dollars in cash. It even made me envious.

There were three huge corned-beef sandwiches, three hard-boiled eggs, a pickle six inches long and fat to boot, four dough-nuts so big that they resembled pitching quoits, a bottle of coffee and milk, a quarter of a pie, and, to cap the climax, an immense raw onion. It was worth a long journey to see Bill eat that onion. He took out his clasp knife, and after stripping off the papery outer shell, cut the onion into thick dewy slices. Then he opened one of the sandwiches and placed several of them on the beef, afterward sprinkling them with salt from a small paper parcel. Having restored the top slice of bread he took a moon-shaped bite out of one end of this glorified sandwich.

"I like onions," said he.

When we first sat down he had offered to share his luncheon with me but I told him I had just been to dinner, and I observed that he had no difficulty in taking care of every crumb in his "bucket." It was wonderful to see.

Having finished his luncheon he went down to the brook and got a drink, and then sat down comfortably with his back among the ferns of the roadside, crossed his legs, and lit his pipe. There was a healthy and wholesome flush in his face, and as he blew off the first cloud of smoke he drew a sigh of complete comfort and looked around at me with a lordly air such as few mon-archs, no matter how well fed, could have bettered. He had worked and sweat for what he got, and was now taking his ease in his roadside inn. I wonder sometimes if anybody in the world experiences keener joys than unwatched common people.

How we talked! From pugilists we proceeded to telephones, and from that to wages, hours, and strikes, and from that we leaped easily to Alaska and gold-mining, and touched in passing upon Theodore Roosevelt.

"I was just thinking," I said, "that you and I can enjoy some things that were beyond the reach of the greatest kings of the world."

"How's that?" said he.

"Why, Napoleon never saw a telephone nor talked through one."

"That's so!" he laughed.

"And Cæsar couldn't have dreamed that such a thing as you are doing now was a possibility—nor George Washington, either."

"Say, that's so. I never thought o' that."

"Why," I said, "the world is only half as big as it was before you fellows came along stringing your wires! I can get to town now from my farm in two minutes, when it used to take me an hour."

I really believe I gave him more of his own business than ever he had before, for he listened so intently that his pipe went out.

I found that Bill was from Ohio, and that he had been as far south as Atlanta and as far west as Denver. He got his three dollars and a half a day, rain or shine, and thought it wonderful pay; and besides, he was seein' the country "free, gratis, fer nothing."

He got his coat out of the truck and took from the pocket a many-coloured folder.

"Say, Mister, have you ever been to the Northwest?"

"No," said I.

"Well, it's a great country, and I'm goin' up there."

He spread out the glittering folder and placed his big fore-finger on a spot about the size of Rhode Island somewhere this side of the Rockies.

"How'll you do it?" I asked.

"Oh, a lineman can go anywhere," said he with a flourish. "A lineman don't have to beg a job. Besides, I got eighty dollars sewed up."

Talk about freedom! Never have I got a clearer impression of it than Bill gave me that day. No millionaire, no potentate, could touch him.

The crew came back all too soon for me. Bill knocked the ashes out of his pipe on his boot heel, and put his "bucket" back in the truck. Five minutes later he was climbing a tall pole with legs bowed out, striking in his spikes at each step. From the cross-arm, up among the hemlock tops, he called out to me:

"Good-bye, pard."

"Stop in, Bill, and see me when you come by my place," said I.

"You bet," said he.

And he did, the next day, and I showed him off to Harriet, who brought him a plate of her best doughnuts and asked him about his mother.

Yesterday I saw him again careering by in the truck. The job was finished. He waved his hand at me.

"I'm off," said he.

"Where?" I shouted.

"Canada."

XIV

ON LIVING IN THE COUNTRY

"Why risk with men your hard won gold?
Buy grain and sow—your Brother Dust
Will pay you back a hundred fold—
The earth commits no breach of trust."

IT IS astonishing how many people there are in cities and towns who have a secret longing to get back into quiet country places, to own a bit of the soil of the earth, and to cultivate it. To some it appears as a troublesome malady only in spring and will be relieved by a whirl or two in country roads, by a glimpse of the hills, or a day by the sea; but to others the home-sickness is deeper seated and will be quieted by no hasty visits. These must actually go home.

I have had, in recent years, many letters from friends asking about life in the country, but the longer I remain here, the more I know about it, the less able I am to answer them—at least briefly. It is as though one should come and ask: "Is love worth trying?" or, "How about religion?" For country life is to each human being a fresh, strange, original adventure. We enjoy it, or we do not enjoy it, or more probably, we do both. It is packed and crowded with the zest of adventure, or it is dull and miserable. We may, if we are skilled enough, make our whole living from the land, or only a part of it, or we may find in a few cherished acres the inspiration and power for other work, whatever it may be. There is many a man whose strength is renewed like that of the wrestler of Irassa, every time his feet touch the earth.

Of all places in the world where life can be lived to its fullest and freest, where it can be met in its greatest variety and beauty, I am convinced that there is none to equal the open country, or the country town. For all country people in these days may have the city—some city or town not too far away: but there are millions of men and women in America who have no country and no sense of the country. What do they not lose out of life!

I know well the disadvantages charged against country life at its worst. At its worst there are long hours and much lonely labour and an income pitifully small. Drudgery, yes, especially for the women, and loneliness. But where is there not drudgery when men are poor—where life is at its worst? I have never seen drudgery in the country comparable for a moment to the dreary and lonely drudgery of city tenements, city mills, factories, and sweat shops. And in recent years both the drudgery and loneliness of country life have been disappearing before the motor and trolley car, the telephone, the rural post, the gasoline engine. I have seen a machine plant as many potatoes in one day as a man, at hand work, could have planted in a week. While there is, indeed, real drudgery in the country, much that is looked upon as drudgery by people who long for easy ways and a soft life, is only good, honest, wholesome hard work—the kind of work that makes for fiber in a man or in a nation, the kind that most city life in no wise provides.

There are a thousand nuisances and annoyances that men must meet who come face to face with nature itself. You have set out your upper acres to peach trees: and the deer come down from the hills at night and strip the young foliage; or the field mice in winter, working under the snow, girdle and kill them. The season brings too much rain and the potatoes rot in the ground, the crows steal the corn, the bees swarm when no one is watching, the cow smothers her calf, the hens' eggs prove infertile, and a storm in a day ravages a crop that has been growing all summer. A constant warfare with insects and blights and fungi—a real, bitter warfare, which can cease neither summer nor winter!

It is something to meet, year after year, the quiet implacability of the land. While it is patient, it never waits long for you. There is a chosen time for planting, a time for cultivating, a time for harvesting. You accept the gauge thrown down—well and good, you shall have a chance to fight! You do not accept it? There is no complaint. The land cheerfully springs up to wild yellow mustard and dandelion and pig-weed—and will be productive and beautiful in spite of you.

Nor can you enter upon the full satisfaction of cultivating even a small piece of land at second hand. To be accepted as One Who Belongs, there must be sweat and weariness.

The other day I was digging with Dick in a ditch that is to run down through the orchard and connect finally with the land drain we put in four years ago. We laid the tile just in the gravel below the silt, about two feet deep, covering the openings with tar paper and then throwing in gravel. It was a bright, cool afternoon. In the field below a ploughman was at work: I could see the furrows of the dark earth glisten as he turned it over. The grass in the meadow was a full rich green, the new chickens were active in their yards, running to the cluck of the hens, already the leaves of the orchard trees showed green. And as I worked there with Dick I had the curious deep feeling of coming somehow into a new and more intimate possession of my own land. For titles do not really pass with signatures and red seals, nor with money changing from one hand to another, but for true possession one must work and serve according to the most ancient law. There is no mitigation and no haggling of price. Those who think they can win the greatest joys of country life on any easier terms are mistaken.

But if one has drained his land, and ploughed it, and fertilized it, and planted it and harvested it—even though it be only a few acres—how he comes to know and to love every rod of it. He knows the wet spots, and the stony spots, and the warmest and most fertile spots—until his acres have all the qualities of a personality, whose every characteristic he knows. It is so also that he comes to know his horses and cattle and pigs and hens. It is a fine thing, on a warm day in early spring, to bring out the bee-hives and let the bees have their first flight in the sunshine. What cleanly folk they are! And later to see them coming in yellow all over with pollen from the willows! It is a fine thing to watch the cherries and plum trees come into blossom, with us about the first of May, while all the remainder of the orchard seems still sleeping. It is a fine thing to see the cattle turned for

335

the first time in spring into the green meadows. It is a fine thing —one of the finest of all—to see and smell the rain in a corn-field after weeks of drought. How it comes softly out of gray skies, the first drops throwing up spatters of dust and losing themselves in the dry soil. Then the clouds sweep forward up the valley, darkening the meadows and blotting out the hills, and then there is the whispering of the rain as it first sweeps across the corn-field. At once what a stir of life! What rustling of the long green leaves. What joyful shaking and swaying of the tassels! And have you watched how eagerly the grooved leaves catch the early drops, and, lest there be too little rain after all, conduct them jealously down the stalks where they will soonest reach the thirsty roots? What a fine thing is this to see!

One who thus takes part in the whole process of the year comes soon to have an indescribable affection for his land, his garden, his animals. There are thoughts of his in every tree: memories in every fence corner. Just now, the fourth of June, I walked down past my blackberry patch, now come gorgeously into full white bloom—and heavy with fragrance. I set out these plants with my own hands, I have fed them, cultivated them, mulched them, pruned them, trellised them, and helped every year to pick the berries. How could they be otherwise than full of associations! They bear a fruit more beautiful than can be found in any catalogue: and stranger and wilder than in any learned botany book!

Why, one who comes thus to love a bit of countryside may enjoy it all the year round. When he awakens in the middle of a long winter night he may send his mind out to the snowy fields—I've done it a thousand times!—and visit each part in turn, stroll through the orchard and pay his respects to each tree—in a small orchard one comes to know familiarly every tree as he knows his friends—stop at the strawberry bed, consider the grape trellises, feel himself opening the door of the warm, dark stable and listening to the welcoming whicker of his horses, or visiting his cows, his pigs, his sheep, his hens, or so many of them as he may have.

So much of the best in the world seems to have come fragrant out of fields, gardens, and hillsides. So many truths spoken by the Master Poet come to us exhaling the odours of the open country. His stories were so often of sowers, husbandmen, herdsmen: his similes and illustrations so often dealt with the common and familiar beauty of the fields. "Consider the lilies how they grow." It was on a hillside that he preached his greatest sermon, and when in the last agony he sought a place to meet his God, where did he go but to a garden? A carpenter you say? Yes, but of this one may be sure: there were gardens and fields all about: he knew gardens, and cattle, and the simple processes of the land: he must have worked in a garden and loved it well.

A country life rather spoils one for the so-called luxuries. A farmer or gardener may indeed have a small cash income, but at least he eats at the first table. He may have the sweetest of the milk—there are thousands, perhaps millions, of men and women in America who have never in their lives tasted really sweet milk—and the freshest of eggs, and the ripest of fruit. One does not know how good strawberries or raspberries are when picked before breakfast and eaten with the dew still on them. And while he must work and sweat for what he gets, he may have all these things in almost unmeasured abundance, and without a thought of what they cost. A man from the country is often made uncomfortable, upon visiting the city, to find two ears of sweet corn served for twenty or thirty cents, or a dish of raspberries at twenty-five or forty—and neither, even at their best, equal in quality to those he may have fresh from the garden every day. One need say this in no boastful spirit, but as a simple statement of the fact: for fruits sent to the city are nearly always picked before they are fully ripe—and lose that last perfection of flavour which the sun and the open air impart: and both fruits and vegetables, as well as milk and eggs, suffer more than most people think from handling and shipment. These things can be set down as one of the make-weights against the familiar presentation of the farmer's life as a hard one.

One of the greatest curses of mill or factory work and with much city work of all kinds, is its interminable monotony:

the same process repeated hour after hour and day after day. In the country there is indeed monotonous work but rarely monotony. No task continues very long: everything changes infinitely with the seasons. Processes are not repetitive but creative. Nature hates monotony, is ever changing and restless, brings up a storm to drive the haymakers from their hurried work in the fields, sends rain to stop the ploughing, or a frost to hurry the apple harvest. Everything is full of adventure and vicissitude! A man who has been a farmer for two hours at the mowing must suddenly turn blacksmith when his machine breaks down and tinker with wrench and hammer; and later in the day he becomes dairyman, farrier, harness-maker, merchant. No kind of wheat but is grist to his mill, no knowledge that he cannot use! And who is freer to be a citizen than he: freer to take his part in town meeting and serve his state in some one of the innumerable small offices which form the solid blocks of organization beneath our commonwealth.

I thought last fall that corn-husking came as near being monotonous work as any I had ever done in the country. I presume in the great corn-fields of the West, where the husking goes on for weeks at a time, it probably does grow really monotonous. But I soon found that there was a curious counter-reward attending even a process as repetitive as this.

I remember one afternoon in particular. It was brisk and cool with ragged clouds like flung pennants in a poverty-stricken sky, and the hills were a hazy brown, rather sad to see, and in one of the apple trees at the edge of the meadow the crows were holding their mournful autumn parliament.

At such work as this one's mind often drops asleep, or at least goes dreaming, except for the narrow margin of awareness required for the simple processes of the hands. Its orders have indeed been given: you must kneel here, pull aside the stalks one by one, rip down the husks, and twist off the ear—and there is the pile for the stripped stalks, and here the basket for the gathered corn, and these processes infinitely repeated.

While all this is going on, the mind itself wanders off to its own far sweet pastures, upon its own dear adventures—or rests, or plays. It is in these times that most of the airy flying things of this beautiful world come home to us—things that heavy-footed reason never quite overtakes, nor stodgy knowledge ever knows. I think sometimes (as Sterne says) we thus intercept thoughts never intended for us at all, or uncover strange primitive memories of older times than these—racial memories.

At any rate, the hours pass and suddenly the mind comes home again, it comes home from its wanderings refreshed, stimulated, happy. And nowhere, whether in cities, or travelling in trains, or sailing upon the sea, have I so often felt this curious enrichment as I have upon this hillside, working alone in field, or garden, or orchard. It seems to come up out of the soil, or respond to the touch of growing things.

What makes any work interesting is the fact that one can make experiments, try new things, develop specialties and *grow*. And where can he do this with such success as on the land—and in direct contact with nature. The possibilities are here infinite—new machinery, spraying, seed testing, fertilizers, experimentation with new varieties—a thousand and one methods, all creative, which may be tried out in that great essential struggle of the farmer or gardener to command all the forces of nature.

Because there are farmers, and many of them, who do not experiment and do not grow, but make their occupation a veritable black drudgery, this is no reason for painting a sombre-hued picture of country life. Any calling, the law, the ministry, the medical profession, can be blasted by fixing one's eyes only upon its ugliest aspects. And farming, at its best, has become a highly scientific, extraordinarily absorbing, and when all is said, a profitable, profession. Neighbours of mine have developed systems of overhead irrigation to make rain when there is no rain, and have covered whole fields with cloth canopies to increase the warmth and to protect the crops from wind and hail, and by the analysis of the soil and exact methods of feeding it with fertilizers, have come as near a complete command of nature as any farmers in the world. What independent, resourceful men they are! And many of them have also grown rich in money. It is not what nature does with a man that matters but what he does with nature.

Nor is it necessary in these days for the farmer or the country dweller to be uncultivated or uninterested in what are often called, with no very clear definition, the "finer things of life." Many educated men are now on the farms and have their books and magazines, and their music and lectures and dramas not too far off in the towns. A great change in this respect has come over American country life in twenty years. The real hardships of pioneering have passed away, and with good roads and machinery, and telephones, and newspapers every day by rural post, the farmer may maintain as close a touch with the best things the world has to offer as any man. And if he really have such broader interests the winter furnishes him time and leisure that no other class of people can command.

I do not know, truly, what we are here for upon this wonderful and beautiful earth, this incalculably interesting earth, unless it is to crowd into a few short years—when all is said, terribly short years!—every possible fine experience and adventure: unless it is to live our lives to the uttermost: unless it is to seize upon every fresh impression, develop every latent capacity: to grow as much as ever we have it in our power to grow. What else can there be? If there is no life beyond this one, we have lived *here* to the uttermost. We've had what we've had! But if there is more life, and still more life, beyond this one, and above and under this one, and around and through this one, we shall be well prepared for that, whatever it may be.

The real advantages of country life have come to be a strong lure to many people in towns and cities: but no one should attempt to "go back to the land" with the idea that it is an easy way to escape the real problems and difficulties of life. The fact is, there is no escape. The problems and the difficulties must be boldly met whether in city or country. Farming in these days is not "easy living," but a highly skilled profession, requiring much knowledge, and actual manual labour and plenty of it. So many come to the country too light-heartedly, buy too much land, attempt unfamiliar crops, expect to hire the work done—

and soon find themselves facing discouragement and failure. Any city man who would venture on this new way of life should try it first for a year or so before he commits himself—try himself out against the actual problems. Or, by moving to the country, still within reach of his accustomed work, he can have a garden or even a small farm to experiment with. The shorter work-day has made this possible for a multitude of wageworkers, and I know many instances in which life because of this opportunity to get to the soil has become a very different and much finer thing for them.

It is easy also for many men who are engaged in professional work to live where they can get their hands into the soil for part of the time at least: and this may be made as real an experience as far as it goes as though they owned wider acres and devoted their whole time to the work.

A man who thus faces the problem squarely will soon see whether country life is the thing for him; if he finds it truly so, he can be as nearly assured of "living happily ever after" as any one outside of a story-book can ever be. Out of it all are likely to come some of the greatest rewards that men can know, a robust body, a healthy appetite, a serene and cheerful spirit!

And finally there is one advantage not so easy to express. Long ago I read a story of Tolstoi's called "The Candle"; how a peasant Russian forced to plough on Easter Day lighted a candle to his Lord and kept it burning on his plough as he worked through the sacred day. When I see a man ploughing in his fields I often think of Tolstoi's peasant, and wonder if this is not as true a way as any of worshipping God. I wonder if any one truly worships God who sets about it with deliberation, or knows quite why he does it.

"My doctrine shall drop as the rain, my speech shall distil as the dew, as the small rain upon the tender herb, and as showers upon the grass."